W9-BJZ-994

THE ADOLESCENT IN PSYCHOTHERAPY

THE ADOLESCENT I

PSYCHOTHERAPY

DONALD J. HOLMES, M.D.
Associate Professor of Psychiatry
University of Michigan Medical School

WITH A FOREWORD BY

RAYMOND W. WAGGONER, M.D., Sc.D.
Chairman, Department of Psychiatry
Director of the Neuropsychiatric Institute
University of Michigan Medical School

LITTLE, BROWN AND COMPANY, BOSTON

LIBRARY OF CONGRESS CATALOG CARD NO. 64-17507

FIRST EDITION

Third Printing

Published in Great Britain by J. & A. Churchill Ltd., London

PRINTED IN THE UNITED STATES OF AMERICA

TO PAULA, ROBB, AND TODD

AND TO KATHERINE AND WILBUR

FOREWORD

In the midst of an active debate on who should be responsible for the psychiatric care of the adolescent, the child psychiatrist or the specialist with adolescents, this book by Doctor Holmes, *The Adolescent in Psychotherapy*, brings a new, fresh, and exciting approach to the perplexing and familiarly frustrating problems entailed in providing appropriate treatment for patients of this age.

The adolescent is neither an overgrown child nor an immature adult but very much an individual, many of whose special problems are closely associated with one of the important stress periods of human life. While adolescent psychiatry is struggling to be born as a discrete specialty, it is important not only to test accepted psychiatric theories but also to explore new tenets. In his interesting and resourceful use of case material, Doctor Holmes has made a significant contribution to our knowledge of handling these problems.

Most of the recommendations have been developed and presented from an empirical standpoint. They are both theoretically and functionally sound; they do work with adolescents. Although practical in purpose and delightfully readable, the book is by no means an exclusively how-to-do-it book. One cannot read the case material and the lucid, provocative theoretical discussions without reflecting on more exact and purposeful directions in psychotherapy with the adult as well as the adolescent patient.

This book is a concise treatise on the principles of psychotherapy. It faces up to the complexities of the subject boldly and treats its fundamentals with a well-deserved attitude of respect and continuing curiosity. By the tasteful avoidance of technical jargon and shopworn psychiatric platitudes, but not through oversimplification, Doctor Holmes has made this work available to all those attempting to aid the adolescent in making a better adjustment. Not only should it come as a refreshing relief in professional reading for the psychiatric clinician, but the timeliness of the subject and the style of presentation will make it important to the paramedical disciplines and the generalist in medicine as well. Reading this work has been an exciting adventure, even for a veteran psychiatrist, and it will surely be an equally rewarding experience for other clinicians and their associates.

RAYMOND W. WAGGONER

PREFACE

"There is no use in telling more than you know,
no not even if you do not know it."—GERTRUDE STEIN[1]

In contemporary psychiatry the fine art of elaborating teaching concepts is sometimes useful, sometimes merely irrelevant, and at other times it impedes more than it helps. A few of the more basic of these concepts have great value in orienting us to the tasks of psychotherapy, but it is often much too easy to infer from them many ideas which do not hold up in clinical practice and, even more, which do not apply at all.

In our teaching we frequently go the way of the arrogant house mouse who advised the shivering grasshopper that he would survive the winter better if he were to change into a mouse. Heartened by the suggestion, the grasshopper inquired how he might proceed with this, and the mouse replied: "I can only give you the general idea—you will have to work out the details for yourself." This book represents an attempt to work out some of the details of applied psychotherapy, particularly in regard to the disturbed adolescent. It is not, and is not intended as, a comprehensive presentation of a closed system of treatment.

In the day-to-day practice of psychiatry, empiricism is still superior to theory. With respect to our treatment of patients we think first of what will work best, what makes the most sense, and what will help the most; only then do we do much theorizing about it. The terms which we use to describe our treatment actions vary greatly with the circumstances in which they are spoken. In seminars, lectures, and professional publications there is an understandable tendency to favor technical terms and concepts. When talking with a colleague about a pressing clinical matter, however, we usually find ourselves speaking with words which, though rather plain and unimposing, combine to form ideas about psychopathology and psychotherapy which are as dynamic and intellectually challenging as some of the more formal theories.

[1] Stein, G., *Lectures in America.* Boston, Beacon Press, 1957.

This partly explains why, in this writing, a careful effort has been made to use traditional technical terms only when there are no better—more specific and clearer—words available. I have tried to avoid excessive use of many conventional psychoanalytic terms and expressions, not because they are thought to be invalid but rather because they are so very valid and generally applicable that one can hardly go wrong with them. Through usage and a natural process of veneration they have acquired a sound of finality and conclusiveness which subtly implies total closure on questions which have not been answered at all. The point is that we need not be embarrassed about talking and writing in the vernacular; ours is a psychologically rich language, and in many applications it is much more specific and scientific than the argot which we often and unwisely use to replace it.

Academic disputes between psychiatric disciplines have been quite real in the not-too-distant past. Over the last few years, however, these disputes seem to have become less and less about real differences in theory and practice and more and more about the equitable distribution of credits and honors among organized groups of practitioners, each of whom has a deeply personal allegiance to whatever affiliation will return the strongest supports to his own personal and professional identity. Perhaps necessarily, we are all a little guilty of violating the ideal of pure scientific objectivity in this way. This is mentioned here as a means of emphasizing that whenever we speak, for example, of a person's thoughts, behavior, or feelings, we are working in the realm of "ego psychology." Work in this or any other area of clinical psychiatry can always be identified better by its content than its idiom.

As in most publications of this type, the clinical case excerpts are intended only to illustrate principles and support assertions, not to prove them. John Pollard, a colleague who was kind enough to read the manuscript prior to publication, suggested that two points concerning the case fragments in this book be clarified in the preface. First, he noted that most of the dialogue used in these passages reads as though it had been transcribed from recorded interviews, which is not the case. Secondly, he observed that many of the detailed inferences about "extraverbal data," which are reported here as having occurred in treatment interviews conducted by psychiatrists other than the author, far exceed what a supervisor could possibly estimate from listening to another therapist's secondhand account. This discordant note results from a well-intended effort to respect the confidence of patients. In most of the excerpts, certain concrete elements of the case which are unimportant to the point being illustrated have been altered for this purpose.

It should be added that these precautions have been taken to keep the patient from being recognized by others; they are not meant to "protect" him from recognizing himself. On the contrary, I assume that a great number of my patients, former and current, will be reading about themselves in this volume. Indeed, one of the strongest theses made in the text testifies to the difficulty of keeping certain kinds of secrets from the adolescent and to our sometimes incredibly naïve belief that we can and should do so. Some confirmations of this expectation have already come to my attention, and there will surely be more. When possible and clinically appropriate, I have already spoken with my patients about their passive but very important part in this venture. Their responses have consistently served to dispel my earlier concerns about their welfare, and have firmly convinced me that if those patients with whom I have not been able to speak should read this book and recognize something of themselves in it, they will be equally understanding and accepting of my reasons for including them also.

Finally, it will be apparent that a few of the case excerpts do not refer to specific persons. These are simply prototypical examples, or sometimes composites, which seemed particularly useful for illustrating a few commonplace principles of psychotherapy with adolescents.

D. J. H.

Ann Arbor

ACKNOWLEDGEMENTS

It is a pleasure to express my gratitude to at least a few of the many people who have contributed not only to the substance of this book but also to the circumstances and inspiration which made the writing of it possible.

Dr. Raymond Waggoner, for his knowledgeable reading and many helpful criticisms of the manuscript and for the friendship and much-needed personal support which he has given so generously in the years I have known him. It is also satisfying to acknowledge, in company with many others here and elsewhere, a great professional debt to him for his pioneering role in the advancement of adolescent psychiatry. Like the Neuropsychiatric Institute itself, our Adolescent Service is—to the best of my knowledge—the first of its kind to be established in conjunction with a university hospital. This significant achievement was largely a result of Doctor Waggoner's dedication to the highest standards of patient care and medical education and to his outstanding administrative skill and vigor.

Dr. John Pollard, friend and colleague, for his critical dissection of the manuscript, which was as valuable as it was merciless, and for his indispensable moral support.

Dr. Harding Olson, for his very helpful assistance in preparing and verifying the bibliographical references.

The resident psychiatrists and other staff members who have served, and are serving, so capably on the Adolescent Service, and especially to our first head nurse, Jean Wood, R.N., who played such an important part in putting the inpatient program on its feet.

The Directors and staff members of the Battle Creek and Huron Valley Child Guidance Clinics and of the Columbus and Kalamazoo State Hospitals.

Dr. Shirley Schneider, Dale Boesky, and Arnold Jones, for their early and enthusiastic support of this writing.

Marjorie Apple, Mary Blair, Verona Little, Virginia Obenchain, and Jacqueline Purcell, for their patience and tolerance, often above and beyond the call of duty, in typing and otherwise helping to prepare the manuscript.

Mr. Fred Belliveau, Manager, Medical Book Department, Little, Brown and Company, for his many helpful suggestions, all of which were offered with the greatest imaginable tact and unfailing good judgment.

I should like to call special attention to bibliographical references number 5 and numbers 16 through 20, which are to some of the published contributions of Dr. Williard J. Hendrickson, as well as to some of the work which we have done together and with others. Doctor Hendrickson has been Chief of the Adolescent Service since its beginning and my friend and teacher for longer than that. Because so many of the ideas and views included in this book came either directly from him or grew out of our joint efforts in developing the Adolescent Service, I have truly found it impossible to accord him sufficient and accurate credit, and thanks, for his contributions to the psychiatry of adolescents in general, and to me—and this book—in particular.

The principal source of material for this book is clinical. The manner of presentation is more informal and speculative than didactic or quantitative. Some of the observations and ideas included here, even though arrived at independently, have surely been specified or alluded to in earlier publications by other workers. An earnest effort has been made to acknowledge these. In any event, the fact that bibliographical references are made to any specific sources at all is less important than that some of the many outstanding contributors in this field have been listed by name. Referring to one or two passages in the publications of at least a few of these leading figures does them a serious disservice, in that it quietly implies that these are the only things they have said which are pertinent and important to the subject at hand. This is clearly not the case. The reader who wishes to look further into the literature of adolescent psychiatry is well advised, therefore, to look first to the authors included in the bibliography and to pursue his study from there, rather than from these few references to a limited number of their works.

D. J. H.

CONTENTS

PART I ADOLESCENTS, ADULTS, AND PSYCHOTHERAPISTS

1

THE ADOLESCENT PERSONALITY AND THE AIMS OF PSYCHOTHERAPY

There are many questions in psychiatry about the kind of treatment for which the adolescent (i.e., the "neurotic" adolescent) is best suited. This is a curiously inverted approach to the issue in that it presumes an answer and attempts to tailor the question to it, rather than trying to answer the question. It is probably more fruitful to examine first some of the personality strengths and weaknesses of the adolescent[1] and then attempt to determine from these what general approaches might prove most helpful to him.

Strengths and Weaknesses of the Adolescent

There are certain elements of the adolescent personality that motivate him strongly to move ahead in his life and, when necessary, in psychotherapy. Because he is so uncertain about what he is and what he is supposed to be, he goes about tautly alert to the fleeting, vivid images of

[1] One aspiration of the troubled adolescent that can be a powerful incentive to his accepting and working in psychotherapy is noted by Fraiberg: "What the child in puberty fears is loss of control, surrender to the demands of drives. What he fears in therapy is the further disturbance of his precarious equilibrium. What he longs for most of all is the restoration of harmony. If our treatment is to have meaning for him, if we can hold out to him a concrete goal, we need to help him see therapy as a means of reestablishing equilibrium, of helping him to become master of himself" [12]. Gitelson suggests that the "ego weakness" of the adolescent is a relative contraindication to intensive treatment [15]. Zachry, considering the other side of this coin, feels that his natural introspectiveness and awareness of intrapsychic difficulty actually facilitates such treatment [33]. According to Hendrickson some of these aforementioned features are similar to those encountered in schizophrenic illnesses, and help to account for the adolescent's strong and opposite feelings—those of desire and dread—toward the idea of psychotherapy [16].

himself which other people can reflect back to him. He is extremely interested in himself and in what others can tell him about himself. He also nourishes a covert interest in how the adult has gone about getting such an easy life for himself. He has a deep curiosity about people, himself, and others, and is actively engaged in a testing, experimental examination of the problems of his own life. If these problems prove to be too much for him and eventuate in his coming to psychotherapy, then his curiosity about himself and others will stand him in good stead. Having the support of an interested adult's superior judgment and good counsel can also enable him to indulge his curiosity with greater safety than if he were to attempt this alone.

Another potential asset to therapy is his increased awareness of the future. In this he differs from the younger child, who enjoys a sense of utter timelessness and vaguely anticipates eternal gratification. The young adult, under the urgent pressures of job, family, community responsibilities, and a swiftly developing appreciation of the temporal limitations of his own life, is impelled to withdraw a large portion of energy from fantasies of the future for investment in plans and actions relating to the present. Through middle life and into old age, there is a tendency for him to resume once more a self-protective sense of timelessness. In no period of life does one depend so heavily upon the promises of the future than during adolescence. Dubo [7] stresses the importance of capitalizing upon this strength in treatment by working actively with the patient to develop a realistic and attractive picture of his own future.

There are some important counterforces to those which motivate the adolescent to accept and progress in treatment. He is by nature skeptical of an adult's promises of good things to come. This skepticism applies to the promises of medical treatment in general and of psychotherapy in particular. He really does not quite understand what it is all about, or just what is the matter with him, or why he cannot "work it out" with his parents.

The adult usually approaches medical treatment with the hope that it will cure him. He comes to the doctor because he feels very bad or is failing at his job or marriage and because he no longer has a person of parental stature to whom he can turn for help. He approaches treatment with the usual resistances, but somewhere among his motives for asking help glows the fantasy that has kept doctors in business for centuries: "I am sick. Doctors help sick people. I will go to my doctor. He is a wise man who has studied for many years to learn about treatment. *I will accept his treatment and that will make me better.*" The patient's faith in this not-so-unrealistic fantasy is in itself a powerful therapeutic force and also one that helps to explain why so many different kinds of treatment accomplish such good results with the same kind of patient and why so many different kinds of sickness respond favorably to the same treatment.

But the adolescent, even when he is outwardly respectful and accepting, maintains an obstinately skeptical attitude toward the miracles of modern medicine. His capacity for blind faith is temporarily suspended, pending the outcome of his own private research into the psychology of adults. Until he has become believer also, an adult, he is much inclined to accept only what is proved to him.

The question of the relative amounts of emphasis to be placed upon various treatment approaches is an academic issue, the real answer to which can be found only in each patient. Whether the adolescent patient is to be probed, supported, directed, or whatever is not really a pertinent question any longer. In all likelihood each and every one of these general treatment measures will enter into his therapy at some time in the course of our first few contacts with him. Often enough the complete gamut is run, however sketchily, during a single evaluation interview.

He will take what he needs of what we have to offer, and if what he needs is not offered then he will be lost to treatment. Even so, the improvement which he enjoys with optimum treatment will depend mostly upon his innate and acquired abilities to desire and tolerate changes in himself. Only to a much lesser extent will it rely upon our humble efforts to assist him with this task.

Aims and Limits of Therapy

The patient and his therapist do not always share the same fantasies about what is to be accomplished in treatment. In one way or another the psychotherapist must attempt to answer this question: "How much should I expect to do through the special agencies of psychotherapy, and how much should be left for my patient to do in the same ways that most people go about doing things?"

George, fifteen years old, was admitted to the adult closed ward with a history of relatively minor delinquencies. He was "an ungovernable child" at home. His complaints, revealed in bits and pieces over the months following his admission, were of anxiety, depression, and an unaccountably heavy burden of "bad luck." In the course of treatment he came to appreciate that much of his bad luck was in the form of "unexplainable" accidents which he perceived as having been inflicted upon him by outside forces. After a while he began to recognize that most of this malevolent influence arose from within himself. Without being aware of it, he did many things which greatly increased the likelihood of his having accidents. For various reasons he and his therapist got only a glimpse at the reasons behind this need. In his recklessness there was an acted-out denial (counterphobia) of a fear of injury, and along with it the hope of satisfying a great anger which had long ago been deflected from parents to himself. Also associated with the idea of being hurt was the fantasy of becoming helplessly incapacitated, which would require that he be given over to the tender ministrations of a "beautiful nurse." During therapy he began to experience intermittent and very unpleasant feelings of loneliness and isolation which for some years had lain under a thin cover of ostensibly tough, reckless independence. He became frightened by the recognition of his mysterious tendency to hurt himself, and resolved—with considerable success—to be more careful. To a lesser extent he also saw extensions of the compulsion to self-injury in some of his self-defeating approaches to friends, school work, and job.

Treatment was terminated when he was somewhat improved. Although reasonably advanced in the direction of living more *for* than *against* himself, there was little doubt that from an exclusively psychiatric point of view he continued to be distinctly neurotic. The decision to discontinue treatment was made chiefly on the therapist's *beliefs* about future probabilities, rather than on knowledge. It was appreciated that George would continue, unconsciously, to try to please his mother, regain his father, and ward off castration anxiety. But it was his therapist's belief, at the conclusion of therapy, that any successes he might enjoy could result just as readily *from* these unconscious efforts as in spite of them. It was presumed that he would continue to pay a price for adapting outside of an institution. He and his therapist hoped that things would be better for him than if he had not been treated. He would certainly continue to have some symptoms, marital troubles, and problems with his children—none of which are too remarkable in the general population.

George could unquestionably have been helped to understand even more about the psychogenesis of his persistent infantile neurotic conflicts, with a theoretical increase in the amount of ego energy liberated from the work of neurotic problem-solving to that of reality. The objection to this view is that it does not allow for the fact that there are outside jobs to be done which one would never feel impelled to do were it not for the pressure of unresolved, unconscious infantile neurotic conflicts. Philosophical reconstruction is not an aim of therapy.

There is not much satisfaction in settling for the general goal of helping a patient to feel better and do better, too often through a half-blind process of cutting and trying, but that is where we stand today in psychotherapy.

2

THE TREATMENT RELATIONSHIP

The frequency with which certain psychiatric shorthand terms and ideas are used provides a useful clue to some of the most troublesome aspects of the treatment process. The available definitions of the "therapeutic relationship," "meeting the patient's emotional needs," "accepting the patient," "resolving the transference (and the countertransference)" provide little reliable counsel about what the therapist is to do about them in the treatment of one patient. To consider useful principles of action requires stepping down at least one or two levels of abstraction and speaking in the terms of the more describable and concrete attributes of the formal concepts.

Attributes of Relationship

Some of the discernible features of a helpful and progressive treatment relationship with the adolescent, or perhaps with anyone else, are briefly summarized in the following paragraphs.

The relationship develops spontaneously rather than by design, occurring as a therapeutically necessary but still fortuitous consequence of the process of resolving realistic problems. Sometimes, however, a helpful treatment relationship can develop in spite of the therapist's self-conscious efforts to achieve one.

It is subjectively satisfying to both participants but *only intermittently*. Expecting the complete fulfillment of an incessantly gratifying love relationship is the impossible dream of infants and psychotic adults, although wishing for it is quite normal.

It survives transiently negative feelings, such as anger, resentment, distrust, and disappointment.

It enables patient and therapist alike to tolerate the falling short of original aims and to readjust to new problems which arise from the miscalculation.

It can also accommodate the patient's improvement in treatment, with its double-edged threat and promise of increased independence, the threat to patient and therapist of impending separation from each other, and the threat of the waning of some neurotic symptoms which may have been almost as gratifying to the therapist as to the patient.

It does not develop overnight and it does not come about easily. A smooth and untroubled treatment relationship with the adolescent which lasts throughout therapy is a reliable sign of one of two possibilities. Either the therapist and patient have managed to substitute an essentially nonprogressive, ceremonial sham for psychotherapy, or the patient did not need treatment in the first place. The latter is unlikely, as it is almost inconceivable that the average, nonpatient adolescent could carry off the stress of such an intimate and protracted relationship with any adult without trouble arising between them.

Therapeutic Alliance with the Patient

A common injunction which bears on the therapist's attitude toward his part of the treatment relationship is that he should attempt to ally himself with certain of the patient's intrapsychic institutions, i.e., ego, superego, or that he win his patient's confidence and trust by joining with him in his struggle against authority and in his competition with peers.

Some of the complications which develop at this point might be simplified by the suggestion that the therapist's best prospects for securing the patient's confidence and trust lie in his attempting to ally himself with the patient's efforts to achieve a clearer and more believable interpretation of reality, and against those forces within him which wish to ignore or distort it. The idea of becoming an ally has a militaristic connotation which supports the commonly shared fantasy, "Let's you and me be buddies against the rest of the world."

Another reckless misinterpretation of the alliance concept suggests encouraging the patient to some fairly benign form of acting out with the general idea of demonstrating "I am not a hard-nosed puritan," or "Now see what a bad job you did of it—you are not a very talented delinquent." This viewpoint neglects the transcendent importance of what the patient and therapist are able to understand about each other. The patient will recognize that this is a purposeful, contrived falsification of reality in which he is being presented with a secretly rigged conflict situation. The therapist can proceed with it only on the foolish assumption that the youngster will not recognize what he is up to, and in the process thus reveal his lack of conviction that it is possible to help without measures which are patronizing, infantilizing, and manipulative.

The approach would also inform the patient eloquently of his doctor's willingness to use the distorting of reality as a valid measure in other areas of the treatment process as well. He might understandably find in this attitude both an excuse and an operational model for doing no more than going through the motions of treatment, for saying all of the "right things," and for resisting the painful effort of productive self-examination.

A misunderstanding of the adaptive value of adolescent rebellion and defiance can also provide a rationale for "joining" the patient by prescribing that he act out. An operational impasse arises from the failure to distinguish adequately between having knowledge of a psychological fact and knowing something of the dynamics which give rise to it. In other words the answer to the question "Why?" is not the same as that to the question "How?" For example, the celebrated rebellion of the adolescent serves, at least in part, the purpose of attenuating his dependence upon adults, and of reinforcing a more confident sense of personal autonomy. This aim is roundly and soundly defeated when his rebellion is sympathetically approved by the too-enlightened adult.

With this additional understanding of the dynamics of adolescent rebellion the therapist may entertain a somewhat broader attitude toward the complicated relationships between a bit of behavior, its meaning to the patient, and what is to be done about it:

A sixteen-year-old boy with a history of aggressive misbehavior was seen for outpatient evaluation. He was found to be deeply ensnarled in a pathologically and mutually dependent relationship with his mother. For several years he had managed a marginal, ostensibly nonpsychotic adjustment by playing the role of a tough, "hoody" delinquent. Through careful attention to clothing, hairstyling, tattoos, facial expression, and posture, he had been able to evoke some transiently reassuring glances of disapproval from teachers, fellow students, and people on the street. In the psychiatric interview he made a heroic effort but, failing to maintain the facade, declared at one point with affected surliness, "There was plenty of times I was going to get together with a couple buddies and get the hell away from home—take off for California or some place." The examining psychiatrist tactfully inquired about why he had not done this. The boy was momentarily perplexed and silent. Then, his eyes reddening and filling with tears, he finally stammered, "Well . . . I wanted to . . . but—but my mother wouldn't let me."

No treatment advantage would be gained by encouraging this youngster to run away. The initial effort would be directed to helping him acquire, in various ways, a higher estimation of his own worth. If successful in this, he might indeed develop enough self-confidence to assert himself to the extent of running away, and upon his return he would surely show some pride in his achievement. As psychotherapists we could understand his very real need to prove himself and perhaps recognize his behavior as a *sign* of improvement. But our satisfaction would be interpreted by him as a tacit message of congratulation and condonement. Whatever good he might have got from the adventure experience would be thereby undone.

The therapist can avoid transmitting such a communication only by appreciating that there was nothing in the act per se which was therapeutic. Although it may have signaled some small improvement, the running away was literally no more than an accessory sign of improvement rather than a cause of the improvement. The therapist should respect the youngster's initiative and daring by treating it accordingly:

"From what you've told me there's been no great harm done by your running away, but don't do it again."

"Aw, I got fed up with this place . . . everybody telling you what to do and staff bugging you all the time . . . If they don't cut it out . . ."

"You know they're not going to cut it out—what you call 'bugging'—so don't set that up as an excuse for taking off again."

"Who's making excuses! They keep pushing me around. Get out of bed . . . go to school . . . don't say any of those naughty, naughty words . . . do your homework . . . do this . . . do that—treat you like a baby!" (Note that he picked only the most reasonable matters to complain of.)

"So you want us to let you stay in bed all day, not go to school, swear at anybody you want to—like that!"

"Ah, it's not going to school and that stuff; I don't mind that. It's that picking, picking, picking all the time. No kidding, they treat you just like a baby!"

"Do what you're supposed to do and they won't have to treat you that way."

"Oh, sure. They're great big important staff and I'm just a kid, so that gives them the right to tell me what to do. Naturally!"

"Naturally. What else?"

"I'll tell you what else!" I don't care if she is staff, if that Smith broad tells me one more time to tuck in my shirt . . . !"

"Now hold on a second . . . Miss Smith, whom you like more than you care to admit, doesn't have much choice but to play your game with you. That's why you left your shirt out in the first place, isn't it? To get her into the act?"

"She thinks she's everybody's big fat mama."

"She does, or you do? You're the one who left your shirt tail out. You keep things going the same old way. (Long silence) Miss Smith told me this morning that you got a letter from your mother yesterday, just before you ran away."

"Oh, that didn't have anything to do with it. I don't care if she never writes to me!"

The act of running away was directly devaluated. Any slight, secondary benefits accruing to the patient from the fact that he was able to break away for a brief period were respected by the therapist's sincerely reiterating the prohibition against running away. The patient made one awkward effort to create conditions which would justify his repeating the behavior, which was clarified by his doctor. He then drew attention to his frightening wishes to yield to infantilization by adults, but did it in a way which revealed that this was only one valence of his contradictory feelings about wanting to be a baby, on the one hand, and wanting to be something even more than just a sixteen-year-old boy on the other. Then the doctor, with some concealed assistance from his patient ("Just because they're staff gives them the right, etc.") was able to take a firm stand on what ought to be a conspicuous reality ("naturally"). From this there developed a more concrete examination of the boy's feelings about particular people. This, once more with the patient's tacit guidance, made it possible for the doctor to bring their attention to a focus on an even more discrete trouble spot—feelings about mother.

In this case the therapist could have disregarded the fact of the misbehavior in favor of turning at once to an exploratory, interpretive examination of its neurotic meaning. Although not intending to approve the runaway as a useful treatment exercise, he would still run a strong risk of unintentionally endorsing it through having interpreted the action as a neurotic expression of the need to rebel, to become independent. It would be as though he were saying, somewhere between the lines, "In view of your past experiences with mother, your actions are understandable—but of course you shouldn't do it." The patient would be encouraged to share his doctor's confusion of cause and meaning, and to entertain the private reservation, "Why shouldn't I do it again? Like he says, it isn't my fault I grew up to have this 'need'—running away is an expected part of my treatment."

Punishment and Discipline—Setting Limits

The setting down and enforcing of certain reasonable standards of behavior, where it is possible to do so, are not things which the psychotherapist does primarily for his own satisfaction. He does them mostly in the interest of trying to meet his patient's emotional needs.

Setting limits. There are some vitally important aspects of the authority issue which are not really covered by the generally accepted tenet that, "Of course it is *also* important to set limits." So stated, this implies that the advantages to forbidding the young patient to tear down walls and build fires in the corridor are secondary, while connoting a hint of reluctance and apology for having interfered with his freedom at all.

There are some primary advantages to setting limits which are less readily recognized [18]. The enforcing of reasonable standards of behavior is an indispensable part of the treatment process, especially with the child and the adolescent. It is likely that certain vaguely unconscious condensations of the different ideas designated by such words as *discipline, punishment, hate, anger,* and *authority* account for much of the uneasy sense of guilt with which we approach this problem. All these sample words connote aggression, meaning that the energy required to carry them into action is necessarily derived from instinctual aggressive energy. In the unconscious "aggression" equals "destruction." But in people's conscious activities, hopefully, some of this energy has been "derived" and converted into aggressive actions which serve the aims of adaptation.

Discipline and punishment. Discipline, though aggressively energized, denotes a complex of attitudes and actions which is consciously intended to help people live more effectively and, in the long run, more happily. Punishment, in contrast with discipline, denotes a type of action which is primarily motivated by the wish to hurt, cause pain, retaliate in the spirit of vengeance. It is much closer to the acting out of primitive, infantile wishes to destroy and cause pain.

Viewed in this way it becomes evident that, as a rule, no reliable decision can be made about whether a given act is disciplinary or punitive by knowing only the nature of the action. This decision turns instead upon knowing something of the individual's predominant motives for behaving as he does. It is an estimation, as Hendrickson [16] has pointed out, that can be made only in a relative sense. That is, it would be quite impossible for a human being to effect even the most legitimate discipline without also gratifying, to some extent, his unconscious need to hurt another person.

This distinction between discipline and punishment in no way diminishes the ease with which one may rationalize flagrantly sadistic, destructive actions as being for the victim's "own good." The psychotic mother of a pathetically brutalized five-year-old child explained matter-of-factly, "Kids need discipline . . . he was still messing his pants when he was two years old, so I started rubbing his face in it and that cured him fast. When he gets sassy with me, I slap his face good. Last week he said he was going to run away, so I packed up a little bag for him and sent him on his way. I can tell you he wasn't gone very long!"

This, on the face of it, is not discipline. On the other hand there are many youngsters who are reared on a standard regimen of spankings and stentorian bawling-outs who never become mentally ill. In many families spankings reflect a sincere parental concern about the child's present *and* future happiness. As an earnest effort to help the child do better by himself, it is a disciplinary measure rather than simple talion punishment.

Still other parents, usually of the upper classes, will spend incredible lengths of time trying to surmount the angry, stubborn wails of their three-year-old with endlessly patient explanations of why he should not play with matches. The three-year-old will regard being sent to his room as far more realistic than a mountain of logic. Even a spanking would be better than all that talk. At the extreme end of the benevolence-malevolence continuum is the exhaustively overindulgent, overprotective parent who, by withholding all visible forms of punishment or discipline, inflicts the cruelest punishment of all. He teaches his child nothing about reality.

AUTHORITY TESTING. The therapist who treats disturbed adolescents, especially if he carries the extensive responsibilities demanded by the inpatient, is subjected to a great deal of testing which is directed at determining just how comfortably he has resolved some of these aggression ambiguities for himself. These tests customarily take the form of accusations which are delivered with passionate simplicity. Each new rendition of the old refrains instantaneously elicits the image of an unhappy and confused youngster still trying to find out *how* and *what* someone feels about him and expects of him. He is still badgering, pushing, and pulling for a little reassurance that someone cares enough about him to risk those disturbing feelings of guilt which he has become so adept at provoking in other people.

The aim of authority in psychotherapy is not to bring an end to the youngster's testing. On the contrary, the business of testing the limits is just another form of reality-testing. It is a most helpful developmental exercise—*if there are realistic limits for the youngster to test.*

Acceptance—Liking and Trust

LIKING. "You don't like me!" means, in translation, "Do you like me and, if so, how much and in what ways? If not, why not, and is there any chance of my changing enough so that someone can like me?"

Disregarding for the time being the intricate details of the defensive, manipulative, transference implications of such a question permits us to consider the kind of answer to which the patient is entitled, and how this may be got across to him.

Up through kindergarten, children say openly to other people, "I like you," and expect to hear in return, "I like you, too." During the elementary years this direct approach becomes a little gauche. Words of affection may crop up periodically, but in the main they are converted to the familiar, extraverbal signs of camaraderie.

The adolescent, in a written note, may deliver himself of a quite sincere, "I can't live without you"; or, protected by the reassuring fantasy that he is lying, an impassioned "I love you," in order to further his progress in a petting session and to enable his girl friend to do the same with honor; but a simple, sincere "I like you" has become an anathema.

The therapist who sees liking the patient as a commendable aim in itself and who replies "But I do like you," will have to work a long time to get the hook out of his mouth. Shortly after kindergarten age if you really like someone, you don't have to say it. If you *do* have to say it, then it must be for some other reason, e.g., to represent yourself as a Warm Helping Person in order to induce your adolescent patient to "accept therapy."

Some oft-repeated answers to the question, when there is occasion for responding with words at all, vary greatly with the patient and the circumstances, but will usually run along the following general lines:

"Since I've only known you about three minutes, it's a little hard to know yet whether I like you or not."

"It's not easy to like you when you carry on like this."

"I don't think it matters much to you whether I do or not."

"Well, after all that has happened in fourteen months of treatment, I really wonder why you even bother to ask. Maybe you're worrying a little that I like you too much."

The answer which the patient will believe and respond to has many parts, none of which are direct verbal expressions of liking.

"You keep me in this place because you hate me," as a rule, rates little more than an indifferent grunt. It is generally a question which, though sounding like an unanswerable accusation, really includes its own answer: "You're keeping me here because you like me, but for God's sake don't say it out loud. Prove it to me. I can't stand any more phony affection." The proof of "liking," then, is much more in what is done than in what is said.

TRUST. The principle of winning the patient's confidence by showing him that you trust him is a misleading generalization which, because of its kindly tone, readily lends itself to damaging misinterpretations and misapplications. It begins to acquire validity when the conditions of trusting are scrutinized with minute care. "Trust you with what, how much, how long, why, and under what conditions?" These are obligatory questions which the therapist directs to himself or, on many occasions, quite openly to his patient.

Hal, a sixteen-year-old boy, was admitted because of his uncontrollably defiant behavior at home. He had also sexually molested a little girl in the neighborhood on several occasions. After some months of treatment he showed definite signs of improvement, but two attempts to confer upon him the burdensome responsibility of pass privileges failed abortively. He made it unmistakably clear that he could not be trusted and that he did not trust himself with this degree of freedom. A few weeks after the second trial at privileges his father became seriously ill while on a business trip in a distant city. After careful consideration we decided that it would be important for Hal to visit his father immediately even though we had to send him on the train by himself. In spite of his inexperience with travel, the complications of an unreliable schedule, and two train changes with long layovers, he turned in a flawless performance. After returning to the hospital he registered a certain amount of justifiable pride in his accomplishment, and of course, immediately requested ground privileges. His rationale: "If I can handle a trip like that, I can certainly handle ground privileges with no trouble at all." When his doctor began to question this reasoning, Hal became angry and indignant: "You don't trust me!"

"With what?"

"With anything! You don't think I can do anything on my own!"

"Wait a minute—which one of us is it that thinks you can't do anything on your own?"

"Well sure, you let me go on a six-hundred-mile train trip all by myself, but I'm the one who did it. Doesn't that prove something?"

"Yes. It proves you can go on a six-hundred-mile train trip by yourself to do something very important."

Sarcastically, "But I can't go out in the side yard by myself for fifteen minutes?"

"Apparently not. We've tried it twice, and you know what happened."

"Oh . . . sure, but that was a long, long time ago."

"You make it sound like ten years ago. Actually, it's been just three weeks since you fouled up our last try at ground privileges. What's happened since then to give either of us any confidence that you can do it better next time?"

"That's what I'm trying to tell you! You make it sound like that train trip was just a little stroll down the street."

"No, it was a very big thing. And ground privileges are a very little thing. Isn't that what you're saying?"

"Well, sure. That's pretty clear, isn't it?"

"I don't need to give you the answer to this, Hal. You know it well enough, but you don't like to look at it."

With an occasional reminder and question from his therapist, Hal then proceeded with a pertinent and meaningful review of certain aspects of his preadmission adjustment. He had been a star athlete, and had also carried out a long and difficult science project which won him much gratifying commendation. But because of tardiness, procrastination, and almost total indifference to routine daily assignments, his course grades were dismally low. He could do the big jobs very well when he chose to, but the small and unpleasant ones hardly at all. He began to recognize this as he talked further about his past experiences, and was visibly impressed by this recognition of something about himself which he had not quite faced before. At the end of the interview he attempted to swap this important step in therapeutic self-understanding for a very small and "unimportant" concession: "Well, now that I see what I've been doing, I'm pretty sure I can handle privileges all right." When his therapist calmly persisted in denying the request, Hal's new insight acquired a new dimension of meaning for him. He not only understood it, he felt it.

Rejection

Like parents, the therapist of juveniles strives to be helpful, and he naturally hopes that his speech and actions will attest to his good conscience. His genuine eagerness to do the job well increases the likelihood of his confusing "looking good" with "doing good." It is a potential shortcoming which is not so easily recognized in oneself as in the parents of one's patient:

Mark, a pubertal thirteen-year-old boy, was referred for psychiatric evaluation by his parents with complaints of frequent and violent temper tantrums, aggressive sex play with two younger sisters, open masturbation in the presence of others, and of having made a number of direct sexual propositions to his mother. During the intake interview the parents attributed Mark's difficulty to "heredity," and described the countless ways in which they had demonstrated their love for him. His mother had first explained the sexual facts of life to him in great anatomical detail when he was four years old, and had continued the didactic portion of his education with regular refresher courses. They did not want him to grow up believing that sex was dirty and shameful, which was also their expressed reason for regularly having sexual intercourse in his presence.

He had suffered severe night terrors since an early age, and at these times his parents readily accepted him into their bed. In order to "comfort him" he would be permitted to sleep between them. As these nightly visits increased in frequency, Mark's father found himself becoming irritated and uncomfortable because of "overcrowding." He solved this problem by moving to Mark's bed. This arrangement became standard during the several years preceding referral.

Upon examination it was apparent that Mark suffered a severe, chronic psychotic illness, and immediate commitment was recommended. Because there was to be an unavoidable waiting period before admission would be possible, the case worker tactfully suggested to the parents that they have Mark sleep alone in his own bed. The father, who had already described himself as a well-trained and thoroughly-read "student of child psychology," demurred on the grounds that "the boy might interpret this as a rejection."

Rejecting a youngster in this fashion is as necessary in psychotherapy as it is in child-rearing, although the indications are not usually so glaring as this. Most of the ways in which a therapist may exploit a patient to serve his own needs, and unwittingly encourage developmental arrest or regression, are far more subtle.

Tender, Loving Care

The procedure for accepting the disturbed adolescent, on the other hand, sometimes requires the application of authoritative control to a degree which appears inimical to the idea of "tender, loving care."

Cynthia, age fourteen, was brought to the hospital by her parents for emergency admission. She was extremely anxious, wild-eyed, flushed, perspiring, and unable to sit still. She shouted repeatedly that she would not go onto the ward. Her generally violent and agitated manner and her swearing caused much anxiety and embarrassment to her parents, to several outpatients in the waiting room, and also to Dr. J, who was attempting to get her down to the ward. After a minute or two of irresolute persuasion, Dr. J took what might be called, perhaps a little euphemistically, a firm stand with her. He exceeded her in vocal volume, interrupted her interruptions, and limned for her a quick, clear picture of imminent reality—that she was going to the ward one way or another without further negotiations. The spirit of uncompromising determination came through to Cynthia, and she was promptly admitted, whereupon she became quieter and much more comfortable. This incident was coincidentally witnessed by a psychiatric staff person from another area who had a strong academic and theoretical orientation to psychiatry and something of a "salvation" concept of psychiatric treatment. After the storm had subsided, she approached Dr. J and respectfully expressed her dismay at this "aggressive approach" to an "emotionally deprived child" who is "mentally ill and in need of love and understanding." Recognizing the futility of a long and abstract explanation in these circumstances, Dr. J replied, accurately enough, "I was simply meeting her emotional needs."

Cynthia's past history was well known to him. It was apparent that she was verging on panic at the time of admission. For some days preceding this she had been growing increasingly agitated, far beyond the ability of her parents to control and protect her from the risks of promiscuity and suicidal gesture. The severity of her illness frightened and immobilized them. Several days before they had taken her to an emergency room at another hospital where tranquilizing medication was prescribed. She had refused this, and in desperation her father impulsively took the medication himself. In the light of her lifelong and recent history, Dr. J recognized that much of her panic was based upon the justifiable fear that she might be abandoned entirely to her own care. She was confused, depressed, and very much at the mercy of her own impulses. What she needed more than anything else during the admission crisis was a demonstrated reassurance that she could depend upon someone other than herself to protect her from the damaging potentials of her own illness.

Meeting the affectional needs of the adolescent patient, like building a relationship with him, is one of the last things a therapist need concern himself about. It is almost embarrassing to talk about a question as closed and undebatable as this one. To propose that you should show your adolescent patient you like him, and are emotionally involved with him, is very much like advising an apprentice lion-tamer that he should be afraid when he enters the cage. In neither of these instances is a conscious effort required to convey the reaction which nature presumably intends.

Positive feelings between people are signaled in many ways and with many degrees of ambivalence. Our affectionate concern for the adolescent in trouble is something which he will infer, quickly and secretly, from our determined efforts to help him stay out of trouble and feel better. Occasionally the suggestion is made that the therapist do something special and out of the ordinary to help convince the patient of his good intentions, such as giving him money, or deliberately encourage him to "act out" as a means of strengthening their alliance. Measures of this sort usually do not help. If the patient is receiving the treatment which he has a right to expect from his therapist, an offer of money would only confuse and embarrass him. It would be redundant. And, as suggested earlier, the idea of allying oneself with the patient is a perilously incomplete action. The treatment alliance is a triumvirate—the therapist, the patient, and reality.

Some Relationships Between Diagnosis, Pathology, and Therapy

Touching upon the "practical syndromes" of adolescence, in conjunction with discussions of treatment principles as illustrated by brief case excerpts, will serve the clinical purpose of this presentation. In the interest of being systematic it is tempting to examine the adolescent from the standpoint of his generic psychology—an approach which has the advantage of simplicity. Various stages of biological and psychological development can be described in terms which emphasize relative shifts in erotic primacy from one body zone to another and in terms of the psychological processes which enable the individual, in normal development, to make a realistic compromise between the conflicting demands of his own desires on the one hand and of his environment on the other.

The parents and siblings of the patient, who constitute the most important part of anyone's psychological environment, can be dealt with as relative "constants." Mothers are maternalistic, fathers paternalistic, and siblings rivalrous. Some general differences in parental types are traditionally indicated by broad terms such as *loving, rejecting, domineering, passive,* and *overprotective*. This effort at scientific control of the psychological variables of the environment, meaning chiefly the personalities of parents and siblings, makes it possible to delineate several developmental directions which are based on relatively fixed patterns of relationship between the growing child and his family. Thus, the youngster has the critically important feeding experience with his mother during the first year of life. Later he is involved in the strenuous oedipal relationship with his parents. After having resolved this stress, he is better able to turn more attention to enjoying and learning about the outside world. The onset of puberty stirs up some of the old conflicts, and as orthodox theory has it, these must be resolved once more through the psychological work of adolescence before maturity can be achieved.

LIMITS OF THE UNIVERSAL FORMULATIONS. These are the general and presumably universal relationship complexes which are so influential in human development. Unfortunately, they are too general to have much value when one tries to apply them *directly* to the treatment of one sick patient. This is probably the commonest single error of the beginning psychotherapist. Having learned these well-established truths about human development from books and lectures, he seeks material from the patient which will verify them all over again. He is then bewildered and discouraged upon finding that insight into these psychological forces has not helped the patient.

General concepts of normal and pathological development, even though they are true, often prove to be irrelevant in psychotherapy. The patient's painful and disabling personal conflicts are exclusively and intimately his own. Understanding the oedipus complex and similar concepts does not make one a psychotherapist any more than knowing that the world is round qualifies him as a geographer. This is why the experienced therapist, usually some years after the completion of his training, finally gets around to approaching each new patient with the more realistic and productive feeling of almost total ignorance.

Freed of the need to prove the fundamental verities of dynamic psychology over and over again, and of the obligation to demonstrate his knowledgeability to patients and colleagues, he is able to approach the patient with a degree of curiosity which can accommodate the intricacies of this one person's unique wishes, fears, resources, and weaknesses. He can try to find out what things are wrong with his patients and to figure out from this what can best be done about them.

LANGUAGE OF THE EGO. The details of "what is wrong with the patient" require the therapist to think in more elemental terms than are ordinarily used to describe the universal complexes. It is usually possible after the first interview to classify the patient, for example, as "passive," "flat," "warm," or "castrating," but one quickly runs out of such terms for thinking about the patient during subsequent contacts. In order to fulfill his treatment obligations, the therapist must turn, perhaps somewhat apologetically, to the unprofessional language of the vernacular.

We soon stop speculating about whether the patient's ego is "weak" or "strong," beginning instead to talk about the person to whom the ego belongs:

May is only sixteen years old and is not as happy as she tries to appear. She is very pretty and healthy-looking. Her manner is affable, brisk, and business-like. She said she was unsure about the reason for the interview. She hadn't questioned her mother about this because "I never do! Whatever she says goes!" She quickly admitted that she had some theories of her own, however, about the reason for the interview. Both of her parents are worried because she spends too much time with her ten-year-old brother, Danny. At first she denied this, protesting that she likes him because "he's a charmer, a real dear. I only wish I could trade places with him."

She couldn't understand what the trouble was all about. Her mother seemed afraid to say anything about it but would occasionally "blow up and tell me to just ignore Danny . . . just stay away from him!" She also complained that some of her friends tease her and make crude remarks to her about treating Danny as though he were her "boyfriend." About this she said, "wish they wouldn't say that . . . it's embarrassing . . . he's my brother and not a boyfriend. After all, he *is* six years younger than I am, and *that* sort of thing wouldn't even be possible. He loves me and depends on me, and I'm almost old enough to be his mother. That's the way he feels about me, like I'm his mother—not that *other* way."

She then began to tell about when her parents separated. Her mother went to California and she remained with her father and a paternal aunt. She described vividly the scene of this separation: "Danny didn't want to go. He screamed and fought, and my father had to help put him in the back seat. When they drove away, he was pounding on the back window and crying. I kept waving to him until he was out of sight."

She paused a moment, appearing deeply preoccupied, and then continued on in a flat, dreamy voice. "I have a car that I get in sometimes and drive eighty miles an hour in the country . . . I almost kill myself . . . I'm not rough or crude or anything but sometimes just not very feminine . . . I have a girl friend and I like to make her fight with me . . . I take her out in a car and drive until she gets so scared she screams, then I can make her promise to hurt me if I stop the car. I carry manicure scissors around in my purse . . . once I got her to punch them into my chest three times . . . sometimes I can't get anybody to cut me like that, then I have to cut myself. A motorcycle is what I like to ride most of all after I cut myself, because that makes me feel the best . . . my mother doesn't like me to do it but I'd rather chew up an ice cube than kiss her . . . but I've got Danny . . ."

To point out that May has some serious ego defects adds nothing to the description above, and contributes no information about how to proceed in the therapy. Her therapist cannot plan treatment on the basis of having learned that she is suffering much guilt over oedipal feelings, that she has blurred ego boundaries, terrifying fantasies of castration, and a punitive superego. He will not be able to determine from his general understanding of her pathology what he is supposed to say to her in psychotherapy. He cannot know whether he is best advised to "uncover" or "support" or "direct." He doesn't even know that it would be within his power to carry through with any of these very general plans. He will have to find out by listening, asking questions, suggesting, guessing, and questioning some more. His uncertainty about her diagnosis and outlook, and about the things which he will be doing in psychotherapy, will persist throughout the period of treatment. May is a new and unknown patient, and the things which he will need to learn about her and do for her cannot be extracted from any general dynamic formulations. In this brief interview there were substantial indications that May is suffering from a "schizophrenic reaction," although she also demonstrates many signs of psychoneurotic conflict. She is also delinquent and sexually deviant.

She is also an adolescent. Treatment measures will be determined not by the final diagnosis which is affixed to her hospital record, but by those highly individual, fluctuating features of her illness which appear to be schizophrenic, neurotic, and characterological as well as by those which are healthy. The chaotic fears and wishes which have become a part of her did not develop in relationship to a "rejecting mother" or a "passive father," but rather with a mother and father who expected, demanded, and permitted that she feel and behave in ways which are infinitely more complicated than the most elaborate electronic computer or dynamic psychological concept.

Many of the common psychiatric syndromes of adolescence are described or alluded to in the brief case excerpts which are used to illustrate discussion of treatment principles. In the main, however, the therapist's most useful reference point in conducting psychotherapy with the adolescent is the normal, or usual, rather than the pathological. The impact of puberty on the youngster, his reactions to it, the emotional tasks which he must accomplish in becoming adult, the positive contributions which his adolescent experience make to his adult life—these are the therapist's most valuable guide lines for making those difficult moment-to-moment treatment decisions in his work with him.

3

ADOLESCENTS

Adolescence is that period of life which lies approximately between the twelfth and eighteenth years of life. The developmental span commonly referred to as latency, during which conscious reflections and fantasies on sexuality are dominated to a large extent by the youngster's attention to the attractions of the outer world, corresponds approximately to the elementary school years. The transition from the relative tranquility of latency to the restlessness and personality changes of puberty generally begins somewhere between the tenth and twelfth years. The onset of puberty is presumably initiated by certain somatic changes, although the exact relationship between these physical transformations and the personality characteristics of puberty is not well understood. Precocious puberty, the premature development of secondary sexual characteristics in children below about eight years of age, is not accompanied by the storm and stress so typical of puberty and mid-adolescence [25, 26]. The parents of these youngsters are often deeply distressed, but not the children themselves [27].

The biological changes of puberty affect the youngster directly in various ways, and also stimulate a number of reflected influences through the emotional impact which they have upon the important people around him.

The direct effect of these changes on the individual might be tentatively classified as (1) those which are experienced as urgent sensations, such as increased sexual excitement and the subjective component of aggressive impulsion, and (2) those which the youngster can observe directly—increase in size and altered body form, as well as his *consciousness* of his increased sexual and aggressive feelings.

The first is the one most emphasized in the discussions of puberty which are based on the conventional scheme of psychosexual development. The biological and emotional equilibrium of latency is disrupted by the increase in the strength of instincts, with a proportionate intensification of genital excitability and aggressive strivings. The relative incompetence of the pubertal child to master these in stride results in a quality of partial ego disorganization which is a necessary preliminary to its subsequent reorganization; it arouses anxiety, motivates the reinforcement and refinement of existing patterns of psychological defense, and stimulates a fuller elaboration of affectivity and thinking.

More difficult to describe are the secondary, sociopsychological effects of these primarily somatic changes. These influences act through the pubertal child's perception of the changes occurring within himself and also through the altered nature of the responses which the changes evoke from other people.

Motives for Progress

There are some sharp modifications in the expectations imposed upon the child by the people in his sphere. He is now seen as being much bigger and stronger, ergo, more self-reliant and competent. There is a time-lag between his becoming aware that more is expected of him and his attaining the ability to respond to this adequately. The dreadful feelings of childishness, of being unable to make the grade, are feared intensely by the pubertal child. His profound sense of being less-than-expected provides much of his powerful motivation for plunging himself into the considerable labors of adolescence. He runs scared—and if he were not frightened, baffled, and filled with doubts, he would have no reason to run at all.

From clinical experience alone we are accustomed to recognizing puberty as an important transitional period in personality development. Great numbers of youngsters are referred for psychiatric evaluation because of their inability to respond satisfactorily, in the opinions of those around them, to the inviting and frightening challenges of growing up. School performance begins to fall off sharply. The will to compete seems to wither. He loses interest in friends because they are doing things which he feels himself unable to do. He fills in as best he can by turning to daydreams and childish play or by overinvesting in latency-type activities (hobbies, for example) in an effort to achieve a level of expertness which will help to support a protective sense of omnipotence. During puberty he may also extend his latency interest in aggressive sexual symbols (guns, knives, etc.) into an awkward, transparently overprotesting, self-defeating imitation of the maturation struggle.

This point of view is an important one to have in mind when beginning psychotherapy with the early adolescent, because he is usually quite conscious of his appalling feelings of impotence, worthlessness, and competitive inferiority. It is rare to find a delinquent antisocial boy, for example, who can long maintain his muscular posturings in the face of a direct inquiry into his own *conscious* estimation of himself. The socially marginal, self-styled "hood," even in the initial interview, usually provides a succinct and deeply meaningful dynamic formulation of the psychology of the hood—his sense of isolation from others, of sexual inferiority, of feeling effeminate, of fear, and of being a monumental bluff who is continually amazed that he can impress others when he himself is not really deceived by his own pose.

Further Excursions of the Adolescent Ego

The latency-age child is interested in the world of things, of toy rockets, dolls, model airplanes, guns, drawing pictures, baking cookies, garter snakes, and cartoons. These interests are not necessarily abandoned in puberty and may even become intensified, but now they join with fantasies which tie them more closely in consciousness with those which they temporarily replaced not many years before. Whereas the latency-age child took his parents and other adults pretty much for granted, the pubertal child experiences again, and with renewed force, some of the same feelings which he had had toward his parents when he was about three or four years old. These include the now-familiar idea of resurgent oedipal longings and fears. However, here it is important to remember that this revival is taking place after some five or six years of further development, during which the youngster has not only continued to mature neurologically, but has also acquired a new sense and knowledge about people. He has learned much about how to enjoy them and get along with them, how to deal with their aggressions against him and his against them, how to make friends and be a friend. In other words, through this experience he has become familiar with the psychological processes by which his feelings for people may be directed to persons *outside* of his own family.

He has also found in his latency adventures and explorations of the world, in his mischief and his secret violations of adult prohibitions—and with the guilt-atoning support of friends—that certain limited transgressions against people do not necessarily destroy them, or him, as he had once feared they would. He has had many opportunities to soften the irrationally rigid, punishing, and constrictive dicta of his childish conscience.

The increase in sexual drive also makes its effect felt through organs other than the genitals. The heightened potential for pleasure in tasting and sucking, looking, touching, skin-sense, hearing, and speaking all impose upon the pubertal youngster a new sense of urgency for satisfaction. His past childhood experiences, from birth through five or six years of age, have afforded him a knowledge of how to go about seeking these satisfactions. In other words, the impetus to perverse routes of sexual gratification has also increased, and in what we conceive of as normal development it is effectively, though not easily, opposed by (1) the relatively greater erotization of the genitals [13], (2) a latency experience which has facilitated the directing of sexual longings to people outside of the family, and (3) a social fabric of rules and customs which both drive and support the youngster in his troubled, strenuous effort to experiment with some new ways to satisfaction.

BOY AT PUBERTY. The boy's latency-age interests in play objects, which are reasonably presumed to be derived in part from the sexual-pleasure potential and aggressive value of his own penis, include a sizeable inventory of long, pointed projectable weapons; pistols, rifles, knives, and arrows are eternal favorites. His play with these toys, often thought of as part of the psychological work of childhood, dwells on such maneuvers as stalking and surprising the enemy, shooting him, being shot by him, collapsing, and writhing about in protracted and highly dramatic death scenes. In puberty and early adolescence there is some shift in interest emphases, but the more striking change is in the new uses to which he puts his erstwhile toys. He begins to abandon models in favor of the real things. Much energy and careful thought goes into the building of usable items, into tinkering with the mechanics of functioning automobiles, boats, and even airplanes. He is not only interested in the principles of vehicular mechanics and in how things work, but also in where they will take him—geographically, sexually, and socially.

The knife is used for whittling art objects and whistles, in camping, and for similar productive activities. Firearms are used for hunting and in a more-or-less disciplined effort to improve marksmanship in target-shooting. Although fantasies of using these "phallic" weapons against people persist strongly, they are no longer tolerated as a basis for formal play. In many sick adolescent boys this play continues in the carrying of concealed knives and hand guns and on too many tragic occasions in their lethal use against other people.

As their highly civilized adult mentors will not initiate them into manhood and womanhood, it is often necessary for young adolescents to take the task upon themselves. They carve up their skin with initials and mystic symbols and then make quite a show of their courage: "It's nothing—merely an awful painful cut on my arm that I just put there for the hell of it." They compare courage and stamina in athletic and scholastic competition and in bending the law without breaking it. The need for self-proving is naturally greater in the mentally ill youngster, as reflected in his correspondingly gaudier, more transparent, and less effective efforts to this end. For many of the sicker boys clothing fads become fetishes. They tattoo themselves with symbols of death, fear, and sex. They attempt to glorify their tortured ambivalence with H-A-T-E and L-O-V-E tattooed across the back of their fingers, one word per hand and one letter per knuckle. They lack the skill and the motive to succeed in looking reckless without real danger. They hurt themselves and others. They break the law clumsily and get caught, partly because they unconsciously "need" to and partly because they lack the imagination and judgment to make the greatest display of nonconformity with the least actual deviation therefrom.

GIRL AT PUBERTY. The interests of the girl at puberty shift from mothering play with dolls to large, stuffed woolly animals. These are to be possessed, loved, and admired but not played with. She is inclined to regard herself similarly as she becomes deeply preoccupied with her physical appearance and sexual attractiveness. Now mostly unconscious of a once keenly conscious sense of being at a physical and psychological disadvantage with boys, she still remains under the influence of these feelings. Much of her behavior seems aimed at compensating for feelings of feminine inadequacy.

Thirteen-year-old Connie was seen for outpatient evaluation because of constant arguing with her father and increasing frequent and severe temper outbursts which were without apparent cause. Not too surprisingly, she expressed strong feelings of "disgust" for her father, although she acknowledged that they had been "very close" when she was younger. She felt that both of her parents were biased against her, and she was also extremely jealous of her twelve-year-old brother. Over the preceding year or two she had developed an intense fondness for stuffed animals. She had also become very preoccupied with a variety of colorful fantasies about horses:

"I love my stuffed doggies. I keep them on my bed and usually I sleep with them under the covers with me. When I was a little girl I had a toy doll but she was too little to hug, so I just let her sleep in her doll bed at night. All my girl friends have stuffed animals, too. I don't know why we like them so much but we do. Whenever we get together we brag about who's got the most of them, and the biggest . . . I don't know . . . Girls have to have *something* to brag about—they don't have anything else. What? Oh, yes—I *love* horses—I just *adore* them! They're so strong and graceful. Last summer I went bareback riding down on my uncle's farm. My little brother was so mad when he found out about it. Well, I'm a little bit scared of horses, too . . . I mean, after all, what if he'd kick you in the stomach? My stuffed animals are safer. One thing I know is, I don't want to get married when I grow up because I'd be too busy taking care of children to go horseback riding."

It would be difficult for a psychiatrist to improve upon Connie's unintentionally crystalline formulation about the "dynamics" of her interest in stuffed animals and living horses.

Whereas the pubertal boy's sexual interests are mainly in the genitals, with some displacement to stature, voice, and body hair, the girl's is concentrated more on the secondary sexual characteristics such as head-hair and on the conspicuous body changes involving breasts, hips, buttocks, gait, and posture. In this general pattern of increasing sexual differentiation, to take a strictly teleological view, the boy's conception of himself as something of a missile is nicely complemented by the girl's development into an ostensibly passive, seductive and attractive target.

Effect on pubertal child of adult's reaction to him. In addition to the internal maturational boost to genital primacy [13], the process of sexual differentiation is strongly supported by the rather abrupt proliferation of secondary sexual characteristics. Not only does the youngster feel the inward intensification of excitement, but the implications of this experience are also made public by the flourishing of other physical features which clarify the direction and rate of his sexual development. People are impressed by his new look, which is in turn an impressive reminder to the youngster that he is no longer a comfortably ambisexual child. A girl's tomboy tendencies are placed in sudden jeopardy by the first suggestive whistle which reaches her ears. A boy's girlish giddiness is tauntingly challenged by one of his more androgenic classmates.

With all of this, the altered feelings arising from within and the reactions to them from without, he begins to expect much more of himself in taking adult responsibilities and forsaking childish indulgences. These same expectations are actively shared by the adults in his environment. When he was ten years old, he could still run and crawl into his mother's lap when injured. At about the age of eleven he might consider doing this if hurt badly enough. But by the thirteenth year he would not be likely to seek out the consolation of maternal cuddling even if every bone in his body were broken. Other people also expect grown-up behavior of him.

Parents and their adolescent children become very nervous in one another's presence. The father develops an irritable intolerance to his gangly, squawky-voiced son's lingering infantilisms. How is he supposed to tell the boy to start calling him "Dad," or "Father," instead of "Daddy"? And mother's heart goes out to her poor boy. Deep down, she never really believed that he would ever degenerate into this lamentably self-centered, perspiring, angular, towering, uncommunicative lout of a half-man, skulking around the house and languishing over-long in the bathroom. The soft skin of childhood is blemished by hairiness and acne ("unbalanced glands"). Masses of muscle deform the cute, sticklike figure of yesterday. The eager, confiding songlike voice of boyhood yields to a surly croaking. What happens now to the tender maternal kiss at bedtime?

The pubertal girl, for many years the apple of her father's eye, becomes something of a foreign body therein. Father and daughter irritate each other. Between them only skinny-bottoms are for lap-sitting and flat fronts for hugging. The old hilarious romping is finished, as is most of the direct teasing and tickling. She has to find other reasons for getting close to him, like crying on his shoulder as though she were still a little girl. But to him she no longer feels like a little girl, with her unripe linearity gone over to a sort of fulminating plenitude. The pressure points of embrace are different. He is angered by her clinging ways, criticizes her appearance, doubts that she is old enough to date, and finds many reasons for curtailing her social contacts with boys—all with the highest of motives. Periodically father and daughter tend to enjoy a vast, mutual disgust for one another.

Many of the acute illnesses beginning at puberty are transparently related to the failing struggle of parent and child to rend themselves free of one another. In many hidden ways the pubertal youngster becomes more helpless and dependent than before, and so do his parents.

The timing of the physiological and social events of puberty lend tremendous impetus to the principal emotional work of the adolescent. They help him with the formidable task of breaking the dependent tie to his parents. To him it has suddenly become a matter of his wanting more than ever to have all those things which he wanted as a child, and at the same time of finding the wishes more insufferable than ever [16, 21].

ADAPTIVE FUNCTIONS OF PARTIAL DRIVES. Some of these infantile yearnings are put to sound developmental uses. For example, the sloppiness and inattention to dress and cleanliness so characteristic of puberty are commonly attributed to an increase in "anality." It may be partly this, by definition, but closer observation will reveal that much energy and cunning deliberation goes into the creation of the same generalized uncouthness which is so natural for the toddler. Great care is required for the effective unpressing of trousers, the color mismatching of clothing, the leaving open of shirt collars, the unshining of shoes, the tousling of hair, and the unshaving of patches of blond whiskers from the face. These things represent far more than a simple pleasure in smearing, being dirty, or offending others. The intensification of pride and the official launching of a calculated campaign for autonomy are signaled by this behavior. They are carefully designed by the youngster to be shocking and alarming to the adults who would have him be otherwise.

The conflict between his feeling of pride, and the guilt engendered by it, is tentatively compromised by the youngster's rendering himself conspicuously unattractive to dissident adults. It is a partial answer to the shyness and self-consciousness which he feels about maturing physically. That part of his rather bizarre appearance and behavior which makes him conspicuous is pleasurable, helps him resist the impulse to phallic exhibitionism. The part which is self-effacing helps to palliate the guilt and fear elicited by the pleasure accruing from the behavior. And the part of it which favors his secession from total dependence upon adults, by dissenting from them, is greatly strengthened by his dedicated alliance with age-mates who are seeking the same goal. The peculiar languages, rituals, dress, haircuts, and make-up are of value to the adolescent only to the extent that they win a good measure of shocked disapproval from the adult. Understanding this principle is essential to a realistic appreciation of the "authority-permission" dispute which arises so often in discussions of psychotherapy with the adolescent.

Jocasta Spurned

In direct observation of the child in his ordinary social activities, we do not see an epidemic of gross sexual collision between the sexes at puberty. The sudden impact of instinctual feelings comes close to fulfilling the conditions required by the definition of a psychological trauma. The pubertal youngster is nearly swamped, from time to time, by the strength of his feelings. The intense longings which pull him back to the known pleasures and dangers of the past are opposed by his anticipation of the unknown and exciting pleasures and dangers of the future. The result is a reversible but rather protracted state of partial psychic immobility, of generalized restlessness, irritability, preoccupation, and indecisiveness. With gentle reassurance, almost any thirteen-year-old will acknowledge that he frequently suffers grave doubts about his sanity. He looks for a way out of chronic confusion. Although mistrustful of adults he is even more mistrustful of himself, and he turns to his peers for help.

To the pubertal boy, of course, a girl of his age is not so much peer as a creature from outer space. In her he sees the image of a grown woman whom he cannot help but view with fascination and excitement, which feelings he next responds to with fear and caution and, depending upon his past experience with adult men and women, perhaps also with disgust, horror, and aversion. In any event, the quality and intensity of his feelings toward the girl are sufficient to disqualify her, for the moment, as one who can help him resolve his fears of her. He turns instead to his fellow sufferers, and together they proceed vigorously with the behavioral business of reassuring each other that they are strong enough to cope with the demands of heterosexuality.

They accomplish this partly through a crash program of self-proving competition and mutual admiration. At this time they value most highly such things as physical strength, athletic prowess, bravery, pubic and axillary hair, the large penis with a capacity for erection and ejaculation, and a studious "contempt" for girls. Their isosexual play is at one and the same time a source of pleasure and a preparation for better things. They argue, fight, and compete among themselves, but with a tacit understanding that each contestant will win something. While struggling together in the pubertal testing grounds, they also praise each other lavishly. Commendation by open admiration becomes their prime medium of exchange. They flatter one another shamelessly in what is probably the world's strongest mutual admiration society.

The success of this operation depends in part upon their overcoming the fear of getting together with girls. The boy's threatening fantasies of being with a girl sexually are minimized by an elaborate process of derogation—of the girl and of heterosexual acts. She is generally referred to not as a person but as a part, by universal obscenities which represent her as being the same as her genitals—no more or less. They find some reassurance against deep-seated fears of heterosexual union, along with substitute pleasure, in rituals of "goosing," genital grabbing, and overt homosexual play. They seek to conceal the implications of their behavior in the guise of masculine recklessness, which in the end is belied by sexual jokes and songs so raw that anyone but the boys themselves could easily recognize that they are indeed whistling by the graveyard. Their conduct, at times, has a semblance of orgiastic abandon, but it is as structured and purposeful as any ceremonial exercise of adult society.

The adolescent's knowledge of dirty words conceals a monumental ignorance—a wealth of neurotic misunderstanding which is in a large measure based on the need to believe something other than the facts. Searching the dictionary for a good definition of *whore*, he looks under the *h*'s. He knows every obscene synonym for the genitalia, but isn't really certain about how they work or whether babies are born through the umbilicus or "from below." His manner is uncompromisingly dogmatic in arguing sexual topics with friends, and in this way he invites information while appearing to impart it. If he becomes a patient, he will do the same thing with his therapist.

Their individual labors are supported by many existing social institutions. It is noteworthy that most of the public schools in our society are divided into four distinct sections, which are usually located in separate buildings or sites: kindergarten, elementary school, junior high school, and high school. It is unlikely that these divisions were made arbitrarily or simply for purposes of administrative convenience. They have evolved in response to society's sensing that the youngsters in each of these age groups share some interests and problems which they can deal with best by well-timed graduation past these concrete developmental milestones.

Youngsters of junior high school age, approximately thirteen to fifteen years old, quit the game playing of recess time in favor of isosexual horseplay and infinitely cautious heterosexual intrigues. Complicated romantic alliances are highly publicized and actively lived out in fantasy, but provide very little relief of sexual tensions.[1] The genital drive is taken

[1] This may be less true of youngsters of the lower socioeconomic classes, who are perhaps more inclined to premarital intercourse at earlier ages than are children of upper-class families.

care of mostly through isosexual play and solitary masturbation. The boys and girls fall deeply in love with each other but usually from a considerable distance. In the main, they make "love" to each other through a complex network of communications and intermediaries, flooding the channels with carefully worded and high-sounding but substantially noncommittal mash-notes to one another.

More often than not their fondness for each other is made public through gossip which relates that they are having *trouble* with each other, that they have *stopped* going together, that they have *given each other up*, and so forth. This is a process which enables them to sample the potential pleasures and dangers of heterosexuality in relative safety. It provides safeguards against the agonizing "narcissistic injury" of unreturned love: "*If* I asked you to go steady, would you?"

Although the boy is likely to declaim on his rather sterile affair with incredible coarseness and bravado, in field practice he approaches girls with a degree of deference bordering on speechlessness. Together, the boys and girls practice the ritual of turning away from each other in the histrionic spirit of grand romance; their love has fallen apart for reasons far grander than both of them.

In middle and late adolescence, through about the fifteenth to the seventeenth years (during high school), this training in heterosexuality undergoes a marked but still incomplete shift from classroom theory to laboratory experimentation. It seems probable that the move from junior to senior high school building, with the reorganization of classes within an expanded curriculum and with the much larger student population, facilitates the breaking of the strong isosexual ties of puberty. It is a time for acquiring new friends with whom to share a stronger, more real interest in heterosexual relationships.

The apparently natural democratic spirit of the elementary years yields to a tacit but complex system of social discrimination in high school, one which begins to bear a close resemblance to the political and social organization of adult society. Social strata are established, recognized, and respected, though seldom referred to as such. A socially active group of "popular kids" is distinguished by good looks and pleasing "personalities," by good though not necessarily outstanding scholarship, and by sophistication or knowledge of the world and its people. Perhaps most of all they are characterized by their talent for securing the favor of others and for rendering themselves liked, respected, and sought-after for the bestowing of social grace upon those of slightly lower caste. They become people of influence. They make a practice of remembering names; they enter a great many activities and are skilled at winning votes and appointive offices. The individual youngster is respected for his abilities and talents, but in the main his movement up and down the social ladder will be determined mostly by the company he keeps. He acquires a "reputation" which is the social reflection of his personal sense of identity. He comes to depend on this. His keen awareness of being *identified by other people*—through their acceptance of his reputation—motivates him to maintain it even if it is "bad." It is a crucial time.

The adolescent's exquisite sensitivity to the value of his own loosely integrated identity attributes, as compared with those of other people, is one of the many paradoxes of his age. His is a narcissism of the truest sort—more easily understood as self-contempt than self-love. He examines himself microscopically for flaws, and observes others with equally minute care in search for "ego-patches" with which to piece out the surface of his own personality. It does seem that his deep interest in others is mostly for his own sake, but perhaps this is not so bad. Adolescents work together, each letting the other know where and how he is weak and vulnerable, and simultaneously provide one another with cues and models for the more finely detailed sculpting of an identity in the adult style.

Elaboration of Attitudes and Feelings

In his "psychological screening" of other people for compatible identity elements and for other self-protective and adaptive processes which he can incorporate, the adolescent is painfully suspicious of counterfeit goods. The loosening of his own defenses under the impact of puberty increases his capacity for seeing through the ruses which older people use to deceive themselves. This is a hidden advantage of the purported "ego-weakness" of adolescence. In his transient frailty he is better able to identify his own deficiencies, and doing this is a necessary prelude to revising and improving them. The adolescent who does not experience this agonizing self-scrutiny in his relationships to others may enter the adult years as a precocious elementary school student, skilled in many ways, and sunnily optimistic perhaps, but still a perennial good pupil who is probably better qualified to work eternally at "pleasing parents" than at completing any job of work, marriage, or parenthood which does not offer a promise of immediate praise or approval. A decided shift in stance is needed to support these burdens adequately.

IDEALISM AND DISENCHANTMENT. The adolescent must pay a price for his heightened psychological acuity. It hurts him to recognize that people are not all they appear to be. Against the ugliness of adult hypocrisy he raises a visor of idealism. He endows selected adults with the perfection and omnipotence which he had accorded his own parents when he was a toddler, but his belief is no longer secure. His idealism vies with feelings of scorn, disillusionment, and loss, until acquiescence to an adult code enables him to accept for himself the comforts of a "socially necessary hypocrisy."

In him we see something of the schizophrenic's impaired capacity for tolerating evidences of self-deception in others. This is reflected in the latter's embittered, hopeless complaints about the falseness of people, of their "hiding behind masks," and "acting things they don't really feel." The artist and the adolescent often seem equally chagrined by recognition of the successful defenses of others, but react with attitudes of cynical criticism and sarcasm. The "great illusion" is something which they view with anger, sadness, and disenchantment but not—as for the schizophrenic—with despair. They still hope.

The well-adjusted adult is naturally unaware of his self-protective operations most of the time. When forced to face himself during moments of personal emotional crisis, he can usually resolve the disturbing discrepancies between wish and reality by the usual philosophical platitudes, some of which may even be true.

The psychiatrist, hopefully, is very much aware of these disquieting incongruities, and strives to be flexible enough to accept them as good and inevitable parts of his personal life and professional work. His ability to do this is crucial in psychotherapy with the disturbed adolescent, to whom a deliberate but well-intended "white lie" seems strangely less damaging than an unconscious deception. Such a lie to an adolescent is a misdemeanor in comparison to the felony of hypocrisy. He has little use for a stuffed shirt, but can occasionally extract some good from one if nothing more nourishing is available. There is no adequate synonym for the deeply meaningful, exquisitely damning adolescent epithet "phony." This is perhaps the worst thing a person can be as far as the adolescent patient is concerned. Curiously enough, many adult patients respond very favorably to therapists who could not even get close to the adolescent.

Disappointment and skepticism. Skepticism is an essentially emotional predilection for questioning the truth of anything and everything, and it becomes a definitive attitude in adolescence. It is a protection against disappointment and an invaluable instrument of reality testing. During adolescence there is a heightening of the latency child's deep concern and preoccupation about the sincerity of people. Moral issues of honesty and dishonesty, of right and wrong, assume a dominant position in the growing youngster's reflections about the people who populate his world.

Perhaps nowhere are the dynamically conflicted relationships between the dreadful pull to the past and the impetus to an unknown future depicted with greater effect than in the stories and novel of J. D. Salinger. The heart of Holden Caulfield, the "hero" of the novel [30], lies with children and their ways. He looks with impotent longing to the remote heights of adulthood and tries to console himself with a sour-grapes profaning of those who have achieved them. He does it by burlesquing pompous adult pretentions to godliness and altruism. He mocks the adult's fear of facing himself—his lack of courage to accept painful truths for comfortable lies. And yet Holden, it seems, lacks the capacity, perhaps even the courage and wisdom, to do the opposite.

New attitudes develop during adolescence which serve partly to reconcile some of the feelings of unhappiness which follow in the wake of improved reality testing. The child's feeling of disappointment, of having received less satisfaction than was expected, is a relatively negligible source of shame prior to puberty. When he becomes adolescent, it is necessary that he react to losses manfully, i.e., as though they do not really hurt. The simple pouting and petulance of latency ripen into cynicism during adolescence. An improved knowledge of the world renders many of the favored myths of childhood untenable. The void created by this loss of comforting illusions is worsened by society's covert disapproval of belief in them by anyone but a child.

The debunking of Santa Claus epitomizes the pubertal youngster's painful but growing doubts about the omnipotence and trustworthiness of parents and other adults, their reliability, and the truth of their beliefs. The lofty, lip-curling visage of the cynic, the feeling of irony, and the "touch" which bears its name are the affective equivalents of the overdrawn and unconvincing idea: "I cannot bear to lose these things, nor can I believe them any longer. They are not true, and as a mature adult I no longer dare to care." The angry resentment engendered by the loss is turned less against "reality," which is an intangible and unresponsive abstraction, than against those who—after having perpetrated and perpetuated these soothing illusions—failed to sustain them against the youngster's expanding knowledge of reality.

The things which are lost are the satisfactions of childhood, and the parent is held responsible. His offense is that of refusing his half-grown youngster the indulgences of childhood. Only the continued, unrestricted provision of infantile gratifications would be a worse crime in his eyes. However, such highly valued attributes of the adult code as forebearance, patience, responsibility, and perseverance are pallid substances which cannot be accepted overnight. During the transition the depriving parents and the other adults who shared their aims stand temporarily accused of peddling counterfeit satisfactions. And yet the adolescent himself is sufficiently threatened and endangered by his own wishes for the earlier pleasures and is so covetous of adult status that he dare not declare his disappointment and resentment openly.

He does not attack the adult for stealing Santa Claus, but holds him liable for having supported the fantasy in the first place. In his own adulthood he will acquire an easier tolerance for his affects, and will be able once again to savor this delicious fantasy as he passes it on to his own children. The St. Nicholas legend with all the feelings surrounding it is an admirable illustration of pleasure's debt to pain. Replacing Santa with perfect reality testing might indeed spare us that sweet-sour yearning for the past, but it would also cure us of wanting to become parents. Until the adolescent becomes adult, he can only rise above his loss, above his own wishes to be little and catered to, by despising the adult with well-balanced respect and contempt for having started it all *and* for having finished it all.

Sarcasm, satire, and burlesque becomes the adolescent's favored defenses against feelings of disillusionment. These are, essentially, attitudinal innovations of adolescence. In satire, and in its broader form of burlesque, the disenchanted youngster attempts to reassure himself through this highest form of wit that his old wishes are more funny than tragic and that the adult's charitable efforts to withdraw indulgences, via diminishing doses, are pitiable and foolish. Through mocking adult posturing he seeks to sever his dependence upon them and to lift himself one level above them. In all of this he becomes society's foremost critic of society's ways of doing things. Pangloss is the archetypal adult, Candide a caricature of prepubertal credulity, and in Voltaire is embodied, among other things, much that is most admirable in adolescence.

NOSTALGIA, REMINISCENCE, AND ORIGINALITY. Beginning at puberty and on through adolescence, the youngster acquires a variety of seemingly new affects and attitudes. Technically, these feelings may not be quite as new as they appear if traced back to their primordia in early childhood, but at the very least their combined effect is a novel one in which the vivid, primary emotional colors of childhood have expanded into a greater and more varied profusion of subtler hues.

Feelings of nostalgia, which are experienced mildly in latency, become a major emotional force in adolescence. The equilibratory, defensive, and adaptive functions of reminiscing serve the adult well. For him it is a relatively elective mental activity in which the recalling of retrospectively distorted, predominantly pleasurable events of the past serves several worthy purposes. Its greatest practical value is in enabling him to "profit from the experiences of the past." But perhaps its most important function is that of helping him to get the most possible out of his short life by remembering and reexperiencing the good things of the past. The extent to which a person is able to enjoy this special premium on his own life is limited by how safe it is for him to do so.

The adolescent, like the adult schizophrenic or hysteric, lives under the threat of recalling too many of the wrong things too quickly. But unlike them he is able to acquire, through a cautious trial-and-error remembering, an aptitude for poeticizing disturbing memories. In adolescence he learns to filter much of the dysphoria from the feelings which were associated with them. The end products of the process are the definitive affects of adult life. They are more numerous, refined, and varied than their childhood progenitors, and it is during adolescence that much of this final differentiation of affectivity takes place. Some representative names of these feelings or states of mind are *bemusement, wistfulness, hope, yearning, sadness, compassion, affection, disappointment,* and *cheerfulness.* They are not popular in the technical argot of psychiatry. Completing the distillation and blending of these life-enriching essences from the raw musk of infantile instincts is one of the major works of adolescence. Until he becomes adept at regulating their magnitude, they sweep into consciousness with hurtful impact. He must have the strength to tolerate them until the relative "flattening" of adulthood occurs. And the adult, for his part, must learn to enjoy life with fewer of them and with even these operating under reduced force.

ORIGINALITY AND AUTONOMY. At adolescence there also occurs an increased interest in words and ideas, especially those which are longer and more impressive. Language clichés, which make one appear "with it," catch on. Logic and formal argumentation replace the explosive, salivary name calling of the elementary years. The great and basic philosophical questions of all history, God, immortality, morality, are reviewed anew as though for the first time.

This increased interest in thinking is more than just another way of "mastering instincts." Under the influence of a compelling inner need to establish his separateness from others, the adolescent strives in all these areas for original formulations—ideas that are his alone. He attends to the concrete data of the humanities and sciences only long enough to gather enough material for building an "original concept" as a monument to his own individuality.

This striving for originality is another aspect of his struggle to negate the stifling sense of being in debt to other people. He must refurbish the thoughts embezzled from them in such a way as to convince himself that he is their author. Rewording attractive ideas is not enough. Their source must first be thoroughly extirpated, driven from consciousness, despised, and depreciated. Father and his political views are denounced by the son in passionate argument, then a few days later, to father's consternation, they are virtuously resurrected by the boy as "new thoughts." The adolescent patient similarly condemns his therapist's idea as "stupid," only to return it a short time later as a brilliant inspiration which "I just thought up this very minute." (The perennial joke comes to mind of the young man's great surprise at finding, upon returning home from college, how much his father has learned during his few months' absence.)

The adolescent's assaultive flourishes against adult authority are more art than craft, but as an artist he inevitably lays himself open to critical review. The adult is the critic of his inspired attempts to reinterpret the data of the external world. The adult's rather defensive smugness and feelings of superiority are continuously and bountifully fed by his recognition that the adolescent's heroic struggle to achieve new frontiers eventually brings him—in the overwhelming majority of cases—not one step beyond the familiar frontiers of contemporary adult society. The adolescent tries to exceed us but fails; and in failing, the normal youngster still wins the compromise benefits of relative emotional tranquility, security, and comfort and a rewarding sense of being a member of the majority.

Occasionally something different comes of his efforts to be original, more often than not something bizarre but in rare instances something novel and usable. When this happens, his offering is ordinarily suppressed by the forces of adult conservatism, which is in itself a significant source of inspiration for the youthful innovator. He nourishes and cultivates his idea until, often many years later, he has acquired a sufficient knowledge and discipline to put a burr under the saddle of orthodoxy. This is the eternal dream of adolescence, the occasional realization of which marks the road of progress in science and the humanities. It is only the rare individual who finds himself unable to make the compromises necessary to "becoming adult," who cannot relinquish that crusading quest for absolute truth which was conceived in childhood, germinated in latency, flowered in adolescence, and—in normal development —deflowered in adulthood.

In this highly experimental and uncommitted phase of his life, the adolescent has little which is permanent and reliable upon which to construct a stable conception of what he is like and how much he is worth. He has no job or career by which he can be named; no house, spouse, or children; no definitive office in the church; or respectable place in the politics and community affairs of the adult. Many of his tasks bear the stamp of "made work," exercises to strengthen him for future labors. He longs with mixed feelings for a real job, at one moment firmly convinced of his competence and at the next gravely doubting that he could last for twenty-four hours on his own without starving to death.

In the struggle to secede from his own childish past, the adolescent is often rather terrible to live with. Even so, the adult stands a good chance of further enriching his own life and outlook by subjecting himself to his sometimes fresh, often disconcerting, but eternally promising viewpoint.

4

TENSIONS BETWEEN ADULTS AND ADOLESCENTS

In some of the aforementioned differences between adults and adolescents in their biological, psychological, and social states, there are certain sources of tension which, if not precisely universal, are certainly usual and expected in our culture.

In psychotherapy with the adolescent it is important to remain deeply aware of these for a number of reasons. Most of the treatment process might be viewed as an effort, by whatever specific means, to ameliorate these tensions in helping the adolescent to become a reasonably comfortable and civilized adult. It is vital to keep in mind that these tensions are *normal:* They serve an indispensable function with respect to the further ego development of both the adolescent and the adult.

As we proceed with the treatment of a particular youngster we must be able to discriminate between those aspects of his personality and ours which are participating in the resolution of these *developmental* tensions, and those which fall outside of the usual range of conflict. We will not respond to these normal, physiological tensions as we do to those repetitious expressions of old feelings toward parents and siblings which are being irrationally transferred and reexperienced in relationship to the therapist. There is frequently nothing worthwhile to interpret in a routine authority struggle, for example. In such work-a-day conflicts the authority is simply applied, rather than understood, because it is an essential psychological nutriment for the adolescent as well as a realistic necessity. We exercise it as a common courtesy, a natural expression of our respect for his strengths and weaknesses in adversity. He is entitled to this much, and it is usually neurotic guilt over our own aggressive strivings rather than therapeutic objectivity which prompts us to withhold it.

Usual Sources of Tension

It is interesting that psychiatric literature abounds with references to the reawakening of certain of the pubertal youngster's instinctual strivings—the same ones which he originally directed toward his parents when he was barely more than a toddler. This one-sided emphasis on the adolescent's liability in a decidedly mutual relationship is a typical adult stance. Little is said of the effects worked upon *us* by the changes in him, or about the ways we have of protecting ourselves from some of these, or about the effects upon him of our altered feelings and attitudes.

Sexual tensions. There is little need to dwell for long on the details of the pubertal changes which cause so much trouble for the adult. As parents, or as adults responsible for the care of children in other situations, we participate vicariously in their "latency" experience and customarily find in this much of the same kind of comfort and safety which they are enjoying. When they cease being "latent" and become disconcertingly "manifest," we will necessarily participate in this as well. The particulars on the manifestations of puberty, as far as simple biological inventories go, have been dealt with at length in countless articles and textbooks. Here, we are interested in considering certain properties of the strain which is introduced into our relationship with a child as he enters adolescence.

He becomes, for example, a much more provocative target for our own sexual and aggressive feelings than when he was a skinny, noisy, more sexually benign five- to ten-year-old. Perhaps it is because he has done the changing, while we have remained the same, which facilitates our holding him responsible for creating these new threats.

Girls become larger and prettier, that is, more like women. Lines and angles give way to curves, contours, and softness. We can detect also a change in the state of mind and affect which accompanies this physical metamorphosis. We sense with growing uneasiness *her* activated consciousness of genital sexuality, our greater responsiveness to her increased sexual desirability and vulnerability, and her heightened capacity for becoming aggressive toward us. The same things are also true of boys. They become tall, muscular, more attractive sexually, and much worthier challengers to the aggressive and sexual supremacy of adult men and women. It is small wonder that we prefer to think of adolescents as older children, rather than as young adults. Clinical evidence is strong that much of the adult's fear of being attacked, raped, or seduced by the adolescent is greatly amplified by the projection to the youngster of his own unconscious strivings. In him, the adult senses an opportunity for either the direct or vicarious fulfillment of his own drives. The unconscious temptation to exploit him accordingly is a significant source of guilt and anxiety for any adult who works with him closely, whether as a parent, a teacher, or a therapist.

The heightened apprehensiveness arising from these clouded wishes has the practical value of motivating the parent to enforce new, age-appropriate controls over the youngster and to provide him with purposeful directions. Concern about the son's or daughter's morals and trustworthiness leads to a somewhat stricter and more business-like approach which is beneficial in at least two ways. First, and most obvious, is the fact that it helps protect the youngster from the injurious consequences of his impulsivity and still-immature judgment. Secondly, the aura of antagonism which invests any authority transaction between adult and adolescent provides a credible *external* rationale for the overdetermined anger, impatience, and disgust which both of them *need* to feel for each other. These patently negative affects protect the combatants from realizing and acting upon their even more frightening erotic feelings for each other by placing a comforting degree of emotional distance between them.

THE THREAT OF COMPETITION. Additional strain is imposed upon the adult-adolescent relationship by the strengthening of the latter's competitive faculties. The adolescent grows intellectually sharper and more imaginative. His aggressive questioning about the aging adult's fixed views of reality are often vexingly original, as described earlier.

Somewhere in this time of life there also blooms that most elusive of human faculties—creativity. This is not just competence, which is honored in other ways and in its own right, but originality in thinking things and seeing things which he fancies no others have thought or seen before. Of all the prerogatives of adolescence envied most by the adult, perhaps it is this *opportunity* to see things in new ways—even if nothing ever comes of it—which inspires the greatest and also least tolerable envy.

To some degree consciously, but even more unconsciously, the adult is also jealous of the adolescent's youth, his special and socially sanctioned license for promiscuous, if incomplete, sexual and aggressive experimentation. He resents the youngster's wider range of affective experience—the general and almost continuous excitement of his age. The adolescent, to put it simply, may be mixed-up, green, and living inefficiently, but the overtaxed and heavily harnessed adult cannot help but sigh occasionally that, even so, "the kid is really living."

The adolescent also threatens us with signs that he is working for certain other psychological developmental goals which we adults continue to seek. When the youngster demands his chance to be independent, for example, we will inevitably feel some guilt over denying him his chance, however unrealistic his specific request might be. Our empathetic involvement in his earnest wish for more self-determination makes it harder to refuse him. When he fears he cannot handle the job which he longs to do, he forces us to keep him safely dependent by demanding his "rights" with such stunning arrogance that—though we dare not grant them—we are still filled with guilty doubts about denying them. In short, he contrives to make it appear that it is *we* who will not let him grow up, and we are inclined to believe him.

The other side of the adult's altrustic intentions is the wish to "take away" from him. The adult's conscious conception of himself as being confidently independent is never entirely reconciled with the unconscious fear that he is still not good enough to hold his own in open competition. We sense that the adolescent is out to get what we have and that we are obligated to stop him by forcing him to accept a compromise alliance with us in lieu of the total victory which he seems to want. There is a panzer-like quality to the adolescent assault against the forces of adulthood which is slighted when one considers only the feeble flailing and thrashing about of a single, angry young man. The threat of our being replaced by him, in time, is very real.

Outgrowths in Therapy of Usual Adult-Adolescent Tensions

Another source of chronic vexation for the adult is the youngster's greatly sharpened alertness to the needs and motivations of other people, and his special sensitivity to that intricate complex of social fictions to which well-adjusted adults have subscribed en masse. We are aware of the smaller child's not-so-uncanny psychological insights, and have all felt the sting of his valid confrontations on those occasions when he has chosen to place his superior appreciation of the "unconscious" in the service of manipulating us for his personal gain.

The adolescent plays with casual skill upon our diathesis for feeling guilty about our unconscious wishes to hurt or exploit him. If he wants a small favor of us, e.g., permission to attend a movie, he is likely to start by requesting a two-week pass to the French Riviera, unchaperoned. Then, with much agony and travail, he gradually reduces each subsequent request in orderly, stepwise fashion—suffering each refusal stoically—until he finally reaches the prize he sought in the first place. By the time he gets to the point, this "last little request" seems so trivial by comparison to the rest, and we feel so much like beasts for having said "no" eight straight times in a row, that it becomes almost impossible to refuse him [16].

He trifles also with the therapist's emotional investment in his therapeutic successes. Over a period of weeks or months the adolescent patient observes that his doctor has begun to swell with pride and self-congratulation over another therapeutic triumph. Just as the doctor begins to enjoy a mental image of himself as a Fine-Warm-Therapist, he is ready for the axe. The patient begins to "regress," pointing out in velvet tones that he is getting sicker because "You aren't giving me a chance to get well . . . If I had full pass privileges, I know I'd just feel better." So reluctant is his doctor to relinquish the facade of success—which indeed may not be entirely spurious—that he unexpectedly finds that *he* is "paying" the *patient* to get better. The patient becomes the supervisor of his own therapy.

So extensive is his appreciation of our soft spots and so determined his purpose to unseat and control us, that even an adolescent of average intelligence—in debate with a highly intelligent adult—will appear to perform like the devil *and* Dan Webster. His skill in argument is scarcely at all dependent upon respect for the rules of "logic" as we like to think of them. He relies, instead, upon misleading and often paralogical sophistries which are administered with dazzling speed and change of pace. The sustained intensity of his feelings distracts us from what he is saying. We find ourselves arguing about whether chair rungs were designed to hold the chair together or as footrests, and then walk off forgetting that, in winning the argument, we lost the issue. (We had gone to remonstrate with him for being abusive to a nurse who had asked him not to put his feet on the sofa, but unfortunately he led us by the nose away from the important question, that of his conduct with the nurse, to an enchantingly irrelevant polemic on the "function of Function" in furniture design.)

The adolescent patient is finely attuned to these sensitive questions of motivation. He protests that we do not really care about him; we are seeing him only out of academic interest, to make money, to feel superior and strong by the cunning device of placing ourselves in close association with people who are mentally ill, to solve our own problems, to seduce him, to enjoy his suffering. Such questions often rush to the foreground during periods of improvement, and even when the improvement is genuine, the patient will find in it an occasion for "testing" whether we like him mostly "for himself" or for what he can do for us.

Probably all his vague suspicions, and others as well, will be partially true. Here the therapist has one of many opportunities to demonstrate his capacity for tolerating certain psychological realities about himself. If the patient's accusations are true, they should not be denied. It is not really possible to hide these things anyway, and ill-advised efforts to do so simply encourage the youngster to attempt extorting special concessions which will favor his reversion to a more dependent, demanding, immediately pleasure-seeking orientation. Treatment deteriorates into a series of covert attempts at a subtle form of psychological blackmail, in which the patient promises a show of improvement in exchange for a quick reward. The lyrics vary slightly, but the tune is usually recognizable if one is not entirely tone deaf.

"I can't stand that math class. If I have to go there one more time, well, I'll just fail it completely."

"Coming in here and talking to you every week doesn't make me feel any better. My father says there's no point coming here anymore if my grades don't get better. I told him if I could just take the car out and drive it around every now and then my grades would get better. Maybe you should talk to him."

When there is at least a kernel of truth in the patient's complaint, one which represents genuine concern on his part, then the therapist can hardly do better than to examine it openly, with a conscious and disciplined determination *not* to dismiss his own liability by interpreting the complaint as "neurotic transference." The patient's accusation that we are keeping him in the hospital just to make money is most likely to appear when he begins to wish and fear that we have some other, even more threatening motive for retaining him as a patient.

Maria, seventeen years old, showed signs of becoming strongly attached to her therapist. She began to accuse him angrily, "You only want me to come in here so you can make more money."

Her doctor reminded her that he was on salary, and his income would remain unchanged whether she continued as his patient or not. She easily countered this psychological irrelevancy by pointing out that he was still profit-sharing with the hospital, in the sense that his income depended on its solvency.

"Well, there's some truth to that. Seeing patients is a part of my job, and I am paid money for doing my job. Is that what you mean?"

"Of course you do it for money—what else?"

"That's a good question. Can you think of any answers? What reason would I have for seeing you, if not to make money?"

"That's what I'm saying—*there isn't any other reason!*"

"Perhaps there isn't, but there certainly could be. You're determined to convince yourself that I'm seeing you only for money. It seems to me that you don't even want to *think* about any other possibilities."

"What do you mean by that?"

"The same thing you're talking about. Tell me, what if I were seeing you and not charging any money for it, and not especially interested in helping you—why would I do that?"

(Beginning to get embarrassed) "Oh, it doesn't matter, I know you're not out to make money."

"But I *am* out to make money. And aren't you glad of that? Otherwise, I might be seeing you *just* because I like you."

"I wish I hadn't started this."

"Well, it's a good thing you did, because there's something to what you're really worrying about. After all, I *did* agree to take you as a patient. No one forced me to."

"You had to, didn't you?"

"No. There isn't enough time for me to see everybody. I have to do some picking and choosing. You see?"

"Yes."

Threat of Regression to Adolescence

These very common sources of stress in the relationship between the adult and his apprentice help us to understand our reliable preference for referring to adolescence as a "developmental stage." We are inclined to minimize its value as a time worth living in its own right, though far less loathe to rhapsodize on the more distant aches and pleasures of childhood's tender years.

These are some things in the adolescent experience, related to the finishing-up of a respectable identity, which are harder to recall and reexamine than are some of the theoretically more threatening "instinct-memories" of childhood.

The adult has occasional opportunities to sample a bit of the shame and embarrassment entailed by reflecting too intensely on the floundering, defensive experiments of his own adolescence. It is not accidental, for example, that only a small percentage of our once deeply meaningful high school friendships are carried into adulthood. High school class reunions are not nearly as delightful as one always dreams they should be. It is not pleasant to be reminded of what a fool you were before you grew up.

The adult seems to have some cryptic, self-interested investment in the youngster's successes and failures which stands apart from the benevolent wish to see him grow up well. There are things about him which remind us that we have not advanced nearly so far from the frailties of our own adolescence as we would wish. As the agent of this unpleasant reminder, the adolescent makes an excellent target for the projection of our most provocative unconscious yearnings. He is an ideal scapegoat. He enjoys withdrawing from us to join others of his age, and together they seem to create, willfully and deliberately, an outcast minority of their own. He likes to make us angry at him. He invites blame and frequently seems to relish it when it is placed upon him [32]. He is too young to have good judgment but is too old to be excused from his transgressions against society on grounds of childishness and immaturity.

It is easier to forgive the small child his deficiencies because his time of life is so remote from our own. When the average adult looks back to his own childhood, he sees a youngster who is very familiar, very close, but not really in atonement with his current conception of himself. Memories of early childhood, whether recalled spontaneously or by deliberate free association can be assigned to this helpless little creature who really exists no longer. This same patronizing and forgiving attitude, which the adult holds toward the mental image of himself as a child, is readily transferable to other little children.

But, for similar reasons, he withholds from the offending adolescent a comparable expansiveness of mood, of understanding tolerance, because he has never forgiven himself for having ever been weak, uncertain, ignorant, foolish, and dependent upon others to help him get on his own feet. He cannot quite forgive himself because, in those brief, flinching glimpses through the amnesia which covers most of his adolescence, he recognizes *himself*—the same person then as now. And he is still not quite certain that he has really made it, permanently and irreversibly. It is true that the pleasure and defense modes of adolescence are not so "alien to the ego" as those of childhood—nursing at the breast and smearing feces, for example—but neither are the latter so temptingly available as bragging, promiscuity, and fighting. Nor is the memory of them so close behind as it is for the cowardice and confusion of the immediate past—adolescence. Those years cannot be dismissed with the same ease as the remote experiences of childhood.

People are able to speak of childhood experiences in rather intimate and seemingly self-critical detail, but these accounts are customarily punctuated with neutralizing laughter, a shrug, and a casual sweeping gesture of the hand which relegates it all to the archives of ancient history. Reminiscences about adolescence are more discriminating, tending to focus more carefully upon recollections which will reflect positively upon one's contemporary image of himself. One's athletic accomplishments, scholarship, social and sexual prowess, dashing adventures, and personal triumphs—such things move quickly to the foreground.

There is an all-or-none quality to reminiscences about adolescence. It is either done not at all, at least not in public situations, or it is done with a somewhat overdetermined delight and enthusiasm. This, of course, helps the adult *not* to remember certain other things which are conspicuously absent from these occasional excursions into the recent past. These are things which are no less gnawing now than they were then and indeed no less painful than the better-known and more widely publicized conflicts of infancy and early childhood. There are the memories of abysmal self-doubting, of plunging despair and hopelessness, of soaring elation which far exceeded its cause. There are also the alarmingly gross failures in reality testing, the same transient fugue flights, episodes of derealization and depersonalization, and transient confusional states which when encountered in the adult patient are generally interpreted as having grave diagnostic implications. And yet they are regularly to be found even in our mildy neurotic adolescent patients, as well as in the adolescent who "passes as normal." One has only to inquire tactfully of these youngsters to hear them speak with surprising candor of such passing lapses in reality sense and testing.

It is reaching the age of "knighthood" which really battens the hatches on the unconscious. The adult cherishes the illusion that he commands a full recollection of his own adolescence, but he retains only highly selected, sentimentalized segments of it. Mercifully, he also forgets the foolish philosophizing, the fears, the stupid fantasies, and the wasted aspirations. These things belong to a way of life which is not compatible with what we conceive of as adultness. When the pressure is on to hold a job, have a family, and be civilized, there inevitably occurs a sacrificing of dreams in exchange for food, clothing, shelter, and an indispensable measure of liking and respect from others. In becoming an adult, the individual will have achieved what Erickson [11] speaks of as a "role," the cost of which is the renunciation of the excitingly grand and hopeful fantasies of the adolescent epoch.

It is extremely important that the therapist acquire, through experience, a reliable sense of these natural, essentially adaptive stresses between adult and adolescent. This is essential to his developing a functional grasp of the ideas of transference and countertransference in treating adolescent patients.

Neurotic Interaction Between Therapist and Patient

The term *transference* is one of the many which lends itself to too loose usage in some quarters and to endless semantic nit-picking in others. It is, approximately, one's experientially determined predilections for having particular feelings and reactions toward other people. For example, an average adult's capacity to enjoy a mutually fond and respectful relationship with another person depends upon his having had such a safe and satisfying experience during his infancy and early childhood. This would be an ideal attribute of a completely mature relationship, but no one is quite that mature. At times one's reactions to other people are inspired by feelings which seem too intense and not rationally related to the circumstances which appear to have given rise to them.

A first-year surgery resident, suddenly finding himself all thumbs in the middle of a relatively minor procedure, was offered some unsolicited advice by the veteran scrub nurse. He erupted in an angry and profane verbal attack against her. He was sufficiently cooled off by the end of the procedure to apologize for his outburst. On the way from the operating room he explained self-critically to the assisting intern: "That's what happens when you have a mother who thinks she knows everything—I've got to watch myself."

A surgeon has some prerogatives which in this instance might have warranted his advising the scrub nurse to reserve her suggestions until they were asked for, but certainly not much more than that. This doctor quickly appreciated that he and the scrub nurse had suffered some transient pain as a result of the long-standing feelings of anger for his mother which under particular conditions he too readily transferred to others.

Certain social customs, such as common courtesy and the respect for protocol, ordinarily provide people with a high level of protection from acting on such predispositions. But there are many other situations which because they are intimate, prolonged, and fraught with heavy responsibilities strongly enhance people's tendencies to react in the present—without respect to the appropriateness of the reaction—as they would have in a similarly crucial spot at some time in their own pasts. Marriage and child-rearing are two circumstances of relationship which facilitate regressive, neurotic, "transference-like" reactions as few others do. Psychotherapy, obviously, is another one.

When a patient experiences an overdetermined and relatively anachronistic response of this sort in the course of treatment, it is usually called, by general agreement, a transference reaction. The therapist's own overdetermined, anachronistic feelings and responses to the patient are referred to as "countertransference," which does not mean, of course, that they are either more or less neurotic than the patient's transference.

Essential to any proper conception of psychotherapy is the idea that somehow, in the course of it, there are revisions in the patient's continuous predisposition to react to other people automatically and stereotypically. Such change may come about in various ways, but it is the one aim which is shared in common by all the theoretically different forms of psychotherapy. Treatment experience with the disturbed adolescent, as with children [14], requires that we reconsider several ideas about transference and countertransference which were developed mostly in connection with the psychoanalytical treatment of neurotic adults.

It is assumed that the neurotic adult outpatient will take care of himself, and the outpatient treatment of the child presumes that someone other than the therapist, usually the parents, will be responsible for the patient when he is not actually in the office. When the patient cannot be relied upon to take responsibility for his own welfare and when it becomes necessary for the therapist to do this for him, then we must recognize that many of the little rules, admonitions, and definitions which grew out of classic analytical therapy will no longer apply.

Transference and Relationship

Danger in overinterpreting transference. At many points in treatment the patient's various reactions are dealt with much as they would be in the case of the "ideal adult neurotic," but seldom is it warranted to treat them as the distilled essence of transference. The adolescent outpatient whose parents cannot or will not take care of him as needed, and the inpatient who has become the almost total responsibility of his therapist, have been thrust into a real and active relationship with the therapist whether either of them likes it or not. The patient *really* must depend upon his doctor for many things, and the doctor, if only for making the continuation of treatment possible, also depends upon the patient. Consequently, a sudden and unexpected outburst of apparently irrational anger, though perhaps neurotically determined, might also have been justified by the therapist's failure to fulfill some important treatment obligation.

Bart, sixteen years old, "blew up" in anger when his doctor denied his request for permission to be relieved of restriction to the boys' side of the ward. At first glance this seemed to be just another repetition of the angry resentment which he had always felt toward his parents whenever they refused him his wishes. But the magnitude of his reaction and the context in which it occurred suggested that there was more to it. A carefully detailed review of recent events enabled Bart to inform his doctor, behind a face-saving camouflage of sullen reluctance, that he had recently succeeded, to his dismay, in making some considerable and rather frightening advances with one of the girls. The staff, for unconscious reasons of their own, had been turning their backs on the matter almost entirely. When proper chaperonage was resumed, Bart returned to his previous "transference" grumpiness.

Similarly, much of the patient's positive feelings toward his therapist *can* occur because he has felt them before with other people, but they *do* recur at this time because he is being well cared for by his doctor. The common rule of thumb that one ought not "interpret the positive transference" with children and adolescents should be understood to mean that one ought not interpret *all* the youngster's positive feelings as belonging to the transference, because they do not. Those feelings which are overdetermined, inappropriate, and unrealistic, even though they appear to be "positive," will not stand the patient in good stead in the long run, and an effort must be made to modify them in treatment. The feelings of fondness which belong naturally to a good relationship usually do not need to be talked about one way or the other. Too great a readiness to "explain" the emotional transactions of psychotherapy by the transference concept feeds into the adolescent's resistive inclinations to make a game out of the serious work of therapy. He will correctly identify overexplanation as the therapist's defense against his own feelings, whether they are of a "countertransference" or "real relationship" nature.

Dr. T sought an informal consultation regarding his outpatient treatment of an eighteen-year-old girl whom he had been seeing for several months.

"Over the past several weeks she's been getting more anxious in the office. She squirms around and keeps smoothing her skirt down over her knees. She started complaining several visits ago about feeling very uncomfortable in the office. I suggested that maybe she was having some feelings about me which troubled her, but she denied that. She said she'd been thinking about having an affair with a boy friend because 'it might help her treatment.' Then she started the next interview by reporting two dreams. They were both about the same thing. In them she was very excited and getting ready to have intercourse with a man whose face kept changing. At one moment it was her boy friend's face, at another her father's, and at another it was mine. I wonder how one is supposed to handle this kind of transference with an eighteen-year-old girl."

Dr. T's consultant suggested that he ask his patient to talk about any *acquired* preconceptions she might have about psychotherapy, if she had been reading books on the subject or talking to amateur experts. He also suggested that she should be advised directly that having an affair for the purpose of "helping her therapy" would be, as she must certainly realize, utter nonsense. Although somewhat skeptical, Dr. T confronted her with these questions in the next hour. She was startled but respectful of the questions, and acknowledged that she had indeed been doing extensive library research on the subject of "dynamic therapy." After this she inquired with a bright smile, "But isn't treatment supposed to be like that . . . where you fall in love with your doctor and your boyfriend, the same way you did with your father when you were little?"

This patient had undoubtedly begun to experience some uncomfortably stimulating feelings toward her therapist, but her defense against them was a high-powered intellectualization which facilitated the denial of its truth. The suggestive signs of this were the sequence and content of certain events, specifically the dreams and the unconvincingly naïve question, all of which were a little too pat. Her half-sober, half-mocking approach to psychotherapy was a resistance, unconsciously aimed at converting the whole process into an entertaining and harmless hobby. It is a general class of resistance which meshes well with the adolescent patient's talent for making dangerous things safe by ridiculing them in fantasy.

COMMON FANTASIES AND BELIEFS ABOUT THERAPY. There are a number of popular notions abroad about psychiatrists and psychotherapy which give aid and comfort to the aforementioned type of resistance. Some of them, like those having to do with beards and couches, are virtually *passé* and usually easy to deal with. Certain others are more subtle fantasies and beliefs about therapy which, rather surprisingly, are likely to be shared by the therapist. A few of these which recur with predictable regularity are worth examining from the patient's point of view.

"You know everything and can do anything, so it's all up to you." The implications of this fantasy, that the therapist is omniscient and omnipotent, are sometimes frightening to the patient and at other times reassuring, but at all times provide a basis for tenacious resistance. It enables the patient to shift the responsibility for his own mental, emotional, and motoric "behavior" from himself to his therapist. In treatment he speaks as though he has signed over his volition to the doctor, which in turn frees him to interpret all his experiences as things which are happening *to* him, rather than *because* of him.

Eileen, age sixteen, had been referred by her parents because of school refusal, somatic complaints, and defiant behavior toward them. They said they had tried unsuccessfully to help in every way they knew and were glad to be rid of her. When she began to show signs of improvement both of her parents became very anxious and started to talk about removing her from treatment against medical advice.

With the skill acquired through many years of diligent practice, Eileen went to work on them. In letters she wrote, "I'm just getting what I deserve. I have no right to expect anything further from you. Don't worry; I'm managing to get along all right in this place." She told them she was so glad that at last they could have some happiness for themselves, now that she was no longer around to interfere.

When she was informed by her doctor that her parents were on the verge of removing her from treatment, she shrugged and replied, "That suits me fine, but I know it will never happen—you'd never let them take me out of here."

She was promptly assured that this was a very risky belief on her part, that there was no way for him to stop it should they remain determined to follow through. She was shocked and frightened by this information, following which there was a distinct change for the better in the tone of the letters to her parents.

In casework with them, they were helped to recognize what had been going on between them and their daughter, and were able to abandon their plans to flee from treatment. However, if Eileen had continued as she had been, there is little doubt about what the outcome would have been. Her influence over her parents was considerably greater than her doctor's. In this area, at least, she was more powerful than he.

"As a psychiatrist you have risen so far above your feelings that they no longer matter to you." The fantasy that the therapist is essentially "acathectic," when shared by him, can become the basis for the most intractable transference-countertransference "binds."

Dr. C ran into serious trouble in his treatment of an intelligent, muscular, "aggression-inhibited" sixteen-year-old autistic boy. After several months of treatment he found Frank increasingly unapproachable, and reported to his supervisor that he was truly afraid of physical attack. On several recent occasions Frank had risen menacingly from his chair during treatment interviews and, trembling with suppressed rage, threatened his doctor with convincing force.

"I could finish you with my bare hands . . . Don't you tell me what to do, I'll tell you what to do. What do you think you could do about it if I decided to knock you around this office for a while?"

In supervision it was suggested to Dr. C, who was a very kind and "aggression-inhibited" person himself, that "it's not possible for a person to face that sort of thing without wanting to accept the challenge, to get angry and counterattack. You may be a little afraid of *him*, but most of all you're anxious about what *you* could do to him . . . think of the fantasies you have when he talks to you that way, like sailing into him and teaching him a thing or two about the realities of assault. There probably isn't anything, any kind of feeling, that makes a psychiatrist more anxious than that one."

Dr. C returned to his supervisor several hours later in a state of acute anxiety. He expressed severe feelings of guilt over the fact that he really had not felt anger toward Frank, and had entertained no retaliatory, aggressive fantasies against him. At the same time he knew enough about himself to realize, or sense, that these feelings were operating within him. He wisely decided, shortly after this, to limit his clinical work to the outpatient treatment of children and adults.

Frank had become increasingly disturbed by the development of intense, ambivalent feelings toward Dr. C, but his testing, through the making of open threats, was mostly prompted by his correctly perceiving that his therapist was also troubled by strong feelings of anger within himself which he could not tolerate well. This was far more frightening to Frank than a show of anger would have been.

"You are a paragon of mental health." Some of the popular, openly hostile jokes about the psychiatrist's eccentricities conceal a half-envious, half-contemptuous reaction against the idea that the psychiatrist might actually be, or might regard himself as being, psychologically flawless and symptom-free, consummately rational and realistic.

Sally, age fifteen, had idolized her father for many years. Her parents had separated when she was quite young, and consequently she'd never had the opportunity to see his eminently human side. Their limited contacts enabled her to dream of him as a considerate, kind, and "giving" father at all times. Although he was a fine person, he could not possibly have lived up to her idealized conception of him. She quickly transferred this to her therapist in treatment, but the circumstances of intensive psychotherapy and residential treatment could not accommodate such innocence. Growing feelings of disenchantment with her doctor were unconsciously regarded by her as a betrayal of the father whom she loved so dearly. For a period of time she became anxious and relatively inarticulate in interviews, then one day began to refer casually and with alarming accuracy to some of the specific neurotic weaknesses which she had observed in various staff people.

"When Dr. F comes down on the ward to see Amy he always clears his throat three times before knocking on her door."

"Miss T (nurse) is real nice, but if one of the boys even smiles at her she blushes every time."

She concluded her inventory of staff neuroses with the offhand remark to her doctor, "I sure am glad you're not neurotic," and sighed with relief. Her therapist, genuinely amused, suggested that she go ahead and tell him about her diagnosis of his deficiencies. With some further support she was able to do this in most telling fashion, following which it was possible for her to proceed in treatment with an improved appreciation of reality. Doctors are also neurotic, perhaps not always but often.

"Psychiatrists aren't supposed to do that." This epitomizes various aspects of the adolescent's thoughtful critique of psychotherapeutic technique. A reasonably complete catalog of the ideas in this category would take a great deal of space, but they are of this general order:

"You are a psychiatrist and you are not supposed to get mad just because I lied, cheated, and deceived you."

"You never ask me what I dream about, and when I do tell you my dreams, you never explain them to me."

"You're not supposed to say anything to anybody about what I tell you in here, but you squealed to the nurses what I told you about how I was going to run away—I'm never going to say another word to you!" (Followed by an hour of uninterrupted monologue)

"You're not supposed to tell me what you think about things; you're just supposed to bring out the best in me."

"I saw you downtown last weekend with some little kids—whose were they?"

"Someone said you had a party at your house last night, but I know that isn't true."

These are not all evidence of pure transference; there is really a widely prevailing image of the psychiatrist as a priestlike person of supernatural intelligence and wisdom, and as one who has no need for wife, children, parties, symptoms, or other petty indulgences of this mortal sphere.

Of these various notions which the adolescent patient is particularly prone to entertain, perhaps the most important, from a practical standpoint, is his dangerous overestimation of our protective powers: "I would run away and get married, but you would only find me and have it annulled." All of these have clearly important transference implications, but dealing with them interpretively, at this level alone, reflects too little respect for the youngster's remarkable penchant for misconceiving our limits. Many things may be said and done about these issues when they come to the fore in therapy, but a careful clarification of reality is one which *must* be done.

"Like it or not we had better face it, I cannot keep you in treatment if you determine to leave it. I cannot make you lose weight. I cannot make you work in school. I cannot always 'get the message' in your behavior in time to do the right thing about it. I cannot read your mind."

The Well-Contaminated Transference

The therapist's attitude toward his adolescent patient is subject to some special influences which vary rather consistently with the youngster's general type of pathology, with whether he is an inpatient or an outpatient, with the specific circumstances of inpatient treatment, and with the professional status of the therapist in the latter setting.

SPECIAL PROBLEMS WITH ADOLESCENTS. As the adolescent is frequently inclined to take a somewhat eccentric view of the mechanics of proper psychotherapy, he can be relied upon to do various things from time to time which will greatly embarrass himself and his therapist. The well-behaved, neurotic adult outpatient makes comparatively little trouble. He keeps most of his problems inside of himself, and takes them home with him when the hour is over. In such an arrangement it is possible, and in the main desirable, for the therapist to communicate as little as possible to students and to other people, i.e., colleagues about his treatment methods and results. It also protects the therapist by keeping his mistakes from the public eye, and often enough from himself as well.

Even the adult impatient is far less likely than the adolescent to discredit his doctor publicly. His acting-out, when it occurs, is ordinarily in the framework of a circumscribed clinical syndrome of some sort. That is, even though he may become grossly psychotic and a difficult management problem for the nursing staff, the therapist is still protected by the fact that his patient is seen more as a sick adult than a "crazy kid."

In the eyes of others the adolescent patient has the privilege of sharing the blame for his misbehavior with his therapist. He is, after all, just a young and inexperienced minor who has not been properly reared by his parents. His doctor, on the other hand, passes as an expert on the psychological complexities of child-rearing. He is tacitly assumed to be such an improvement over the "bad parents"—those who "made the youngster sick" in the first place—that he will be expected to work therapeutic wonders on a moment's notice. Further, even though everyone knows better, there are many times when they cannot help but think that the youngster's pathology, meaning his misbehavior, is a *direct* and *immediate* consequence of the bad home influence; once he is removed from that it should be a simple matter for the doctor to settle him down. When this dream fails to materialize, there is a strong tendency for adult staff members at all levels to blame the doctor and for the doctor to become overdefensive and belligerent.

Nurses also have a very hard life at the hands of adolescent patients. Among the staff there develops a great need to place the blame on someone other than oneself. When there is sudden trouble, the doctor's first comment to the nurse is likely to be, "You shouldn't have approached him that way," and the nurse's first question an accusatory, "What did you say to him in interview? He's been upset ever since he left your office." The supervisor calmly suggests to the resident that he has acted injudiciously because of countertransference distortions, and the resident complains that he was the victim of unwise and inept supervision.

Commonly enough these frantic recriminations are tentatively resolved by a compromise agreement among all parties to lay the blame on someone who is not there to defend himself, the parents, a previous therapist, or perhaps a public school visiting teacher who once said the "wrong thing" to the patient a few years back. When the sounds of battle die away, however, and it becomes apparent that there have been no monstrous errors made by any members of the staff, it usually proves most therapeutic to lay the responsibility at the feet of the person who can use it to best advantage—the patient. "Holding him responsible" is exactly the opposite of adjudging him "bad." It is moral, rather than "moralistic."

Practicing psychotherapy in a goldfish bowl is far short of the ideal from the standpoint of the therapist. The immediate results of his efforts are visible to all. He can hardly avoid the feeling that his professional talents and disabilities are constantly on the block. These are perhaps some of the reasons why inpatient treatment is not too popular among psychiatrists, why the treatment of adolescents is even less popular, and why the treatment of adolescent inpatients is notoriously unpopular. Psychiatrists of high seniority, those who are professors, clinical directors, psychoanalysts, or Board Certified child psychiatrists, for example, are understandably loathe to risk their established reputations by practicing their uncertain art in the clear view of others. In psychiatric training centers the high-status person is usually not eager to treat patients on the same ward with those of the residents whom he is supervising. Treating inpatients is also more time-consuming, tiring, and often less rewarding because of the more serious forms of illness encountered in this population. Finally, it is an experience which does little to support our most cherished fantasies about what psychotherapy *ought* to be like.

Active intervention and transference. By custom, the psychotherapist feels constrained to avoid certain actions toward the patient, out of concern that the effectiveness of some future interpretation might be impaired by his having provided the patient with a realistic basis for defending the validity of a neurotic transference reaction. The principle of "minimum active intervention" in the patient's life distinguishes orthodox psychoanalytic treatment from other forms of psychotherapy, but in no sense does it provide the only basis for dynamic, interpretive psychotherapy.

When the patient's sickness demands more than that he be asked occasionally to recognize something about himself which he had not known before, the mandate necessarily changes from "don't intrude," to "intrude as necessary," and *then* both therapist and patient try to understand how the intrusion has affected the treatment relationship.

In both approaches the treatment principle is the same. We try to understand, and help the patient understand, why certain of his feelings are not rationally related to the reality circumstances which seem to have evoked them. This work can be carried on in a relatively sterile field with the adult neurotic outpatient. When the latter complains that he is doing poorly because his analyst will not go out and find a job for him, the neurotic transference distortion is rather easily pointed out: job-finding is truly and properly not a part of the analyst's responsibility.

The sharp contrast between neurotic and realistic expectations is not so simple with the hospitalized delinquent. For example, he claims to have mended his ways completely and accuses the doctor of interfering with his healthy adaptive efforts by advising the court that he should remain in the hospital. There is some truth to his objection. His doctor *is* compelling him to remain in the hospital, and the reality distortion which needs clarifying is the idea that enforced hospitalization is the only factor preventing him from improving. This could be true, but the therapist cannot know one way or the other without trying it. This, though, would require that he subject his patient, a dependent and delinquent minor who is *supposed* to be grown up, to what might be a serious risk.

Dr. L was interviewing an acutely psychotic fourteen-year-old girl on the adult closed ward. In the course of the interview she became extremely excited and disorganized, and began to shout her intentions to carry out a sadistic sexual attack against one of the ward nurses. She made a sudden lunge for the office door with the manifest aim of implementing her fantasy. Dr. L had no time to deliberate on the nuances of the transference, and leaped to the doorway to block her path. The ensuing interpersonal transaction entailed what might be delicately spoken of as a certain amount of "physical contact" between them, but which was a violent and erotically charged collision between two real bodies which belonged, however unfortunately, to a doctor and his patient. In a post-facto conference, some note was taken of the fact that Dr. L had indeed made a significant contribution to the transference-countertransference snarl by acting in a way which was, inevitably, instinctually stimulating to him and his patient. However, it was generally agreed that he should not have acted otherwise. Transference complications would have to be "worked through" on the grounds that it would not have been good for the patient to attack a nurse or for Dr. L to permit her to do so.

The rather literal taboo against "activity" in therapy has undoubtedly been supported to a degree by the somewhat greater authority of classic psychoanalysis in matters of theory. This has made it a little too easy for the psychotherapist to make certain clinical decisions more by rule than by reason. For example, most hospitals and communities have enough doctors to make it possible for the psychotherapist to keep his own field of treatment relatively "clean" by referring his patient to another physician for various routine medical procedures. Even so, the adolescent patient will occasionally wonder why his therapist, a medical doctor, will send him to a complete stranger to have his sore throat examined. When there is good cause to give an answer, it is usually enough to explain "It keeps things simpler between us—you will understand it better as we go along, if you don't understand it already."

The proposal here is not that it is either good or bad for the psychotherapist to perform medical procedures on his patient, but rather that he feel himself free to decide the issue on the basis of available indications and contraindications whenever the question arises. Many therapists scrupulously avoid "activity" to prove that they are "dynamically oriented." Others operate on the thesis that one should "lay on hands" in order to prove that he is not afraid to touch, or to demonstrate that he is a "Compleat Physician," or that he is definitely *not* a psychoanalyst.

Laura, fourteen years old, was admitted with a diagnosis of "personality disorder, antisocial type." She was not, nosologically, a psychotic youngster. She was admitted to the closed adult ward, and after two weeks of quiescence launched into wholesale temper outbursts, defiance, and destructiveness. After being removed to the seclusion room, she soon became quieter and more controlled. A little later she complained of headache, chest pains, and coughing, then of an itching rash on her neck, and finally, approximately a day later, of nausea and abdominal pain.

Although she had a long history of "crying wolf" with physical symptoms, a surgical consultant was asked to see her regarding the possibility of an acute abdominal disease. Laura was very unpleasant to him, refusing to cooperate and intentionally falsifying and exaggerating her complaints. She howled loudly and deliberately contracted her abdominal muscles when he attempted to examine her. An abortive rectal examination revealed nothing but the patient's exquisite distaste for the procedure. The blood count was of dubious significance. The consultant recommended waiting and watching.

Returning several hours later, her therapist, Dr. S, found her subdued, somewhat preoccupied, and much more reasonable. She was lying on the right side with her thigh flexed and was complaining of lower abdominal pain and "gas." She looked pale and uncomfortable but still had no fever. A repeat white count revealed only slight elevation. The consulting surgeon, then in the operating room on an emergency, recommended temporizing until he could see her again later in the evening. Dr. S, having the advantage of firsthand observation, decided that immediate reexamination was necessary and that he was the best person available to evaluate any changes in findings. This time abdominal palpation revealed continuous, involuntary muscular rigidity and focal right lower quadrant tenderness. Laura tolerated the rectal examination quietly, and showed a pronounced pericecal pain. Dr. S ordered preoperative medications (she had refused food all day), sent her to the surgery suite, and then made his actions known to the surgical consultant. Another team was called in promptly, and surgery revealed a distended, richly purulent appendix on the verge of rupture.

The medically melodramatic overtones of the incident should not obscure the fact that the therapist's intervention resulted in the diagnosis of an acute appendicitis which was about to become an even more serious peritonitis. Although appreciative, Laura did not subsequently suffer from a constrictive sense of gratitude. Fantasies related to the sexual and aggressive implications of the physical examination were strongly dominated by her awareness that it had been a necessary procedure. She matter-of-factly regarded her therapist's intercession as appropriate to the urgency of the circumstances and to his physician's role. The transference was influenced and therapy was complicated, but not nearly so unworkably nor adversely as would have been the case had he waited too long to "suspend psychotherapy." It is even remotely conceivable, of course, that his actions may have "helped her therapy."

There are certain functions which belong naturally and realistically to the roles of the adult, the doctor, the nurse, the teacher. Consequently, if the therapist is doing a competent job of something which he was trained to do, and is doing it in his patient's interest, he will have in this a better basis for comparing neurotic transference reactions with "reality" than if he were to renounce some of the obvious functions of his role as one-who-treats-the-sick.

A doctor's professional role does much to protect him and the patient from the usual threatening fantasies of sexual and aggressive exploitation. In examining Laura's abdomen, for example, both doctor and patient were aware that his fingers were in potentially exciting contact with her skin and perineum. However, the potential was significantly negated by the fact of her being in pain, in genuine physical danger, and also by their shared awareness that interposed between the doctor's fingers and her abdomen was a tough, invisible membrane formed by centuries of medical tradition.

Beyond this there may even be some advantage to the adolescent patient's realizing that his psychotherapist is also a physician. It could be argued that the therapist's willingness to rely at all upon the luster of his role has a neurotic taint; and yet feelings of pride in accomplishment and the satisfaction of being respected for the worthwhile things which one does are natural and inevitable. A patient usually will regard such feelings in his therapist as more credible and palatable than an implied attitude of paternalistic altruism or the pose of abstract emotional neutrality.

There is no list of specific things which the therapist ought not to do in order to avoid unmanageable transference complications. The specific action which he takes, or declines taking, is entirely secondary to his reasons for doing either.

5

INFORMATION EXCHANGE BETWEEN THERAPIST AND ADOLESCENT PATIENT

Some Compound Meanings of Behavior

The celebrated rebelliousness of adolescence can be too readily accepted at face value by the apprehensive adult. If the youngster were truly as angry, resentful, and dissident as he frequently sounds, then we adults would be much too busy saving ourselves to think about helping him. If we interpret his belligerence too literally and fail to appreciate the remarkable extent to which he covertly allies himself with adult values and aims, then we will hardly find ourselves in a sufficiently amiable frame of mind to take a realistically critical, helpful attitude toward him. His antagonism is not usually what it appears to be.

Shortly after earliest infancy even the smallest segment of an individual's behavior accomplishes three things for him. It relieves tension (discharge of instinctual energy), protects him from the pain which his instincts threaten to inflict upon him (via the mental mechanisms of defense), and communicates something about him to another person.

These are not all true of the newborn who first experiences his expressed feelings quite apart from any consideration of their possible effects on other people. We assume that he does not realize other people exist, but are certain that he begins to learn this almost immediately. With advancing age the pleasure motive becomes less and less *apparent*, though no less real, and the defense-adaptation and communication functions become increasingly manifest. These three simultaneous functions of behavior are translated many times a day into the concrete work of psychotherapy. Behavior of apparently small significance often informs us of something extremely important about the patient which he cannot state directly, either because he does not know how or is too ashamed, frightened, or angry to do so.

Many of the commonest errors in psychiatric evaluation, planning, and psychotherapy result from the failure to assess the communication import of an action by comparing its content with such important corollary factors as: who did it, when, how, to whom, and in the presence of whom.

What does it mean when a fourteen-year-old boy deliberately breaks a window? Mostly, it supports a projective psychological *defense* if, for example, he is psychotic, hallucinating, "out of contact," and screaming that he is "trying to get the poison gas out of the room."

It is *instinctual* gratification if it is a window in the car of an enemy, which he breaks in the spirit of vengeance and with sufficient caution to avoid being caught.

Or it is mainly *communication* if it is a window on the ward which he breaks with a defiant, sidelong glance at the nurse shortly after she has generously offered to support his request for a special pass.

There are a number of crude but useful indices which may guide one in estimating the relative degrees to which an instance of adolescent behavior is aimed at instinctual release, defense, and communication. These can also help improve one's judgments about what is being communicated. The estimate is worth making because it will often prove to be the most reliable basis available for reaching important clinical decisions. Strangely, one of the most neglected of these indices is actual outcome of the behavior. Injurious and irreversible consequences, e.g., homicide, tend to bespeak a predominantly direct instinctual aim. As an after-the-act appraisal this might seem a useless bit of information, and yet we are regularly astonished by man's fantastic ability to reduce momentous actions to utter insignificance by designating them as "accidents," the normal prankish behavior of youngsters, or as random whims of fate.

Ned, aged thirteen, was referred for evaluation because of total nonachievement in school for the preceding two years. One casual detail, passingly referred to in the referral information, indicated that two years earlier a loaded deer rifle had slipped from its wall rack, discharged upon hitting the floor, and killed Ned's five-year-old brother. The tragedy was investigated by the parents, law officers, and youth workers. Logical explanations were rapidly given and accepted as to how the accident had occurred, and the almost instantaneous assumption that it was an accident was swiftly confirmed by all concerned. During the investigation and for the two years following, no one asked Ned if he had removed the rifle from the wall and fired at his brother, whether "playfully," accidentally, or deliberately. When this question was finally put to him in the evaluation interview, he burst into tears and told the whole story. He had become enraged with his little brother and fired the rifle at him intentionally, although he had done so with a child's ill-formed concept of death.

Most of the adolescent's more important behavioral communications are not too difficult to "read" correctly once one has identified and renounced his own neurotic inclination to cooperate with the youngster in concealing the message.

Fritz, a fourteen-year-old delinquent boy, was referred to the clinic by a community agency with complaints of school truancy, petty pilfering, and defiant behavior at home. The various adults encountered as he passed through the registration procedure, routine chest x-ray, and blood examination made jocular little comments about the loaded revolver which he was carrying tucked in the front of his belt. When he went for his electroencephalogram, it was tactfully suggested that he hand the weapon to his mother "because it might interfere with the tracing." After the study was completed, his mother promptly returned the revolver to him.

In the psychiatry outpatient clinic he was first seen by a young woman resident whose cultural background had ill prepared her to cope with this awkward situation. She deemed it best not to mention the pistol at all, and instead submitted an urgent request for consultation. When the senior staff psychiatrist appeared on the scene, Fritz greeted him with a facial expression which mingled defiance, helpless misery, and extreme anxiety. Dr. K started to introduce himself, and then noticed the revolver which Fritz had in the meantime made conspicuous by removing his jacket and slouching down in the chair. The greeting ceremony was temporarily set aside, and Dr. K observed, "Say, that is a revolver you've got in your belt?" because he was genuinely startled and incredulous.

Fritz attempted to be hard and sneery. "Sure it's a revolver. What did you think it was?"

"A revolver. You're not supposed to be carrying that around. Hand it over."

In his haste to comply Fritz nearly fumbled the weapon, and the wave of relief which came over him was unmistakable.

When his mother was later asked why she permitted him to carry the gun, she replied innocently, "Well, I've always understood that boys his age have a need for guns." With further questioning, she also revealed, "Sometimes he get mad at me and goes upstairs and fires his shotgun into the back alley. It helps to relieve his nervous tension."

Fritz was a very angry boy with many troubled feelings about his mother, and yet history and interview revealed that he had taken careful measures to avoid really hurting anyone despite all the saber-rattling. His revolver was loaded with blanks, and he had fired the shotgun into an empty thoroughfare. He was mostly trying to make it known to someone that, in addition to trying to frighten his mother, he was also trying to please her, that he was profoundly confused about his feelings for her, and that he was desperate for someone to notice his confusion and give him some help. These aims were conscious; he revealed them directly in the interview. Why not before? Because no one had asked him. There are some things a boy is too proud to admit, unless he is "forced" to do so.

Flora, aged fourteen, was admitted to the hospital with complaints of truancy from school, running away from home, and "bizarre behavior." Her father was a floridly psychotic man who passed in the community as an eccentric. He had frequently forced Flora into incestuous relations with him since she was eight years old. More recently he had begun to humiliate her in the presence of her friends by appearing on the school grounds during recess and delivering "love letters" to her which he signed "your sweet sugar daddy."

Mention of Flora's allegedly bizarre behavior referred to the manner in which she ran away from home. She threw clothing, toilet articles, and a pillow into two blankets and fled from home in the dark of night. Her escape ended six blocks away in a vacant lot directly behind the town police station, where she calmly proceeded to make camp in plain view of the entire community. It was a clever solution to a serious problem: how to get help for herself without causing her father's imprisonment by informing on him verbally.

These are examples of complex social behavior serving as a medium for relaying highly important information which cannot be declared openly. Like so much of the adolescent's telegraphy, it attracts one's attention with a showy feint from one direction as the real message is being delivered from another. Certain other modes of communication, though common to all people, deserve special attention because of the extent to which they are favored by the adolescent for various purposes.

Other Extraverbal Communication

A certain small percentage of spoken language means what it says, i.e., can be taken at face value. In addition to literal content there are the *semivoluntary expressive* media, such as voice tone and inflection, facial expression, hand signals, and body posture. We also rely upon the *involuntary expressive* signs which are mediated by the autonomic nervous system, e.g., blushing, pallor, perspiration, and a variety of visceral reactions which can have communication significance. A high degree of automaticity is a characteristic shared by all of these modes of communication, and the distinction made on the basis of their being voluntary or involuntary is only a relative one. Far and away the greatest part of a person's motive for initiating any of them is, like the bulk of their content, unconscious to him. Further, each form has its own kinds of communication tasks which it can accomplish better than the others.

Autonomic reactions. Autonomic reactions excel, for example, in the expression of such basic feelings as anger, fear, anxiety, and sexual excitement. The psychotherapist, often without realizing it, depends heavily upon these as measures of the meaningfulness of any transaction which is going on between him and his patient. The validity and effectiveness of an interpretation which has been made to the patient, even though received in silence or casually denied, is often strongly and convincingly confirmed by such signs.

Harold, a fifteen-year-old boy, had been sent to the clinic by the court with a two-year history of defiant, aggressive behavior at home, in school, and with his peers. He was muscular and square-built, with a heavy stubble of black beard. He could easily have passed for five or more years older than his actual age. His manner was imperturbable and confident. He spoke unconcernedly of his truancies and of his lippy antagonism to all persons in authority. He remarked matter-of-factly, "This so-called trouble bothers other people more than it bothers me. It's very simple—if I want to go to school, I will; and if I don't want to, then I won't."

When reminded that this attitude had got him into the juvenile detention home, he observed with continued equanimity, "Sure, but it took three full-grown men to get me there, and I'm still not in school. They won't keep me long."

Everyone who had contact with him regarded him as an aggressive, "impulse-ridden" youngster who had little concern for himself or others. He presented an almost perfect picture of this, the only discernible incompatibility being a moist, red-eyed look which he could not entirely conceal with his mildly bored, scornful facial expression. The examiner spoke directly of this:

"I could be wrong, but it looks like you have feelings that other people don't know about. You look sad . . . you have tears in your eyes."

Harold yawned, shrugged, and said something about having an allergy, to which the examiner replied, "You look at least twenty-one years old. You've probably bought beer plenty of times without having your license checked. A fifteen-year-old boy with a beard and the muscles of a man wouldn't want to admit to anybody that he's got tears in his eyes, but you have—I can see that, and I think you know it, too. Can you remember when you were a little kid, when you first started going to school?"

With this Harold's manner became openly depressed, and he began to talk about certain suppressed memories of his childhood, of the "empty" feeling which he experienced each day when he left his mother to be in school, and of his struggle to keep from revealing himself as a baby, which he did by fighting instead of crying and by being mad instead of sad.

These signs belong so intimately to *immediate* feelings that the therapist will always *start* to sense them intuitively. In order to avoid turning away from them, because of the anxiety which they will cause him, he will need to make a conscious effort to recognize and interpret them as another variety of language. Most of these autonomic signs have a sufficiently uniform relationship to affects that their appearance makes it possible to talk directly with the patient about actual and immediately experienced feelings. In this respect the treatment of the adolescent differs from that of the "ideal adult neurotic," in that the latter is obligated to report his feelings spontaneously, whereas the former must often have these reported *to him* by the therapist.

Mask of depression. Facial expressions and bodily attitudes and mannerisms are identified and approached similarly. The "depressive grin" is a broad, fixed, unconvincing smile which is reinforced by a too-happy, glittery-eyed look. It is all teeth and no mirth. It must have its defensive value clarified openly before it is possible for the patient to acknowledge any ideas or feelings which do not square with his starched mask of cheer.

Autistic look. The autistic look, often covered by signs of exaggerated attentiveness, boredom, or friendly compliance, is also betrayed by these same signs. Stereotyped verbal rejoinders, "yeah, I guess so . . . yeah, I guess so . . . yeah, I guess so," in conjunction with perseverative head-nodding in the negative or affirmative and an expression of intense interest whether anything interesting is being said or not seldom conceal completely the patient's dreamy preoccupation with his own thoughts. The therapist stimulates him to return to the present moment by pointing out these revealing accoutrements of expression which help to maintain the appearance of being "in touch." He encourages the youngster to make a conscious effort to stay with the conversation, to concentrate his attention on what is being said, and arbitrarily to compartmentalize and limit his retreats to the "inner sanctuary" for particular times.

"When I say something to you, especially if I ask you something that might bother you, you look real interested and nod your head, but I can tell that you're not even thinking about it. You probably don't even know you're doing this, do you? Everybody does it some, daydreaming, not knowing what's going on around them, but you do it a lot more than other people. You're nodding your head again, but I don't think you really heard what I said—it's something you do automatically. You know, we've got to get around that somehow if we're to get anyplace. Let's go over this again, and you try real hard now to stick with me this time. Daydreaming is OK in its place, but I want you to try and save it for when you're not talking to me and when you're not in school. Now let's see if you can tell me what I've just been talking about; that way we can get to work on this trouble."

Importance of nonverbal communication. Any attempt to catalog the remarkable variety of ways in which the patient can convey things through "body language" would exceed the bounds of this writing, even if the author were equal to the task. Some comment is justified, however, if only to counteract the negative effects of positive lip service. It is too easy to sidestep the special effort required to recognize and use communicative body movements in psychotherapy by the time-honored dodge of labeling them categorically, e.g., "non-verbal communication." This little device enables us to pay our respects to a troublesome idea that we may more promptly return to the relative certainty of words and ideas.

It would be much closer to the truth to say that people carry on only a very circumscribed amount and type of interpersonal business through the literal content of words and that most of what they have to say to each other—especially those things having to do with feelings—is expressed otherwise. Perhaps the only exclusive function of *manifest* speech content is to carry out the pedestrian business of the day; it is for ordering groceries, giving directions to tourists, and describing how an atom is split. Its hidden function is a protective one—one which enables people to do some things together which have, at the very least, a sustaining appearance of importance and pertinence, and to do them in an atmosphere of civility. It protects them from being too close together in the strained silence which prevails in an elevator full of strangers, in the stunned aftermath of an embarrassing faux pas, or in the first few minutes when an adolescent boy and girl are left alone together under the awful pall of romance.

These, and the periods of silence in the psychotherapy interview, are often situations of burgeoning tension in which people are faced with the danger of conveying too much about how they really feel by the looks on their faces, their squirming, or their evident withdrawal into private thoughts. It is the kind of silence which, because it is too intimate to bear as a routine means of exchanging emotional information, must ordinarily be broken by the soothing sound of words before it goes too far. The awkward silence following a social blunder can be dissolved by a well-timed joke, the silence of the elevator by arriving quickly at one's floor and getting off, the silence of the adolescent boy and girl together by a practiced embrace (whether necking or dancing) or by its defensive opposite—an animated discussion of love, God, the universe, and sex.

Meanings of Verbal Communication

Direct statements. We are often reminded that words are used to conceal meaning as well as to communicate it. The experienced therapist of adolescents would probably find more food for thought in a corollary notion: that words are sometimes used to communicate meaning directly as well as to conceal it.

Indeed, the peculiar sensitivities, vulnerabilities, and strengths of the adolescent on the one hand and of the adult on the other seem almost to be arrayed against each other in a way which precludes direct verbal communication on all but the most prosaic aspects of the daily routine. A typical example of a kind of statement by an adolescent is one in which the intended communication is contained specifically in its literal content but is nonetheless concealed by the steaming hyperemotionality with which it is delivered.

Elaine, aged fifteen, had been secretly violating the conditions of her pass privileges for several weeks and becoming increasingly anxious at finding it possible to continue undetected in a kind of behavior (telephoning an old boy friend with whom she had been involved in several prehospitalization delinquencies) which was potentially damaging to her. She effectively initiated a helpful resolution of her dilemma by suddenly demanding of her doctor "a weekend pass by myself, so I'll have a chance to think about things . . . see if I can get along with some of my old friends without getting into any trouble."

Although her doctor was unaware that she had been abusing her pass privileges, this patently unreasonable request prompted him to inquire matter-of-factly about her reasons for making it. Instead of attempting a rational justification, which she could easily have done, she erupted into a rash of angry, sarcastic accusations: "You won't let me do it! Sure, I'd go out and get into all kinds of trouble with Hank! You just can't trust me for a minute!"

The literal statements, stripped of their sarcastic charge and viewed as though they were detached observations on her part, specifically informed her doctor of the kind of trouble she was having. They also instructed him on how to handle her request: "Don't give me the pass. I'm having trouble about Hank. I am not to be trusted, by myself nor by you."

Recognizing this, he had only to inquire, "Oh, have you been seeing Hank or talking to him on the telephone when you've been on passes?"

This enabled her to answer with face-saving anger, "Well, what's so wrong with that?"

On the surface it appeared that her doctor had shrewdly deduced her misbehavior from the scantiest of clues, but a second look reveals that he could have missed the message only as a result of an overpowering need of his own to do so. Such messages are usually to be encountered in the injured protest, the unexpected outburst of manifestly hostile sarcasm, the accusation: "Of course you're going to restrict me." "Oh, sure, I think you're wonderful—you're so wonderful I can hardly stand it!" "You think I'm crazy!"

These often appear to be projections—fears about himself which the patient is ascribing to someone else. Usually they are not projections because the youngster is quite conscious of liking his therapist "too much" or of "feeling crazy," and will acknowledge this easily and with evident relief when it is called to his attention openly.

The central communication of an overdetermined declaration is easily recognized once the therapist has become accustomed to the idea that he is not really the target of a personal attack. Whenever the patient's expressed attitude about something is negative, conciliatory, angry, or cheerful to a degree which far exceeds what the reality of the situation justifies, then we are well advised to "look to the opposite." Hence, the general reaction of "You disgust me, I can't stand you" may be tentatively understood as an expression of the patient's fear of his growing erotic feelings for the therapist.

Overselling. In "overselling" an idea or a plan, the adolescent will often, if given a little time and opportunity, carry himself with elaborate arguments and subtle persuasions to a complete refutation of what he started out to defend. He will unwittingly disprove his own point.

Lydia, aged fourteen, had been making a major nuisance of herself with heated complaints about having to be in the hospital instead of at home. When asked by her doctor to talk with him about this, her strongest arguments progessed in the following fashion: "Why shouldn't I be home? My mother doesn't give me any trouble. She works all day and lets me do what I want to. So what if my father does drink? Sure, he tries to beat me when he gets drunk, but he's usually too plastered to catch me. I hate this place! It's nothing like home! Sure, everybody treats you pretty nice here, and my grades have gone up to A's and B's, and I have a lot of fun with the other kids but—well—it's just not like home!"

TESTING. Ordinarily these communications are directed less at securing the therapist's indulgence than at eliciting from him a believable answer to some fairly simple question about reality. It is as though the patient were asking, "I'm quite sure that I know what is true about this, but I just wanted to know if you think so, too, and if you're willing to stand behind your belief with courage and conviction."

In a small, spontaneous group discussion Ted took the lead as chief rabble-rouser when one of the staff doctors thoughtlessly voiced some sympathy with a few of their standard, conversational complaints about ward rules. (Sympathy is inflammatory to the adolescent.) In a few minutes' time the boys were heatedly demanding to know why they were required to get up at 7:00 in the morning. The doctor gave them all the usual logical explanations for this to no avail. They grew increasingly irascible and aggressive until they were finally told, rather curtly, that they had to get up at 7:00 in the morning "because all over the country, all the other kids are getting up at that time too—that's the way things are done!"

At this they quieted promptly, and Ted said, "Oh," quite acceptingly. This contented, comprehending "Oh" is a familiar conclusion to such exchanges, and it seems to function as an abbreviation for "OK, just checking to see if you knew it, too. Why didn't you just say it that way in the first place?"

Preferred Communication Mode as an Index of Progress in Psychotherapy

As in any other intimate relationship between two people, most of the work of psychotherapy goes on quite apart from the literal content of the audible dialogue. This principle is so reliable that a therapist has strong cause to question the therapeutic value of any transactions, i.e., those having to do with feelings about people, which either he or the patient *can* translate into words.

This is a difficult idea to defend, but there is that familiar feeling of frustration which one experiences when he knows that, although his efforts with a patient have been genuinely helpful, he cannot satisfy himself that the customary explanations for how this occurred are really adequate. It is a feeling that something else very important happened in the course of therapy which neither he nor his patient can explain, and paralleling this is the disturbing suspicion that if the modus operandi had been successfully explained, i.e., rendered more fully in words and ideas, that it would not have been nearly so effective.

This issue is reminiscent of the difference in the approaches of the artist and the critic to matters of human emotionality. The actor or writer scrupulously avoids statements which explicitly analyze what he is trying to get across. That the message be conveyed indirectly, with the least possible amount of intellectual analysis, appears to be an indispensable attribute of the artistic creation. From concrete data and simple imagery the reader or viewer is left to extract its emotional essence without being able to describe how he does this. Only the critic offers to tell us what the artist is "attempting to say," and he needs many, many words to accomplish this. It often seems that a similar relationship exists in the transactions of psychotherapy, between the extent to which the process *can* be described and the effectiveness of its impact on the participants.

Deals, Covenants, and Contracts

It is in some of the glaring discrepancies between the latent and manifest meanings of a patient's words that we can discern evidences of the more paralyzing, stalemating consequences of his profoundly ambivalent relationship with parents.

In treatment we find him compulsively repeating with us the behavioral and attitudinal expressions of this ambivalence, simultaneously testing and pressing for a better resolution of it by subjecting us to repeated provocations. He seems to draw from almost endless resources—meaning his many years of unhappy exercise with his parents—to inspire in us the greatest amount of immobilizing ambivalence toward him which we are capable of experiencing. It is a class of behavior which is ordinarily referred to as "manipulation." At least two people, each with particular qualifications, are needed for the process: one who *can* manipulate and one who *can be* manipulated.

One person is manipulating another when, either consciously or unconsciously, he behaves in such a way as to place the manipulee in the position of having to give him something which he *wants*. In a conscious manipulation, e.g., the acquiring of a monopoly, all parties involved realize what has happened once the entrepreneur has succeeded in secretly buying up enough of the commodity to control the selling price. This is a particular kind of power play, the mechanics of which are not difficult to understand after the act. The unconscious manipulation of one person by another ordinarily remains secret business before, during, and after the campaign. The goal here is the psychological control of another person, which is accomplished by keeping him in imminent danger of certain of *his own* unconscious wishes and fears.

Abbey, aged fifteen, was very fond of expensive clothing. Whenever she wanted a new article of clothing, she would badger her mother unmercifully for it. The latter was a genteel, inhibited person who took great pride in her emotional equanimity. Abbey would keep after her until she would finally lose control of herself and counterattack angrily. At this point Abbey would burst into tears, and her mother, overcome with guilt and anxiety, would invariably atone by giving Abbey what she wanted.

This garden-variety manipulation is probably practiced to some extent in every family, but many others are not so obvious.

A disturbed fifteen-year-old boy was admitted to the hospital at the request of his parents who declared unreservedly, "We've had all of him we can stand. We've done everything possible for him, and nothing has worked. Do whatever you want, and we'll agree to it." The boy made a calm, untroubled adjustment to the ward, and seemed totally unconcerned by this apparently total rejection. Two or three weeks later, when asked by his doctor why he had written no letters to his parents, he explained virtuously that he did not want to "bother" them. But by this time they were already bothered to the point of agitation. They began calling his doctor at an increasing rate of frequency to inquire about what was going on, to complain about the cost of hospitalization (which they were not having to pay), to protest the dreadful inconvenience of their weekly twenty-mile trip to see the case-worker, and to demand a clear and concise explanation as to why their son had not yet been cured! At about this point the boy finally considered them "ripe" for a loving, forgiving letter along the following lines:

"Dear Mommy and Daddy: I miss you both very much (especially you, Mom) but I know that this is the best way. I am just getting what I deserve, and I have to admit that it's helping me a lot. My doctor is the smartest man I ever met, and thanks to him I'm almost a changed person. He explained to me how all the things that happened to me in my childhood caused me to turn out this way, but he says I shouldn't blame you. I don't. Say, Mom, could you send me the rest of my clothes and all the other stuff in my room? Also, could I have a picture of you and Dad to keep in my wallet? Tell Dad he can have that .22 rifle he gave me last Christmas because I won't need it here. I wish you all the luck in the world, Mom and Dad. All my love!"

"Mom" and "Dad" arrived at the hospital one hour after receiving the letter, bent on removing him against medical advice, and it proved impossible to dissuade them from this.

The therapist of the adolescent can expect to find himself the perpetual target of similar manipulative efforts, and must recognize and treat these as expressions of transference. Hopefully, he will regard each such attempt as a covert inquiry from his patient about some question of reality which he and his parents have never been able to answer satisfactorily. Abbey, in one of the above cases, was far less interested in having a new dress (indeed, she could never get enough of them) than in trying once more to find out if her mother loved her enough to deny her the total gratification of her every wish. The letter-writing boy did not want to get out of the hospital as much as he wanted to learn whether his parents were sufficiently concerned about his welfare to tolerate the prospect of his becoming nondelinquent and more independent of them.

In the course of his treatment, the adolescent patient will direct countless questions to his therapist, all with the same essential meaning: "Can you stand your own feelings about me well enough to give me what I should have and deny me what I should not have?" Translated into psychiatric idiom, "Will you have the same kind of countertransference problems with me that my parents had?" In specific rendition, this will take many slightly different forms:

"Now that I understand why I used to wreck my father's car so much, will you help me get my driver's license back?"
"But no one would ever have found out that I cheated on the test if I hadn't told you—it isn't fair for you to make me take it over!" (Is it?)
"I'm not blaming you for sending me to the state hospital, but this week is the last chance I'll have for a long time to be out on my own. Can I go see some of my old friends tomorrow?"

The communications import of these variants on a central treatment question is emphasized to illustrate that an adequate and effective answer will take the form of action first and words only secondarily, if at all. Recognizing and responding realistically to the adolescent's manipulations become second nature for the experienced therapist, but time and again we find the youngster casually hamstringing inexperienced residents and seasoned veterans alike.

In his power struggle with the adult the youngster naturally aims at improving his own relative position by degrading his opponent. One excellent way of doing this, especially in psychotherapy, is to seduce the therapist into stating the obvious. It is so easy to find one's self deeply immersed in a long and eloquent discourse on some utterly foolish truism without even realizing how the patient got it started or why.

Another effective and often quite complicated manipulative device is that of hiding a delinquency within a delinquency, within a delinquency, etc.

After having reached a firm understanding with her doctor about deferring further contact with a particular boy friend, Jill was permitted to go home on pass. That evening her parents had a party and, as Jill later told her doctor, "I felt so lonely I couldn't stand it." She called her boy friend in a distant city and spoke to him for an hour and a half at her parents' expense. Following this she felt quite guilty, and after returning to the hospital became upset and demanded an "emergency" interview with her doctor.

The emergency was fictitious. Jill had been in treatment for many months and was markedly improved. In this instance the conspicuous delinquency was the spending of some sixty dollars of her parents' money on a long-distance call. So compelling was this problem that her therapist had to force himself to recognize that the expense of the telephone call per se was less important than her unauthorized call to the boy friend, and also less significant than her demand that her doctor come in on a Saturday evening for a matter which she could have saved—to her own treatment advantage—until the following Monday.

There is the related mechanism of hiding a delinquency within a virtue.

Mort turned in six firecrackers to Dr. A after being approached about his possible involvement in a firecracker episode of the night before. Dr. A proudly reported his coup to a senior colleague, who deflated him by asking if he had stopped to consider how many firecrackers there are in the average packet. Without comment Dr. A returned to the ward and curtly directed Mort to turn in the rest of the firecrackers, which he then did without question.

Confiscating contraband was not the important issue. This, rather, was a matter of casting doctor and patient in appropriate roles in a cat-and-mouse game which Mort had hoped would prove him "smarter" than his doctor.

As clever as some of these illustrative operations sound, it still should be emphasized that they are of characteristic adolescent quality. They do not compare favorably with those which are practiced with such consummate, though unconscious, skill by the average, stable, well-adjusted adult. Unfortunately, perhaps, the limits of the present subject do not permit a digression into this area, one which has—perhaps for reasons of self-preservation—remained largely neglected by our profession. The interested student is referred in all seriousness to Stephen Potter's pioneering exploration into the theory and practice of civilized, adult manipulation [28].

The adolescent must achieve maturity in order to master advanced gambitry: the finesse and the euchre, the damning with faint or unearned praise, sophisticated sycophancy, slow ego corrosion by benign nuance and benevolent innuendo, the amiable bluff, and the marvelous powers of virtue turned to the service of manipulation, of arrogant humility, and cunningly aggressive pacifism. Until he matures, the adolescent must rely strongly upon such primitively magical mechanisms as direct effrontery, bald provocation, and simple extortion.

6

THE TREATMENT CONTRACT

The adolescent patient and his therapist must arrive at certain understandings about the division of treatment responsibilities between themselves and also about the practical mechanics of the psychotherapy process.

The conditions of the treatment "contract" in general psychiatry vary with such factors as the following: age of patient, type and severity of his illness, attitude of the family, theoretical orientation of the therapist, and whether the patient is an outpatient, an inpatient, or an ex-inpatient who has become an outpatient. Significant changes in the terms of the treatment contract occur when any one of these factors is altered.

Postadolescent and Postinpatient

For the adolescent patient who grows older and is discharged from the hospital to be followed as an outpatient, there will be extensive revisions in the contract. He is no longer a dependent minor. He must begin to take more responsibility for himself than he did previously. If a ward of the juvenile court, he must leave its jurisdiction somewhere between the ages of seventeen and nineteen years. In many respects he is regarded by society as an adult when he reaches the age of eighteen. The law does not require that he attend school; he may volunteer for military service; in many states girls may marry without parental consent. The new post-adolescent is relieved of the restrictions of child labor laws and is eligible to seek employment at will.

Certain alterations in his psychological status also raise the familiar question about whether or not it is best for him to continue with the same therapist, if he is to continue at all. The consideration commonly given to changing therapists at this time probably has very little to do with the matter of the doctor's subspecialty, i.e., the fact of the patient's having grown older has little to do with whether he should continue to see an adolescent-psychiatrist or one who specializes in the treatment of adults.

It can be difficult for the patient to continue seeing the therapist who knew him so well when he was a teenager. This problem is shared, of course, by the therapist. Of the several things which account for this new strain in the treatment relationship, one of the more important is the patient's sharply revised concept of himself. As a young adult with many new responsibilities, he must feel greater self-reliance, and this depends upon his being strongly supported by a mental picture of himself as a mature, strong, capable, independent adult.

The adolescent does not enjoy the adult patient's advantage of having started therapy with tangible proofs of his capacity for doing most of the things which an adult is supposed to do—one which could help him immeasurably at the strenuous business of self-revelation. Both he and his therapist are bound to remember him as he was—an obstreperous, irrational, clinging, overprotesting caricature of a real adult. Finding himself repeatedly confronted by an eyewitness to his adolescent frailties does very little to strengthen his adult defenses.

The postadolescent patient must also resist the pull to resume a dependent attachment to his doctor, which cannot be accomplished by simply "resolving the transference." The regressive inclination is fostered by the reality of the past. As an adolescent he was genuinely dependent on his therapist for many of the things which the normal youngster receives gratuitously from his parents.

Ordinarily, the patient who has done well enough in treatment to maintain himself independently does not elect to resume intensive psychotherapy with anyone. Occasionally he will return to his previous therapist for a cursory examination of some current problem. More often, one gets the impression that he stops by for a rest, to retire momentarily from the arena of daily living and to remind himself that there is a haven to which he can turn should desperate need arise. Most of all, perhaps, he returns infrequently to reassure himself that he doesn't *have* to return regularly.

Basic Rule for the Inpatient

There are also some striking differences between treatment contracts which we have with the adolescent inpatient and outpatient, because the youngster in residence becomes the almost total responsibility of his therapist with respect to his behavior, his adaptive progress (e.g., school performance), his safety, and the fulfillment of many of his affectional needs. The major responsibility for the outpatient, on the other hand, remains with the parents. The latter will frequently blame the therapist for intercurrent trouble, but in the end this is mostly their liability and headache.

There are other clauses in the treatment contract of the adolescent, whether he is an inpatient or outpatient, which are distinctly different than those for the adult. For practical purposes these differences may be classified under the headings of "obligations of the patient to treatment" and "treatment obligations of the therapist."

The adolescent need not formally agree to become a patient in order to benefit from therapy. It does not work out well to expect him to read, understand, and subscribe to the treatment contract at once. With enough suitable help from his therapist, however, the prospects are fair for his doing this in time. Whether he can do it will depend greatly upon how effective his therapist is in conveying an accurate, believable appreciation of how things must be done to make his treatment worthwhile. Sooner or later, for example, it is usually necessary for the therapist to contradict most of the popular prevailing notions about psychotherapy and also to explain some of the special refinements which distinguish it from ordinary social relationships. Initially the patient will have many misconceptions about psychotherapy, some of which were mentioned earlier, which will need clarifying; and then, as he begins to understand it better, he may be counted upon to use this knowledge for developing some additional, highly sophisticated, and subtle resistances to treatment.

Generally, he will favor the idea that psychotherapy is "talking," and more often than not that it is talking in the office, as though the things which he does at other times have nothing to do with treatment. He presumes that he is expected only to stay out of trouble, be pleasant and cooperative, and confess a few carefully preselected tidbits about his sexual fantasies and behavior. He will readily participate with the therapist in regarding himself as a hapless victim of "pathogenic parents," one who is, therefore, not at all responsible for what he is and what he will become.

Disabusing him of these cozy notions is one of the first and most important tasks of therapy.

After being denied a third helping of dessert, Hank, a sixteen-year-old inpatient, called the nurse a "crummy bitch" and then strode angrily from the dining room without permission. When confronted by his doctor, he apologized contritely and explained, "I just got nervous and upset." He expected this to bring an end to the incident. When his doctor persisted in probing for more information about the episode—for associated fantasies and any possible relationships between this outburst and other difficulties which he had been having in the preceding several days —Hank protested impatiently: "I apologized, didn't I? What's all this got to do with my treatment?"

The incident also indicates another common fantasy—which again reflects the positive value which we tend to attach to symptoms—that being upset will justify almost any kind of behavior.

"I refused to go to school because I was so depressed."

"The reason I took off and swiped that car is because I was so disappointed I couldn't stand it when my father said I couldn't get a driver's license."

This device reaches the summit of inanity when the adolescent patient begins to predict pathological behavior on the basis of *anticipated* symptoms: "I know I'm going to have trouble tonight—I'm getting so anxious I just can't stand this place." He lays detailed plans for "losing impulse control."

Closely related to this is another idea which the therapist is usually prone to share with his patient. Being a psychiatric patient or a psychiatrist tends to engender a certain sense of loyalty to the cause of psychopathology. The adolescent patient is not affecting sarcasm when he argues, "What am I supposed to go to school for—that's why I'm here—that's my problem!"

At such a point the therapist might try to get across to his young patient the essence of the following statement: "Look, as a psychiatrist I am naturally interested in the emotional problems of adolescence, but you have plenty of them without deliberately trying to make more. You are a psychiatric patient because it's necessary, not because it's a good way to live. You're supposed to work at being well, not sick." The adolescent patient will frequently try to please his doctor with little gifts of psychopathology, and too often the therapist will unwittingly accept these with an unintended expression of gratitude which, regrettably, the patient will readily detect.

Teaching the Adolescent About Therapy

Psychotherapy takes place wherever and whenever it is needed. The activities of a routine day may be fun, hard work, or just passing time, but they are also grist for psychotherapy. A visit home is more than just a visit; it is an opportunity for the patient to learn something more about himself, about other people, about the world. Getting this idea across to him is not easy. The adult therapist will find it most disconcerting to be haughtily advised by his adolescent patient that some extremely meaningful event in his current life is "none of your business!" There is little cause for distress in this. One clause which is almost always absent in the "contract" is the patient's explicit acknowledgment that he is in treatment. As a rule he prefers working under formal protest, progressing well even as he voices determined resistance to the whole idea. Then some months later he soberly observes, "I've finally decided to accept therapy—what is it?"

There is much more cause for concern when, very early in the course of treatment, a youngster brazenly volunteers to become "involved in therapy."

Jack was an intelligent, sixteen-year-old boy who was admitted to the hospital because of certain consequences of his remarkable ability for controlling and manipulating his parents, teachers, and other adults. A number of previous efforts to hospitalize him had failed because of this knack for "explaining away" his delinquencies and for convincing people in authority that he had finally reformed, once and for all. Following admission, and after failing to convince his doctor of the therapeutic value of discharging him immediately, he suddenly announced a noble decision: "I don't like being here but I know it's for my own good. I'll probably never have another opportunity like this again, so I'd better make the most of it. Tell me what *you* want to know, and what *you* want me to do, so I can get well. Do you think I can be well enough to leave the hospital in a couple of weeks or so?"

Psychotherapy with the adolescent inpatient usually begins with a rather protracted period—weeks or perhaps even months—of mutual indoctrination. It is not a very happy time for either patient or therapist, and the former will sometimes complain during this introduction that he is being "brainwashed." For many youngsters with severe character disorders there is perhaps a grain of truth to this view as far as means are concerned, but certainly not about aims. He is separated from a home which, however humble and horrible it might be, is still the only home he has ever known. The treatment program also seriously frustrates his automatic efforts to defend himself by the mechanisms he has acquired and used with some success in his past life. The props which held him up are shaken. He is in a mental hospital and under the care of a psychiatrist. He suffers a severe loss of *positive* self-esteem, and responds to this either with massive revolt or a desperate turning to his therapist for support or direction. It is an extremely difficult transition in many ways, but it can also do much to help him appreciate the purpose of those measures of treatment which are so painful and difficult to understand.

People no longer respond to him as he has learned to expect; what he (unconsciously) attempts to provoke is withheld. In his resulting frustration and perplexity he begins to sense that there is a point to his doctor's curious injunction that he try to "practice" and "exercise" at doing some things differently, and that it is really not much fun to be so automatic and predictable, like a puppet with six strings.

Buddy, a very disturbed fifteen-year-old boy, had a long history of minor delinquencies which had brought him to the attention of the school authorities and the juvenile court on many occasions. In the classroom his chronic "show-off" behavior, talking out of turn, and ridiculing of the teacher had been so disruptive that it became necessary to expel him. He violated curfew and baited police officers relentlessly. The people in the community dismissed him as a grinning, insolent nuisance.

During the first few weeks following admission, every reasonable effort was made to curb the momentum of this defensive behavior which he naturally attempted to continue. His therapist was not able to resist the inevitable temptation to "interpret" the defensive import of his impudent, provocative manner, but this, of course, had no effect. Out of treatment necessity he was pressed vigorously into routine activities, where he found little support for disruptive behavior from fellow patients or staff members. His attempts to carry off his role as a devil-may-care delinquent assumed a quality of desperation. The pressure was kept on, and as his ability to resist began to flag, he grew visibly depressed. He frequently choked up with tears, and would then try to explain away his dreadful unhappiness as a direct result of the "mean" way he was being treated. In this he momentarily found justification for intensifying his nuisance behavior. He would leap on empty stretchers or food carts and scooter them down the hall, laughing, singing, and carrying on in a way which did not endear him to anyone.

He scoffed when his doctor suggested, "You think you're doing those things because you *decide* to, but the truth is you can't help it. You need those ways of making yourself look like an obnoxious fool, just like a dope addict needs his dope. You couldn't stand the feelings you'd have if you didn't give yourself a shot of that food-cart routine or something like it."

Buddy accepted the challenge and within three days was in abject misery—profoundly depressed, weeping openly and almost constantly, and suffering a recurrence of an acute neurodermatitis which he had not had since childhood. He told his doctor that he couldn't stand it and begged for some kind of help. An empirical trial of psychotropic medication relieved him temporarily (it would have had no effect at all had it been administered earlier with the intention of "modifying" his behavior), but it was not enough. Finally, he saw no alternative to talking with his doctor about the things which disturbed him so deeply.

The patient also begins to learn during this period of acclimatization that immediate relief from psychological pain is not the prime goal of treatment. He is asked to work consciously at not seeking it, at keeping requests for emergency interviews to a minimum, at trying hard to understand that, by the standards of civilized people, the ability to tolerate psychological pain is valued over the infantile mode of relieving it at the expense of others.

It is not easy for the therapist to take this position. For a physician the inability to provide symptomatic relief for severe pain makes him appear professionally helpless. He will feel guilty of having let his patient down, and as a result of this may be left with an unrecognized need to make atonement by offering the patient some unrealistic compensatory satisfactions of one sort or another. Under the sway of such feelings he will be especially vulnerable to his own unconscious wishes to overprotect and infantilize the youngster with excessive displays of sympathy and gestures of appeasement. This is not helpful for the adolescent patient who is struggling in the best way he knows to win the increased self-respect which comes with being less of a cry baby.

The adolescent patient has to be reminded a few times of some of the do's and don't's of therapy. He should not talk about his interviews out of the office. In the competition for status it is not uncommon for several youngsters to start keeping score on who can log the most total hours per week of treatment time.

There are many other ways in which adolescents can subtly belittle a serious business. Overdramatizing the content of interviews in order to attract the attention and interest of other patients is among the favorites. For a girl to return weeping from an interview with her doctor is customarily a mark of social grace. Other choice measures include burlesquing the therapist's mannerisms, treatment contrivances and techniques, and mimicking some of his preferred platitudes and clichés.

Joe, a sixteen-year-old boy on the adolescent ward, was defiant and insulting in his relationships with women staff members, just as he had been with his mother. He was an intelligent, articulate boy who had participated readily with his doctor in searching his own past for experiences which had contributed to his hostile and disparaging attitude toward women.

One day he became unbearably offensive in his manner with one of the nurses and was called by his doctor for an on-the-spot interview in the nursing station. The other boys, who had been contentedly watching the action from the sidelines, greeted him eagerly upon his return from the interview. Inspired by their eternal expectations of Hammurabic retaliation, they wanted to know immediately what happened. One of the attendants overheard Joe's scornful reply: "Just some more Tinker Toy psychiatry—that's all I ever get from him."

After the adolescent patient has begun to get some idea about the modest benefits to be enjoyed from the insight-producing part of psychotherapy, he will gradually become a little more willing to accept a few specific instructions regarding procedure. It is frequently necessary to put these in very concrete form.

FANTASIES. Most youngsters, for example, construe the word *fantasy* to mean *fantastic*—something too preposterous to talk about. Being reminded of the universality of fantasies—that they are enjoyed and suffered by all people of all ages, that they do indeed sound ridiculous when put into words, and that they will not be made too much of by the therapist—will often make it easier for the patient to report his own "preposterous" ideas. Sometimes it is even helpful for the therapist to prime the pump by recounting one or two of his own—hopefully not too revealing—adolescent "dreams of glory."

Although accustomed to declaiming loudly on grand feelings which he hopes will support the picture of "that's the kind of person I am," the adolescent finds the describing of such simple feelings as tenderness, longing, and homesickness to be an abhorrence. He can scarcely conceive that anyone would really expect him to say these words out loud. He also needs help in overcoming the automatic "switch off" which is activated by the question, "What are you thinking right at the moment?" We must remember that he is rarely the intelligent, literate analysand of the type favored in published case reports. He needs to be taught some of the words which people can use to describe their feelings (e.g., love, cry, afraid, lonely), and to be reassured about his conviction that outside of the office they would indeed be as socially inappropriate as the obscenities which he ordinarily uses to deny them.

One of the most important therapeutic forces in the treatment of the adolescent is that which acts through his unlearning—through the reporting of ideas and fantasies—his magical infantile belief that thought and deed are moral equivalents. He is usually greatly reassured to find that he can speak openly of angry, destructive, and perverse sexual wishes without acting them out and without suffering the retaliation which he has long feared and partly invited. He is usually so thoroughly imbued with the talion principle that he fully expects us to regard his having the fantasies as equal to his perpetrating them: "But I can't tell you what I think about that—you'd never let me out of here." This *decon-*

tamination of fantasies can be accomplished only in a real relationship with another person—with someone who can provide living opposition to living fears.

The adolescent's reluctance to talk about himself stems largely from his quite normal aversion to making *open* covenants with any adult. He cannot *openly* agree to strive for self-critical detachment because this would require an almost treasonous degree of public collaboration with his therapist. There are, however, some ways in which he can be assisted to do this by subterfuge until he is sufficiently secure and trustful to let it be known that he is not all muscle and grit.

He will be relieved, for example, to learn the difference between free association and free action, between describing his feelings for another person and acting on them.

Farley, aged fifteen, had been in the hospital after being admitted for complaints of unmanageably rebellious behavior at home and in school. He became very angry at his doctor one day for denying him something which he wanted.

"You bastard—you think you can make me do anything you want!"

He was interrupted by his doctor at this point. "Hold it a minute! We've got to get something straight here. Where did you get the idea that it was all right for you to call me a bastard?"

"I didn't get it anywhere—I'm just telling you what I think!"

"That's fine. That's what you're supposed to do—let me know what you think. It's OK to tell me you *think* I'm a bastard or you *feel* like calling me a bastard, but it's *not* all right to go right ahead and *call* me a bastard."

"So what's the difference! If you are one, that's all there is to it!"

"Lots of difference—the big *if!* Am I a bastard? I could very well be, but you'd be about the last person to know it. You haven't known me long enough to know whether I'm a bastard or not. You don't have the least idea what I'm like and apparently you don't even care to find out. You're just calling me the same thing you've always called anyone who ever made you do something you didn't want to, or doesn't give you something you want."

Farley shrugged.

"How about it? Can you name one person you've known in the past three or four years, say, who you think has given you a hard time, that you haven't called a bastard or a son-of-a-bitch or something like that?"

"Sure! Plenty of them!"

"That doesn't seem very likely to me. How about telling me about one of them?"

"Aw, this is a bunch of crap."

"What?"

"I said I *think* this is a bunch of crap. That's what *I* think."

"Fair enough. Now, how about that person you never swore at?"

The therapist's chief aim in the procedures of the psychotherapy interview is to support in all reasonable ways the patient's efforts to carry out his responsibilities effectively. In addition to the examples above, other general measures include providing the youngster with the greatest possible protection from humiliation, protecting his confidence, and giving him good cause to believe that his therapist will always make a strong conscious effort to tell the truth—however bitter it may be.

Confidentiality. Protecting the confidentiality of the interview with the adolescent frequently presents some special problems which are related to the fact that he is legally a minor, often in some kind of trouble with the juvenile authorities, and morally committed to the familiar adolescent dictum against "squealing."

He cannot be given the same assurances of confidentiality which are usually accorded the adult outpatient. He knows this, and his efforts to exact such promises are generally aimed at accomplishing something else anyway. In the overwhelming majority of instances he understands well that we seldom have occasion to reveal intimate information about him which would cause him embarrassment. He is also aware that he has no right to expect us to remain silent about matters which have a vital bearing on his or another person's future welfare.

The only guarantee which is made to the patient is that we will always try to act in his best interests. The treatment contract does not absolutely obligate him to reveal everything he knows about fellow patients, but it does enjoin him to open up about actions which might be important to his own welfare. As it works out, his attitudes and behavior toward fellow patients, whether they are "friends" or "enemies," are practically always important to his own welfare.

"I can't tell you what he did—he made me promise not to."

"He has no right to demand that kind of a promise from you, and you have no right to give it."

"Yes, I have. He's a friend of mine, and I don't want to get him into trouble."

"Have you considered the possibility that you might get him—or yourself—into even worse trouble by not telling about it?"

"How could I do that? He's the one who did it. It's his problem. I didn't do anything wrong."

"Maybe not, maybe yes. But you're wrong about its being just his problem. You know about it, so that makes it partly your problem, too. Whether you're doing anything wrong or not depends on what happens to him as a result of your keeping quiet about it."

"Nothing's going to happen to him. It's all over and done with."

"That's a pretty big decision to make. You know the odds are in favor of my having much better judgment about it than you."

"But I'm sure about this one. It's all over and done with. He just did it once and he's not going to do it again."

"Well, if you're really that sure about it, then he certainly isn't going to get into any 'trouble'—as you call it—as a result of my knowing about it."

"Yeah, but I promised him I wouldn't tell. Look, if I tell you, do you promise not to tell his doctor?"

"I know better than to promise something like that in advance. I'll use my own very fine judgment about it, as you well know."

"Well, a couple of weeks ago he got this letter from his father asking him if he wanted to get out of here. He wrote back that he wanted to get out because he wasn't getting enough to eat. He said he's feeling worse than when he came in and it isn't helping him a bit to be here. You know, a whole bunch of lies. Then his father wrote back that he was going to get a lawyer and go down to the court to see the judge and get back custody."

"Well, what do you think about all of this? It sounds like his idea might work out. Are you real happy for him?"

"Well, no, I wouldn't say I'm happy for him. He's just going to keep right on getting into trouble, but if he really wants to go . . ."

"Well, with friends like you he doesn't need many enemies, does he?"

"What am I supposed to do about it?"

"You've already done it. You've told me about it, maybe not too late. Are you willing to hear some good advice?"

"I guess so."

"Well, I don't think he really knows what he's doing. If he isn't careful, his father's actually going to get him out of here. You might just tell him that, and tell him also that he'd better let his doctor know about it pretty quick."

"But what if he doesn't?"

"Then let him know you told me about it. I'm willing to talk with his doctor."

"He sure won't like that—me breaking my promise."

"I'm not so sure. Try it and see. If he really holds you to your promise, then I won't say anything about it, unless he forces my hand some other way. Trouble is, we wouldn't be able to do anything until we hear from the court, and by then it would probably be too late. But if you go to him like that, then it really will be his problem. Why don't you try and get him to see that?"

There are other circumstances, such as possible suicides or homicides, which will not justify returning the responsibility to the patients involved. A fifteen-year-old girl inpatient confided such a problem to her doctor.

"I'm scared. It's something about that new girl, but she made me promise not to tell."

The exchange which followed led quickly to the first revelation: "She has this big bottle of medicine she brought from home, and she's hiding it in her locker. She says she's going to take it all tonight after bedtime and kill herself."

"OK. I'll let her doctor know right away, and he can go down and see her about it."

"But you can't do that! I promised I wouldn't tell!"

"I don't really think you're too worried about breaking that promise. You certainly don't want her to kill herself."

"But I don't think she's really going to do it."

"Maybe not, but you also know we don't have any right to take a chance on that."

"She'll hate me for telling on her."

"Not likely. You're practically a complete stranger to her. Why do you suppose she told you in the first place?"

"You mean she wanted me to tell you about it?"

"It looks that way, doesn't it? Anyway, you did the right thing to tell me about it. Now I'll call her doctor."

Keeping secrets. It is also futile and inadvisable for the therapist to try to keep secrets from his patient about matters which are of important, realistic concern to him.

At a staff conference Dr. M discussed the unfortunate consequences of what he called a "security leak," pointedly indicating to the nursing staff that they were indiscreetly revealing information to the patients which could be harmful to them. He referred specifically to certain complications which had arisen during the past week or two in connection with his efforts to plan a disposition for Ben, a sixteen-year-old boy.

He explained, "Ben knows he'll be leaving here in several weeks. This is a rough time for him. I didn't want him to know his father was fired from his job and deserted the family . . . that his brother was picked up by juvenile officers for breaking and entering. But somebody told him! He's been having more and more trouble for the past week. When I asked him about it this morning, he told me that it was because he was worried about all the trouble at home. He accused me of keeping this secret from him."

The problem was reviewed in supervision; after some further discussion with the nursing staff it became increasingly evident that no one had said anything directly to Ben about the troubles at home. Nor had he received such information from his family. A step-by-step examination of the specific transactions which had taken place during psychotherapy over the preceding two weeks revealed the hidden source of the information.

Dr. M had begun to see Ben a little more often and for longer periods of time, in an unconscious and sympathetic effort to compensate for the loss of support from home. He was not able to disguise his reluctance to talk with Ben about the current family situation. He had become increasingly conciliatory and indecisive about Ben's more frequent requests to call his parents or to visit home on a pass. It was Dr. M who had "leaked" the information.

There is no magic in this. It is not mental telepathy or radar. Subtleties of facial and vocal expression, of faint aversion reactions and shifts in interest, are often more revealing of emotionally meaningful issues than words would be. There are entirely too many transmitting frequencies in a person's expressive system to be kept under full, conscious control all the time. One can only try to be alert to his own feelings and attitudes about the patient and about some of the lively current issues which are important to him, and then subject all of these things to open review with him at regular intervals.

This is in part simply a matter of accepting the futility of trying to keep certain kinds of things secret, but there are other reasons for being candid about such problems. The patient has the right to know about matters of importance to him even if the knowledge causes him pain. Withholding information from him about trouble at home, for example, presumes that he does not have the character resources necessary to endure this stress. It is a telling vote of "no confidence," conveyed by the therapist's overprotectiveness.

Sometimes it is recommended that one ought to be very conservative about revealing some kinds of information in order to enhance the opportunity for the patient to make a self-revealing, "projected" interpretation of a stress situation. This idea might arise, for example, when the doctor is unable to keep an interview appointment. If the patient is informed only that "your doctor won't be in today," he will have to construct his own explanation. The content of this idea will indeed give us further information about him, but the same end can be accomplished by advising him, "Your doctor has a mild case of flu but expects to be back to work in a day or two." This approach makes more sense to the adolescent, who is inclined to become suspicious and guarded about mysterious-sounding, offbeat approaches.

"But weren't you told why I couldn't see you yesterday?"
"Sure, I guess so."
"Then tell me—why couldn't I?"
"Oh, you had the flu or something like that."
"But from the way you say it, I gather you had some other ideas about why I wasn't here."
"I believed it! You think I was sitting around here worrying you had a heart attack or something?"

7

THE TONE OF CONVERSATION WITH THE ADOLESCENT PATIENT

It may be futile to tell a therapist how he is supposed to behave in an interview with an adolescent, but it can be helpful to speak explicitly about some of the things which he *may* do even though they might violate convention a little. Allowing the beginning therapist to infer that there is a precise technique which he must learn in order to interview effectively places an unnecessarily heavy burden on him. Until experience teaches him otherwise, it leaves him to struggle alone against the idea that he must assume a particular manner and way of speaking to be considered a proper psychotherapist. The folklore of psychotherapy, if not the actual teaching, continues to sustain the image of the psychiatrist as one whose wonderful arts will be judged less by the canvas than the frame which supports it. The objection here is not to how the individual analyst or psychotherapist actually works in his own practice, but rather to his guilty reluctance about conveying an accurate version of his therapy activities to students and colleagues. Psychotherapists of different persuasions undoubtedly differ greatly with respect to some of the gross, observable things they do, but as a matter of definition the therapeutic forces which they introduce into the treatment of patients must be pretty much the same for all.

As far as the choice of "technique" is concerned, it is well to note that the psychotherapist is just as prone as the next person to make professional virtues of personal deficiencies, and indeed he can do little else. As a psychiatrist, however, he is expected to know something about his deficiencies—specifically the ways in which they can and cannot be usefully employed—and to direct his professional efforts accordingly.

Many adolescent boys who are fearful and frustrated in their feelings about people express compromise interests in becoming forest rangers or veterinarians. There are also many similarly inhibited bright young psychiatrists who professionalize their limitations through examining and thinking about these conflicted feelings in other people and, of course, in themselves as well. Much of their motivation for undertaking this worthwhile investigation, and their capacity for understanding and interpreting what they observe, depends upon their own conflictedness. But by the same token they will be inclined to favor treatment measures which offer the greatest protection from painful emotional entanglements with patients. One of these stems from the idea that the therapist's over-involvement would not be good for the patient. This is reinforced by the formal establishment of method, regularity, and technical structure in the treatment arrangements. In other words, therapists with similar assets and limitations defend those rationales of treatment which are best suited to them personally as well as to the kind of patient whom they usually select for treatment.

Having the need to maintain a considerable emotional distance from the patient does not warrant the general advice that this is the best way. Nor does having the need to be more active, more emotionally involved, justify the claim that one must pursue this course in order to treat effectively. Probably the differences between the two general approaches are only superficial. There are reasons for suspecting that the orthodox analyst, for example, becomes just as emotionally involved with patients as his rather more talkative colleague in general psychiatric practice, and that the latter has his own ways of avoiding antitherapeutic overinvolvement. In all likelihood the therapist's helpful attitudes and understandings about the patient are communicated by his thoughtful silence in the one case and by his interested talking in the other. Our effective actions in psychotherapy are governed far more by our attitudes than by the techniques of therapy of which we speak with such sober fondness.

Directness with the Adolescent

By and large, it is necessary to engage the adolescent patient rather actively, with directness, spontaneity, and a minimum of technical method. The new adolescent patient is greatly threatened (to put it mildly) by the strangeness of psychiatric treatment. Unlike the more sophisticated adult patient who comes willingly because he has some idea about how treatment will help him, the adolescent patient feels the need for help at least as urgently, but has only the fuzziest and most distorted ideas about what it is.

As a rule he doesn't know the difference between a medical doctor, a psychiatrist, a truant officer, and a psychologist. They all look pretty much the same to him. He has usually heard vague rumors to the effect that a psychiatrist sees "crazy kids" in order to "help them with their problems." Most of what he will come to know about the process and substance of psychotherapy will be taught to him by his therapist, less through direct instruction than by his manner of speaking, dressing, sitting, and "interpreting reality." The idea that the technical operations of therapy will yield effective results regardless of who directs them has been pretty much left by the wayside. It still persists in our mythology but hardly at all in practice.

The therapist reveals much of his personality for two general reasons: (1) he can't hide it from the adolescent anyway and (2) there is no good reason to try to hide it even if it were possible. The adolescent is able to tell too much about us even when it is our intention to tell him nothing at all. Our efforts to operate as emotional technicians of some sort are transparent to him; they only increase his embarrassment and uneasiness in a situation which is already strained at best. A conversational style which would appear to the average adult to be one of *abnormal candor* contributes much to the atmosphere in which the adolescent can work best. This will do far more than an explanation of the "basic rule" toward making it possible for him to let us know what is on his mind. He will approach the work of therapy according to his therapist's lead.

The idea suggested by the expression *abnormal candor* will strike a discordant note with the average person. The survival of a society depends, of course, upon the willingness of its constituents to participate tacitly in an incredibly complicated system of what might be called "socially necessary reality-distortions." The working proposition for present purposes is that people could not live together in civility without the protection afforded by these unconscious lies of courtesy, diplomacy, and politics and that effective psychotherapy cannot proceed with it. If psychotherapy has anything to commend it over the automatically evolved forces of society, such as education and common sense child-rearing, then it is this opportunity to get a better idea about what is true and what is untrue by taking at least a few quick glimpses beyond the barriers which people use to keep from knowing too much about too much for too much of the time.

Concerning his own personal attitude about the operational value of the adult's views of reality, the adolescent stands about midway between the child and the adult. He continues to be deeply troubled by remnants of his childhood suspicion that adults are so nice, diplomatic, and courteous in order to ward off their partial tendencies to murder and rape each other. He inwardly concedes that there are some conspicuous merits to these ends, but is tormented by serious doubts about his ability to believe in the means by which they are reached. His ability to accept, at the right time, the psychological compromises necessary to the attainment of a second latency depends mostly upon what he has learned to expect from his own past experience about the ultimate reliability of adults.

In normal development the adolescent will have long since discriminated between socially convenient bending of reality on the one hand, and, on the other, those crushing violations of trust which so gravely impair the child's capacity for believing in anything or anyone. The past experience of the mentally ill youngster has been critically dominated by the latter; for him every little pose and pretense seem to mask another terrible lie of the kind he has come to know so well.

The degree of forthrightness that one takes with the adolescent should not be confused with making "wild" or "deep" interpretations. Although there are other good reasons for not beating around the bush when interpreting something which is thought to be unconscious to the patient, in most instances a bluntness of approach is primarily meant to help him talk about something which, though conscious, he guards against revealing because he considers it an unspeakable secret. Doing this as quickly as possible, meaning as quickly as the therapist has a reasonable guess about the nature of the secret, is intended to spare the patient the unnecessary anguish of confiding something which, as a rule, adolescents and adults simply do not talk about together. In this sense it is quite different from the attitude of watchful expectancy which the therapist assumes with the patient who is trying to recall and "work through" unconscious problems.

There are, of course, many times when it is useful in treatment to interpret a patient's unconscious wish, defenses, or communicative behavior. Both the reasons and the methods for doing this vary greatly with what is being interpreted, to whom, and under what circumstances.

In general, we probably worry too much about the possible damaging consequences of uncovering too much, too rapidly. In most instances the adolescent who is in serious psychological straits, even if he is terrified and psychotic, is usually more relieved by having a chance to look the monster in the face than by being left to suffer with the knowledge that the monster is there but frighteningly nameless.

An extraordinary degree of forthrightness is ordinarily more merciful for the acutely tormented adolescent than is well intended circumspection. From his standpoint too much diplomatic temporizing becomes a psychological version of the Chinese water torture. But directness alone, of course, is hardly enough. If the therapist himself is inordinately anxious or embarrassed, his efforts at candor are likely to come off badly. If, on the other hand, he can take a reasonably relaxed approach to those things which the patient anticipates with such dread, then this alone will help to reassure the patient. The attitudes of the therapist toward the task at hand, as reflected in his literal approach, have an immense influence on the adolescent patient's response to it.

Wendy, a fifteen-year-old outpatient, came for one of her regular interviews shortly after having had a routine physical examination at the private school which she attended. Although rather distraught at this time, she was an unusually intelligent and introspective girl who was able to recognize some of the *immediate* sources of her anxiety by comparing the recent examination with another which she had had a few months previously.

She correctly discerned that her two quite different reactions had been determined more by the approach of the examiner than by any significant change in her own feelings about being examined. "The last time I had a physical the doctor told me to get undressed and jump up on the table. So I got undressed behind the screen and put on one of those hospital smocks and climbed on the table. He started asking me questions while he was examining me, and I can remember thinking from the way he did it that he must have done physicals on thousands of people. I don't mean he wasn't friendly; he just seemed to know what he was doing and it didn't bother him any. When he checked my chest, he just had me sit up and drop that smock all the way off, and I was kind of surprised. Well, he checked up here to see if I had any lumps, you know; well, I guess he was trying to make sure I didn't have any breast cancer. I don't know why, but it was real easy. But it was different today. There was this new doctor and he was . . . well, he was real nice but kind of official. I got on that smock again and got on the table and he had the nurse cover me with a sheet . . . and for the whole examination he just went around lifting up little corners of the sheet and pulling down and lifting up this gown just enough to get to whatever he was examining. It felt like he was undressing me. I blushed all the way through it. I was never so embarrassed in my whole life; if you have to be naked, it's easier to be all the way naked instead of part way."

In addition to the transference import of Wendy's account, it also included some wise counsel. Ideally the psychotherapist takes an approach with the adolescent which is similar to the first doctor's. Straining to spare the patient's feelings enhances rather than diminishes the sexually exciting and frightening potential of a necessary examination. When the therapist has good reason to believe that something is true about the patient, it is best that he make this thought known with as little delay as possible. Being wrong in a speculation is not damaging unless he has somehow given the patient to understand that he regards himself as omniscient and infallible. This applies equally to the interpretation of aggressive strivings and to threatening affects which the patient is struggling to hold in isolation. Even in the initial diagnostic interview this rather quick, direct approach is taken, usually not electively, but because there is an urgent treatment need to be met.

Many of the acute disturbances of puberty and early adolescence respond very favorably to a short period of rapid-cadence psychotherapy. The very young patient of this type is often frozen with fear at the time of the first interview, in which case the customary attitude of sympathetic listening and watchful expectancy will only increase his anxiety. It becomes essential that the therapist take the lead, and often enough the first interview is less a dialogue than a quizzical, speculative, exploratory monologue by the therapist. He goes about it a little like a bloodhound on the trail, sniffing first in one direction and then another, depending mostly on his sense of smell to help him sort out the hot and cold scents and to bring him to the main trail as quickly as possible.

Jennie, aged fourteen, was referred with an acute history of frequent running away from home, school truancy, and using many sexual obscenities within earshot of classmates and teachers. This had started very abruptly about a week earlier, prior to which she had been a quiet, pleasant girl with a good school record. She was well liked by her friends and classmates, and had never been in any trouble with the authorities. When first seen she was flushed with excitement and appeared to be very angry. At the outset of the interview she attempted to dominate it with extravagant expressions of resistance. The examining psychiatrist took control of the interview by advising her, with a shading of emotional emphasis, to "quiet down and get hold of yourself."

She did, but continued to insist that she had nothing to say. She repeatedly challenged the doctor to "go ahead and send me to reform school—you can't scare me that way!"

"I didn't say anything about sending you to reform school. Did someone else say you might go there?"

"No! I don't care if they do!"

"It sounds as though you'd just as soon they would."

"So go ahead and do it! See if I care!'"

"That's what I mean. You're telling me to go ahead and send you there, and I might even do it if there's no better answer. Do you figure you absolutely *have* to go to reform school?"

"You might as well go ahead and do it because I'm not going to say anything."

"You already have. You're telling me to send you to reform school, which is about the same thing as saying someone had better lock you up to get you out of trouble or keep you out of trouble. Which is it?"

"That's what you think?"

"That's what I think. Right. What do you think?"

"I told you I'm not saying anything more."

"Then I guess I'll have to. I read over your history from the court, and there's . . ."

"Big deal. Is that supposed to scare me or something?"

"Something is sure scaring you. You quiet down for a minute and maybe I can tell you what it is, since you can't tell me."

"There's nothing to tell!"

"Well, to an outsider, what's happened to you doesn't seem to make much sense. It's beginning to make some sense to me, though. From what it says here, you've had a lot of trouble with your father." (Silence) "It says here he doesn't let you date, won't let you talk to any boys on the telephone, gets mad at you, and calls you all kinds of dirty names if you argue with him . . . lots of trouble."

"So? What of it?"

"Is he always like that? Isn't he ever nice to you?"

"Of course he's nice to me. (Bursts into tears involuntarily) When he's drunk, he's nice to me."

"Oh, like that. Maybe he's too nice to you sometimes."

"He didn't use to be. When I was a little girl, he was always nice to me, but not anymore . . . not anymore!"

"He was different when you started to change from a little girl into a —you know—more like a woman?"

"I'm just not going to stay there any more. You might as well go ahead and send me to reform school!"

"We'll see about that after we finish with this. Sometimes he's too nice to you, only it's not really nice. He doesn't act the way a father's supposed to act with his daughter? He gets—well—fresh with you, and things like that. Tell me what happened with him that got you started on all this trouble during the past week."

"He came into my bedroom. (Still sobbing bitterly) He was drunk and I couldn't make him stop . . ."

Jennie was asked bluntly about the possibility of her having been sexually approached by her father because there was enough historical and clinical information available to suggest that this was the immediate cause of her acute illness. She had been able to adjust fairly quietly in her chronically neurotic relationship with her father, but her various ways of doing this broke down in the face of an overt sexual approach from him.

Nothing was said in this interview about the unconscious wishes and fears which prompted her severe anxiety, her feelings of guilt ("send me to *reform school*"), and the emergence of a counterphobic defense ("I don't care!"). The latter could well have precipitated her into promiscuous sexual adventures away from home, but she had sufficiently publicized her desperation to win the protection of residential placement.

Positive Value of Arguing with the Adolescent

Getting into arguments with the adolescent, patient or not, is both inevitable and useful. It does not signify either a loss of dignity for the therapist or a disruptive lapse in treatment.

It is the one medium of verbal communication in which the patient of this age is likely to feel the most comfortable. It is his natural conversational habitat. When arguing, he is able to reveal things about himself which he could not possibly speak of in a quiet, expository tone.

Recalling his general position in relationship to the adult—of having to secure help and the gratification of dependency needs without asking for them openly—largely explains his preference for conducting himself in ways which invite controls, attention, and advice even as he appears to resist them mightily. Further, his surly, insolent ways maneuver the adult into being just as indirect in supplying these supports as he is in asking for them.

A quiet respect for the positive values of contentiousness in conversation with the adolescent is especially valuable early in treatment. It is also useful in the outpatient evaluation, where we must usually find out a great deal in a short period of time but in a way which will not be too upsetting to the patient. If given the opportunity to rear up on his hind legs a little, he is able to confide much information about himself without experiencing the serious loss in self-esteem which would come of submitting helplessly to an omnipotent adult and pouring out his heart like a baby.

The issue is also worth examining from the standpoint of what is accomplished in the usual family or social relationship between adolescent and adult. The therapist's willingness to yield at appropriate times to his own impatient urges to "argue back" signals a measure of respect for the youngster's increasing capacity for self-determination. He is given a stimulating chance to take a firm stand of his own and to defend it. The fact that he is frequently illogical does not at all mean that his efforts should be regarded as neurotically determined. His therapist ordinarily will not attempt to help him resolve his apparent anger by interpreting its origins in a remote infantile experience when by simply attending to the reality aspects of the content, it will usually come out promptly that the anger was not "real" in the first place. The following is a paradigm of a standard exchange between adult and adolescent (therapist and patient) in which a simple question receives a simple answer:

A sixteen-year-old girl says, "I'm-going-to-get-out-of-here-and-get-an-apartment-and-get-married-and-you-can't-stop-me!"

Her doctor replies, "No you're not, and yes I can."

She acknowledges, quietly enough, "Oh."

The patient's question is inverted, but the doctor's answer is direct. *The adolescent is emotionally ungrammatical in that he so often uses an exclamation point where a question mark is called for.* Efforts to appeal to self-critical faculty in the midst of argument and to be logical and reasonable usually tend only to increase his resistance to thoughtful introspection. Through his eyes the analytic interpretation is often experienced as just another adult gambit aimed at compelling him to submit like the child he once was. If, instead of this, the therapist honors the youngster's singularity by joining him in a vigorous adversary review of the reality issue, the proud challenger is often able to concede the point with self-respect intact.

Arguing also provides an opportunity for patient and therapist to enjoy a modest degree of tension-relief through the mutual acting-out of a modicum of controlled aggression. In view of the psychological necessity for adolescent and adult to confront each other in this way on many matters, it would be necessary to suspect that an absence of argument in any protracted relationship between them signifies an excessive neurotic inhibition of aggressive strivings on the part of one or the other, or perhaps both. As used here the word *argument* is to be distinguished from *quarrel* in which even the protective semblance of objectivity is replaced by direct, unrefined attack. Nor does it refer to prolonged, emotionally overdetermined struggles which do not lead to some tentative resolution of differences within a relatively brief period of time.

In the development of an argumentative pattern of exchange, there will always occur a resurgence of significant transference-countertransference feelings which must not be permitted to lie forever under cover of dispute. Hence, the therapist is required to exercise a great deal of flexibility in shifting from the position of a reality-oriented adult, arguing work-a-day issues just as he might with any recalcitrant adolescent, to that of a psychotherapist turning his special skills to the service of a youngster whose capacity for reality testing has been at least temporarily subverted by mental illness. [19].

Adoption of an antagonistic tone by the therapist is by no means associated in all instances with the application of authority, of controlling and prohibiting. It commonly dominates the tone of a transaction in which a calculated overpermissiveness, a devil's advocacy, is being used to highlight a specific treatment issue so that it may be dealt with interpretively.

Suzanne, aged sixteen, was mechanically perpetuating a long-established defense pattern, that of warding off erotic feelings for her father, by waging a militant-appearing but otherwise desultory romance with a boy who lived three states away. She introduced this problem into treatment by demanding much too heatedly that she be allowed to exchange letters with him. When this was immediately granted, with no resistance or comment at all from the therapist, Suzanne was visibly disappointed. A few letters passed between the two youngsters during the next several weeks, throughout which time Suzanne became increasingly anxious and antagonistic. Finally, she indignantly accused her doctor of reading her mail.

"No, I don't happen to be reading your mail. If I thought I should, I'd talk with you about it first. You know that."

"Well, anyway the nurses always tell you when I get a letter from him!"

"Of course. As usual, they tell me a lot of the ordinary things that go on with you and the other kids. What's wrong with that?"

"Because it's none of your business if we want to write to each other!"

"Well, I'm not too sure about that, but in any case I certainly haven't forbidden you to write, and I'm not reading your mail either!"

"Well! We'd write to each other even if you did tell me we couldn't!"

"You're sure working awfully hard to pick a fight about this. I guess maybe those letters aren't as much fun as you hoped they might be. Maybe it was a dirty trick for me to let you write to him in the first place. (Then, tongue-in-cheek) Would it help, do you think, if I ordered you not to swap any more letters with him? Then you could smuggle them on and off the ward—that would spice it up some."

"That is a stupid idea! It's *impossible* to smuggle mail in and out of here!"

"Oh, come on! Sneaking letters on and off the ward is easy as pie and you know it. Now, tell me what's the matter."

"I don't know. Oh, his letters are OK, but it seems like I don't miss him very much—I do miss him!—but I . . . Oh! I don't know what I'm missing so much. I feel like bawling . . ."

Attempting to represent reality as accurately as possible to the patient is fundamental to psychotherapy. It is the touchstone of the process, and should dominate the therapist's intentions in everything he says to the patient in any situation. The psychotic delusion is no exception.

Managing Delusions

Acutely psychotic adolescent boys, by way of illustration, are frequently convinced that they have prophetic powers. A youngster will claim that he can predict infallibly the outcome of a toss of a coin or, by extension, of anything else. When questioned about this, he presents his belief as a deep-seated conviction and seems insulted that the doctor would even question it. If there were reason to assume that such a delusion is an essential mechanism to the patient for maintaining his optimal level of integration, then we might be justified in temporizing by leaving the claim uncontested. However, it is necessary to consider the proposition that the delusional patient who *tells* the therapist about his delusion is neither completely convinced of its validity nor critically dependent upon it to stave off further personality disorganization. In speaking of it aloud he is, in addition to reinforcing an important defense by announcing it to another person, seeking to test the doctor's reaction to his muddled conception of reality. He is also expressing an unstated willingness to at least consider the outcome of that test, and then, perhaps, to proceed to more disturbing fears which he can recount only if he can trust his doctor's truthfulness. He is not looking for agreement and appeasement, as he so often seems to be, but for an improvement in his version of reality.

Roger was an acutely psychotic fifteen-year-old boy who was brought to the emergency room after having had "a series of convulsions" over the preceding day or two. History and physical examination were strongly suggestive of a psychological etiology, but he was admitted to the neurosurgery service for some further studies. He proved to be unmanageable there. Although not combative, his arrogant refusal to cooperate with ward procedures was intolerable. Psychiatric consultation was requested. Roger readily acquiesced to an interview but persisted in his haughty, supercilious manner. He claimed to know everything about himself and denounced all doctors as morons. He obtained his information about the universe by direct audio communication from Venus and asserted that he could predict the future as fully as he knew the past.

"I think it would be very easy to prove to yourself that you can't predict the future. Have you ever tried flipping a coin and calling it?"

"Many times. I never miss. You toss and I'll call."

"Then what?"

"Then you'll know I can predict the future. If I miss just once I'll go with you to the psychiatric ward voluntarily."

"Well, I'd expected you to do that anyway. The main reason I wanted to do this experiment is because it isn't right for me to leave you believing something that isn't true. Besides, you're being so snotty about everything I can hardly wait to prove you wrong."

"It's true. Go ahead and toss the coin."

Roger then proceeded to give his doctor a bad moment by correctly predicting the first seven tosses. But fortunately the law of averages prevailed, and he missed eight of the next ten. At the conclusion of the experiment Roger was more sheepish than unhappy and commented, "I figured all along I couldn't really do it, but I keep having this idea that I can. There's something wrong with my head, but I don't know what it is."

Pseudoresistance

The adolescent is not greatly consoled by benevolent offers of affection, sympathy, or help. The very least of his resistances are those things which most appear to be: the verbal challenges, the hyperemotional outbursts against us, the plangent disclaimers of any interest in treatment whatever, and the belligerent promises of perpetual revolt.

All are a part of the usual day's work with the adolescent patient, and the therapist who is currently treating one or two of them would not have to reach back more than a few hours for an appropriate illustrative excerpt. These flourishes of pseudoresistance are often in clearest evidence when the question of hospital admission is introduced.

Wally, an intelligent but very disturbed sixteen-year-old boy, was referred to the clinic by the juvenile court after he was picked up for his fifth episode of breaking and entering. Even among adolescent boys, he was an unusually hostile and paranoid youngster.

In pale, straight-faced anger he railed against the juvenile authorities for the multiple injustices which he had suffered at their hands. He accused his father in similar tones, and then turned his attack against the clinic and the examining psychiatrist for "interfering in my private affairs, which is none of your goddamned business!"

Dr. B reminded Wally that his troubles had become the business of the clinic and inquired more carefully into the details of his torrential complaints of "injustice." Wally suddenly turned his ever-mounting anger toward the juvenile officer who had dealt with him following his several arrests:

"That bastard Johnson is after me . . . he won't let me alone for a minute and I've had all I'm going to take!"

"I don't get it. You've been picked up five times for breaking and entering. Officer Johnson has always put you back on unofficial probation. Isn't that true?"

"Yeah. Big lick! You should hear the way he talks! The second time I was pulled in he told me if I ever did it again he was going to send me up to reform school! He's a real big shot!"

"That was after the second time. Since then you've gotten three more counts against you and you're still not in reform school. What happened when you broke in the third time?"

"Nothing happened! When my buddy and I got out the window we split up and I cut for home. They picked him up a block down the street and he told them everything. I didn't give a damn what they did about it. I hung around the house most of the day and about four o'clock big shot Johnson called up and said he was coming out in a couple of days to bring me in for questioning. I told him he could keep right on headed for California as far as I was concerned."

"Oh. Now I see. So he broke his promise? He didn't pick you up like he said he would. Well, Wally, we've been over everything pretty carefully and you've got a lot of trouble on your hands. It's time something was done about it. We'll start arrangements to get you in the hospital."

"Hospital! Make all the arrangements you want to—I'm not going into any hospital!"

"Well, don't get yourself all trapped in a spot like that. I think what you mean is you don't want to come into the hospital, which is all right, but you need to be in anyway so we'll just do what needs to be done. You can argue with me about whether it's fair or not, but let's not spend a lot of time arguing about whether it's going to happen or not."

"Fair! You guys don't know the meaning of the word! Do you think

I'm nuts or something? Anyway, just how do you think you're going to get me into a hospital if I don't want to come in?"

"I don't know. Frankly, I haven't thought about it. Like I just told you, you will be admitted, so I wasn't thinking too much about how."

"Well, I'll tell you one thing right now, there aren't enough cops in this town to catch me and even if they catch me they couldn't get me into any nut house!"

"Oh, I expect they could all right, but why put yourself to the trouble if you know it's going to happen anyway?"

"You guys are all the same! I've got nothing to say about it, huh? *I'm* the one who's going into the hospital, but *I* have no choice about it—is that what you're trying to tell me!"

"Right."

"It's wasted. It's the stupidest damned idea I ever heard of! I've got nothing more to say about it!"

"Then I'll go ahead and call your doctor, and we'll get you admitted."

"What do you mean!? I thought you were my doctor!"

An excruciating exercise of will is often needed to hold one's ground against such a convincing display of resistance. The temptation to placate, apologize, and defer is very strong. However, when it is made clear to the patient that his passions are not always decisive in conflicts with adults, that necessary things will be done, he is able to put up a dignified show of resistance prior to "surrendering": "I have no choice!" A desperate youngster's typical response following the resolution of such a crisis is sometimes embarrassingly grateful and affectionate. It is a reaction which even though it occurs time and time again is always surprising.

Adolescent Ultimatum

Dealing with the "irrevocable" adolescent ultimatum is a routine clinical chore. This standard mandate is rendered by the patient as an absolute prediction about the future outcome of an immediate authority conflict. "I don't care what you say—I'll *never* go back to school!"

"I'm going to take off from here and you can't stop me!"

"You can make me go to study hall but you can't make me study!"

These declarations are frequently made with unnerving intensity, which fact is the first item of business to be dealt with. The therapist observes, in effect: "You know, when you say it that way you put an end to everything. There's no place to go from there. You set things up to make it almost impossible for you to change your mind even if you wanted to. Why don't you just say you've decided you absolutely *don't want* to go to school, so you can at least change your mind if you ever want to. It's a lot different than saying you *won't* go to school."

There is usually an abundance of personal historical data available which will help to clarify with the patient that his reckless ultimata have repeatedly gotten him into self-defeating, paralytic binds with many other people in the past.

"You told your father once you were going to take off from home and he couldn't stop you. He must have believed you, because you'll remember he didn't even try. You didn't leave yourself a way out, so it ended with your getting yourself in a spot you didn't like one bit. You never leave yourself a way out, do you?"

Even though it sounds like a supreme act of self-determination, the ultimatum is really another way the adolescent has of turning all decisions about his own future over to someone else, or to "fate." It is an unqualified imperative statement which appears to demand an equally absolute response—presumably one which will instantly define the course of an otherwise uncertain future. Its essential, implicit question is, "I say you can never make me do this—can you? I say you can't possibly stop me from doing this—can you? I say I can force you into missing the whole point—can I?"

The passionately challenging tone of the ultimatum often stuns the therapist into an impulsive response which promises more than can be delivered.

"You might run away all right, but the police will just pick you up and bring you back here before you get to the city limits." The content of the mandate deserves, as a first step, some better clarification than this, i.e., a point-by-point analysis of the extent to which it squares with reality.

"You say you absolutely will not go to school, but I guess you don't really believe it or you wouldn't say it so loud and so often. Let me help convince you that what you say really is true. I certainly cannot make you go to school, at least not so it would do any good. But I can make you *not* go to school, and as things stand right now that's exactly the way it is. No, I don't know what's going to happen next, because what you just said is true—it's mostly up to you. What? Of course I want you to go to school, and I'll do everything reasonable to help you get there, *if* it will really help. Sure, I know you don't want to go to school, but what's that got to do with whether you *should* go or not. If there's any chance of your getting something good out of it then you should go, but there's certainly no point in our having a make-believe argument about whether I can force you to. I can't."

Or, "If you just think back you'll remember nobody here ever told you we could keep you from running away because we can't. Oh yes, I could put you on the closed ward and that would make it a little tougher, but still not too hard. No, I can't guarantee the police would pick you up before you had time to do yourself some serious harm. I know they've always found you right away in the past but that's only because you gave them plenty of help . . . you know, by keeping on with this constant threatening to run away you have a very neat way of avoiding saying anything at all about *why* you run away."

These general responses are not of the same unrealistically permissive genre as: "The only way I can help you is by helping you understand yourself." Rather, they advise the patient that we will do anything, including the liberal application of personal pressure and physical confinement, which has a reasonable chance of supporting his progress in treatment. At the same time we acknowledge certain realistic limitations on our ability to control, restrain, and protect him from the consequences of his own actions.

As suggested earlier, some of the most formidable resistances are those which are least apparent. A youngster's direct request for psychiatric treatment, his sincerely expressed wish to cooperate in psychotherapy even before he has the least idea what it is, or his sober praising of the therapist's abilities, are all representative of the kind of resistance which sends shivers of apprehension through the therapist who is experienced in treating adolescents.

Intuition and Guessing in Psychotherapy

The experienced therapist is familiar with the frustration of trying to render a satisfying description of even the most minute and circumscribed transaction between himself and his patient. Attempting to explain the reasons for having said one thing or another to the patient is a discouragingly formidable enterprise.

It is not feasible to discuss the verbal exchanges of a treatment interview with the implication that each of the therapist's statements had been made with a specific purpose, or were justified by a clear preconceived plan of psychotherapy. In practice, the understanding and the treatment of a mentally ill patient proceed simultaneously, and in many instances an "act of therapy," e.g., a statement by the doctor, precedes his knowing why he said it. Usually he never becomes conscious of his reasons in their entirety, but this deters him little from (1) giving them anyway and (2) doing the right thing anyway, most of the time in spite of his abysmal ignorance.

An intelligent, civilized outpatient who doesn't cause too much trouble nicely accommodates the therapist's need to fancy that he knows exactly what he is doing. This is far less easy to do in the necessarily erratic, quizzical, and speculative approach to the frightened and defiantly skeptical adolescent. He will not join his therapist in the work of treatment until he is convinced that he is in the hands of someone who is able to ferret out and understand the feelings and thoughts which he has long contemplated, in lonely desperation, as unique and incomprehensible. He can be counted upon to require his therapist to be right much of the time, although he will not expect him to be omniscient. The therapist must be equally tolerant of his own fallibility and constantly prepared to acknowledge his frequent errors as an inevitable part of the therapy process.

"All right, I'm missing the point. If what I just guessed isn't true, then what is? Try to tell me. Don't expect me to do all the work."

"But I don't know!"

"No, you don't. But you can guess just as well as I can, at least about some things. What happened just before you went out that night? Did you feel OK? The way you usually do? Or was there something different? What did he look like? What did you say then? Why? Maybe you didn't really mean what you said—it sounds like you just wanted to scare him. No? But you were scared . . . why are you getting mad about it—what's so wrong with being scared in a set-up like that?" And on it goes. The therapist does most of the "free-associating" for the patient at times.

Although patently rejecting the "basic rule," with tactful and tacit assistance the adolescent will practice an equally serviceable type of free association. He requires a little more stimulation, more nudging, pulling, and pushing, and only rarely a bit of bulldozing. The therapist's approach is crudely analagous to the physical examination of a patient who presents a difficult diagnostic problem. One tends first to apply the stethoscope and listen. In a good, straightforward disease of the chest auscultation alone might provide the answer, but the value of inspection, percussion, and palpation increase in proportion to the complexity of the problem. There are probably some psychological equivalents to vocal fremitus, ballotment, and fluid wave, but the analogy is not worth extending in these terms. The main point is that with the adolescent it is essential that the therapist acquire a high level of confidence in his clinical intuition and accept the information acquired in this way as being often just as valid, and many times much more so, than that which he obtains through conscious design.

The psychiatrist has some good reasons—if not adequate excuses—for relying too much upon definitive and logical explanations for the too frequently unexplainable events of psychotherapy. More is being said these days about the psychology of intuition and the hunch and of their place in psychodiagnosis and psychotherapy. Intuition is a mystery only in that it has not been thoroughly explained and understood. There is nothing magical about it: no telepathic communication, no "flowing together with the patient's unconscious," no "psychological osmosis." No matter how these matters are finally explained from the standpoint of theory, we know that in practice the clinical guess is experienced as a rather sudden, distinct, subjective impression which inclines the therapist to one side or another of a conflict situation which requires decision. The resulting conclusion, which is statistically far more likely to be correct than a random selection, is reached by "prethinking" processes which go on beneath the level of consciousness. How accurate the psychiatrist's intuition might be in one situation or another is something which he must establish for himself through the trial-and-error of experience. Some find their intuitive promptings to be trustworthy and useful, while others learn that they dare not rely upon their spontaneous tendencies to thought and action in decision making. Past experience has taught them that they do better to take the time to assemble as much relevant data as possible for conscious processing by logical thought.

It is not necessary to make a value judgment about the relative merits of these two general modes of operation. However, the therapist who is fortunate enough to bring a sound set of "reflexes" into the field of therapy will be somewhat more comfortable and effective with the disturbed adolescent than will the man who must contemplate the problems of therapy at leisure. The adolescent's movements are swift and covert. Keeping up with him, or hopefully one step ahead of him most of the time, requires more than just very superior intelligence.

There is no way to train psychotherapists to become keenly intuitive, nor does it become us as scientists to commend the unconscious intuitive process over that of conscious logic. The fact remains, however, that the therapist's intuition is still his most valuable instrument of diagnosis and therapy, and he is obliged to use it in treatment until mere intelligence can improve upon it. The point is emphasized because contemporary psychiatry, as a relatively new and very demanding discipline, stands with some embarrassment and sense of inferiority among the classic quantitative sciences. In seeking to make itself respectable, it sometimes reaches too far and too eagerly to garner an adequate semblance of scientific respectability. In the course of this the intuitive process has got a very poor reputation. It is not proposed that one should substitute intuition for thinking when the latter is appropriate to the task at hand, nor would the serious psychological scientist neglect to examine as thoroughly as possible, *after* the act, the precedent determinants of an intuitive judgment.

A remarkable personality feature of the adolescent is his willingness to accept our sensible, intuitive answers to his countless irate demands for logical explanation. As an ex-child he retains a quiet respect for the other person's ability to make wise and realistic judgments without really knowing how he reached them. He is equally sensitive to the average adult's reluctance to admit that the cerebral cortex, though a valuable addition to the lower levels of the central nervous system, has not yet rendered them obsolete.

Jane, a sixteen-year-old girl, was admitted with a long history of delinquencies which included much aggressive-destructive behavior and sexual promiscuity. She could not be adequately contained on the adult closed ward. She broke windows, inflicted numerous cuts on her arms and legs, and was intolerably loud and aggressive in her behavior toward other patients and the nursing staff. When all reasonable efforts to calm her failed, it was finally necessary to place her in the "quiet room." (This is actually a seclusion room, although we do not like to call it that.) She continued to create much disturbance there, but after a few hours she gave it up in favor of a new tactic. She became compliant, cooperative, and unconvincingly sweet, and began to say all the right things about her intentions to cooperate in treatment. She concluded her impressive pledge to reform with a request that she be returned to the ward. Although uneasy about his decision, her therapist finally denied the request, to which she responded with a furious demand for "a reason . . . give me one good reason!"

Her doctor, feeling that he owed her this, made a sincere but fumbling effort to supply it.

"You've been in seclusion many times before because of trouble like this. You always say that you'll be able to do better when you come out, and I think you even mean it at the time, but the trouble comes back anyway."

"But how am I going to learn how to get along better on the ward if I don't ever have a chance?"

She then continued to play on his guilt by accusing him of punishing her. When she recognized that this was not accomplishing her purposes, she suddenly became more docile and asked him when she would be permitted to return to the ward. He replied that he really didn't know, that there was no answer to the question.

"Well, how will you be able to tell when I *am* ready to go back? What do I have to *do*? How long do I have to *behave* myself in here?"

Her doctor did not know when or how he would be able to make this decision, but he felt that there would be a time when he would "feel" that it would make sense to try again. He advised her accordingly:

"There is nothing I can tell you about how you have to behave, or what you have to say, to persuade me that you're ready to go back to the ward. The best thing I can tell you is that I'll probably have a feeling about it when it's got a chance of working. That isn't much to go on, but I really don't have a better answer—I only wish I did."

This explanation proved to be entirely acceptable to Jane. In a relatively short period of time she became more convincingly and genuinely responsive to the staff and gave believable indications of having begun to develop some increasing concern about herself.

8

TREATMENT PRIORITIES, PACE, AND COURSE

One can sympathize with the teenager's sense of urgency about completing the psychological labors of adolescence before it is too late. Although clear scientific proofs are lacking, there is persuasive evidence that certain essential "emotional nutriments" are age-specific. They must be administered at a certain time of life in order to be effective.

A hormone of the anterior pituitary produces normal longitudinal growth in young children, but after closure of the bony metaphyses these organs are able to respond only with lateral growth, which results in skeletal abnormality. Maternal love, however it might be defined, is needed in infancy. If this is withheld, and attempts are then made to supply it when the child is eight years old, it will not accomplish the same psychological effects which it produces in the infant. It is probable that the same principle applies in the adolescent's growth to adulthood. If he has not made substantial gains in this direction by the end of chronological adolescence, then it becomes increasingly difficult for him to do so as he grows older. His impatience with the status quo makes itself felt in therapy.

In a characteristic course of long-term treatment with an adolescent there are fairly protracted periods of time, on the order of weeks or even months, which are spent at what appears to be a relatively pedestrian review of his routine adjustment. One of the therapist's most tiresome tasks is that of remaining moderately interested and very attentive to his supervisory responsibilities. As things now stand in clinical training, many of these vital but spectacularly ordinary chores will not square with the student's conception of what he *should* be doing as a psychotherapist.

These periods of equilibrium are occasionally punctuated by small flurries of conflict which are usually externalized to the therapist, to another member of the staff, or to a patient. They often appear in the guise of ostensibly resistive emotional outbursts—anger, complaint, accusation, threat, or ultimatum. Psychotherapy progresses through the piecemeal resolution of these conflicts and through the scrupulous maintenance of a supportive and realistic daily activities program. The latter is in itself therapeutic, and it also provides certain of the preconditions needed to render therapeutic some of the more formal operations of psychotherapy [18].

In the treatment of any patient the therapist has good reasons for applying general treatment measures in a certain sequence. In the basic model of psychoanalytic therapy, for example, we are reminded that the patient's defenses must be analyzed before he can gain access to the unconscious wishes against which these have been erected. The order of treatment in psychotherapy with the adolescent sometimes resembles and at other times differs from that which would apply to the neurotic adult outpatient. One of the biggest differences hinges upon the rather opposite ways in which these two patients enter therapy, the one walking and willing and the other dragging his heels and clawing at the door jambs. Thus the first order of business in the treatment of the adolescent is to get him into treatment, and the next is to keep him there.

We would not dream of attempting anything resembling intensive psychotherapy with an adult who resisted the idea with such devotion. Even though the adolescent's great show of reluctance is more apparent than real, there are problems associated with his breech delivery into psychotherapy, speaking metaphorically, which are more complicated and carry a higher morbidity rate than those belonging to a standard occipital presentation. There are some important measures which may be taken to prevent or correct these in support of effective treatment.

External Supports to Treatment

Parents. We find little reason to believe that the parents of an adolescent patient are "sicker" than those of a child patient, but one gets the strong impression that they are often much more desperate about being separated from him for purposes of psychiatric treatment. Increased feelings of guilt, liability, and ambivalence are suffered by the parents of adolescent patients who require hospital treatment.

These reactions are partly explainable by some of the same terms used to describe the expected and unusual tensions in the normal relationship between adolescent and adult. The adolescent is older and more experienced than the child. Comparatively speaking, he is able to take more responsibility for himself in his relationship to others. Although technically the "child" of his parents by law and custom, everyone recognizes that his development is carrying him further and further away from emotional dependency upon his parents. This dependency means more than a simple need for turning to mother or father for affection and protection. It also means depending upon them to preserve and perpetuate the old patterns of neurotic family interaction which, though damaging in many ways from our point of view, have also done much to preserve the umbilical bond. Somewhat less evident is the parents' profound dependence upon their sick and troublesome child.

In a sense, removal of the sick adolescent from the home brings an end to many years of unconscious labor which the entire family has put into the development of a stable, neurotic equilibrium. The removal of one of its more forceful components, the disturbed adolescent, is usually extremely disruptive. He may be urgently needed as a source of vicarious satisfaction for one of the parents, as a "chaperone" between a husband and wife who cannot bear to be alone together, or for many similar reasons. The guilt which parents feel as a result of sensing that they have done a poor job in rearing their child is intensified and made more imminent by their adolescent youngster's accelerated approach to the more final appearing, perhaps irreversible, sickness or "badness" of adulthood. This is less true in the case of younger children with whom it is easier to nourish the fantasy that there is still plenty of time left to rectify the damage. Beyond this, it can be made to seem that the damage is not so much after all, because we do not expect little children to behave like adults. The adolescent is necessarily regarded as a more finished character, much closer to being that which he is soon to become, finally and definitively, as an adult. For the little patient in hospital treatment the prospects are fair that he will return home eventually, but the adolescent is more likely to be outward bound to a boarding school, college, military service, or perhaps to independent employment. The proof of the developmental pudding is about to be made known.

These are some of the explanations for the extreme difficulty which is often encountered in keeping the adolescent patient in treatment and in assisting his parents to recognize and modify their own contributions to the shared family illness. The problem is significantly amplified, of course, by the adolescent's native talent for provoking in his parents the fullest possible realization of their latent feelings of guilt-provoking and anxiety-provoking hostility. Even the most heroic efforts to help parents tolerate these painful stresses are often futile. Carefully coordinated casework, medical authority, and unrealistic last ditch attempts at appeasement are frequently too little to stem the family's immense need to restore its previous neurotic stability. Several of the case excerpts, used to illustrate various points in other sections, also demonstrate something of the magnitude and dynamic characteristics of this problem.

JUVENILE COURT. When it is apparent that medical measures alone will not be enough to preserve a workable treatment arrangement, it is often helpful to secure additional external supports. One of the most effective of these is the benevolent authority of the juvenile court [19]. In taking temporary custody of the patient, the court does *not* terminate parental rights, contrary to popular belief. In actual practice it does not even seriously diminish them. Unless parents have been extremely negligent, and sometimes even when they have been, they will ordinarily have little difficulty in regaining custody within a very short time if they are determined to do so. A few days of grace, however, are often enough to help parents resolve the acute stress which prompted them to seek termination of treatment.

Probably an even greater advantage of temporary court custody lies in its providing the parents with an effective antidote to the guilt which they are inclined to feel about having voluntarily given up their child to the care of others. The arrangement lends strong support to the idea that "We do not want to give him up but have no choice—the court is forcing us to leave him in the hospital."

The problems of separation are serious enough that we commonly find it necessary to stipulate temporary juvenile court custody as a condition of inpatient treatment. Almost as often, however, this will not be a lasting protection unless we are able to enlist the patient's assistance in making it possible for the parents to tolerate his improvement during treatment. Accomplishing this requires that he be helped to appreciate the enormity of his influence over his parents and to be aware of the unfortunate consequences of his exercising this influence "testingly," which he often does for little better reason than that it has become his habitual means for controlling them and retaliating against them.

POWER OF THE PATIENT. There are a number of times in treatment when it becomes important to remind the patient of his power, i.e., particularly at times when he is showing visible signs of improvement. However, the adolescent's astonishing eagerness to act in his own best interests is never more dramatically illustrated than when state hospital commitment is being recommended for a severely disturbed youngster who appears to be openly antagonistic to the plan.

Chuck, a fifteen-year-old boy, was referred for help with a severe and far-advanced psychotic illness. Since puberty his only interest had been in weight-lifting. He had no friends—only enemies. He believed that his classmates at school whispered false accusations against him behind his back. The boys, he was convinced, considered him a "queer," and the girls conspired to humiliate him by refusing to look at him or speak to him. He had severely beaten his eleven-year-old sister on several occasions, and had recently choked her into unconsciousness. When the parents were finally prompted to take action, he threatened to kill them.

In the evaluation interview he was flushed with anger, and his manner was openly threatening. The examining psychiatrist took a dominant, controlling position but allowed a tolerable atmosphere of mutual antagonism to prevail. This enabled Chuck to reveal abundant intimate detail about himself, more than enough to confirm the seriousness of his illness and the urgent need for hospital commitment. When this plan was discussed with him, Chuck saw no alternative to remaining loyal to his furiously overdetermined protests against any "interference" in his life. The psychiatrist recognized that his influence over his family was so great that it would probably be impossible for them to carry out commitment without Chuck's overt support. This was brought directly to Chuck's attention; his cooperation was openly solicited by the psychiatrist's simply *speaking past the manifest content* of his violent protests, as though they had not even been expressed. He spoke instead to their latent meaning, which permitted the vital "face-saving" function of the furious opposition to remain intact.

"They're not sticking me into any goddamn nut house. I'll kill them if they try it!"

"That's where the trouble comes in. If you fight it, they won't be able to do it. That worries me. They're awful scared of you."

"They damn well better be!"

"I didn't mean especially that they're scared you're going to kill them. They might be; I don't know, but from what you've said it seems like they've always been afraid of crossing you up in any way at all, maybe because they're afraid it'll hurt you or something. Do you know what I mean?"

Chuck was silent.

"I see you do. Well, what it means is that you don't even have to threaten to hurt them to stop them from getting you into a hospital. Look how long it took them just to bring you over to see me, even after all this trouble you've been having for the last three or four years."

"They knew they better hadn't."

"Right. They couldn't stand to hurt your feelings, or something. They couldn't make themselves do it until you practically choked your sister to death. Maybe they can't help being that way, but they are. You tell me, Chuck, what will they think about my advising that you go to a state hospital?"

"They won't like it!" Then, having almost forgotten himself, he hastily added, "Neither do I! I'm not going there!"

"I'm thinking about it some more. You know, if you keep on threatening them or beat up your sister again, they might be able to get the point and go ahead with it. The more I think about it, the more I think there's a better way for you to stop them."

"What do you mean? How!"

"Just get well. You know, the same old way. Just tell them everything's OK now. You feel better since coming over here. Tell them different things . . . like going to a hospital with a lot of crazy people will make you go crazy . . . things like that. It would work, wouldn't it?"

Chuck remained silent again.

"Well, anyway, you know all the different things you can do to keep them from sending you to the hospital."

"I sure as hell do."

"So don't do them. If you do, they won't be able to let you go."

"Yeah? Well that's good, because I don't want to go!"

"Look, I know that, and you know you need to go anyway. Let's don't argue about that because we don't have an argument."

"What's it like out at that dump?"

"The hospital? Well, some good, some not so good. I'll tell you about it in a minute, but let's settle this other thing first. Do you think you can get them to let you go there?"

"You're the boss, what the hell! If you're going to send me there, then go ahead and do it. I can't stop you."

"Oh yes, you can. That's what I'm talking about. If I could just call a car and send you on out there, I'd do it and save us both all this sweat. But we can't get you in unless they go down to the court and file this petition of mental illness . . ."

"Mental illness! Are you trying to say I'm nuts!"

"Of course I am! Well, not "nuts"—that's your word. Mentally ill, or sick, is the way I say it. Look, let's don't worry about naming it. The point is, if your folks don't go down and file the petition, you're stuck. Can you get them to do it?"

Very quietly, "I guess so."

"Then you'd better stay in here with me while I talk to them, because the first thing they're going to do is get all nervous and wonder what you think about it. They should be able to go ahead no matter what you think about it, but I doubt if they can."

"I don't want to go out there."

"I know—I'll tell them that and you tell them, too. Then when I explain to them that you need to go anyway, you just tell them it's their nickel or there isn't any choice or some such lie. See what I mean?"

"Yeah."

Chuck followed through as planned, and then some. He put his psychiatrist to shame by declining the invitation to lie—even in a good cause. When they anxiously raised the predicted questions he told them, arms folded and staring grimly at the floor, "Listen, you brought me here to get some advice and now you've got it. I don't want to go out there, but I'd like to see if you can take someone else's advice for a change. If you don't, you'll be sorry." He was able to "save face," have a little revenge and tell the truth at the same time.

Perhaps it should be added that this pattern of resolution, in this very type of intense anxiety-provoking situation, is the rule rather than the exception. It is something which cannot be believed until one has seen it happen, and even then it is hard to remember when the next occasion arises. The sick adolescent does not like being sick any more than he likes admitting to it or asking to be helped with it. But he will seize upon the opportunity for help if given a way to do this with honor and without being lied to.

Assuring patient against external threats. Adequate insurance against precipitous removal from the hospital, however, is not always enough to convince the patient that he is truly in treatment. Because of their past experiences with adult inconsistencies and betrayals, many of these youngsters are able to sustain fantasies of being in control of the situation with only the flimsiest reality supports. Without the therapist's knowledge, parent and patient may be protecting themselves from the threats of treatment by a secret contract [16], one which provides, for example, that father will "hire a lawyer and get you back home if you're not cured in six months"; or "if you'll keep it to yourself, I'll let you drive the car when you come home on passes, but you have to promise not to go over seventy in *this* county. They might never give your license back."

No matter how firm the various external supports to treatment, there is no psychotherapy until the adolescent has had an opportunity to test conclusively the newly restricted limits of his own power to control adults. There may be detention, benevolent care, humane patterning, helpful pharmacotherapy, an opportunity for spontaneous remission, but no intensive psychotherapy. This is under way only when the patient realizes that for an indefinite and highly uncertain time virtually all the child-guiding authority of society has been vested in his therapist.

At first glance this condition would seem important only in the treatment of the delinquent, hospitalized adolescent. In practice it applies also to a great number of youngsters in other diagnostic categories and in a lesser degree to many outpatients as well.

It is true that there are some types of psychoneurotic and quietly "schizophrenic" adolescents who can receive appropriate help in a more or less traditional form of outpatient therapy. However, there is something incompatible between the idea of a circumscribed, self-contained illness on the one hand and the psychological turbulence of adolescence on the other. The adolescent girl with a simple hysterical paralysis, for example, who has always been a cooperative youngster until the onset of her illness, may prove on close inspection to be quite depressed, intransigent in her refusal to attend school, defiant with her parents, and given to swallowing conservative overdoses of aspirin and inflicting epidermal lacerations on her wrists when displeased or frustrated.

Before he can accomplish anything else, the patient must have strong assurance that he will be protected from such major external threats as on-going sexual seduction by an older sibling or irresistible delinquency sanctions by a parent; from the threats posed by internal impulses, such as suicide, homicide, premature marriage, or some other kind of behavior which is more apt to get him into prison than into a psychiatric hospital. The therapist attends first of all to the crucial external problems in his patient's life and only then to those which are internal and tastily psychodynamical.

Interpreting Defensive Behavior

When it becomes possible to initiate intensive psychotherapy, there is a further order of treatment priorities to be observed. It is unfortunately common for experienced as well as beginning therapists to approach the patient with a constricted and fascinated focusing on the neurotic manifestations of an illness which is far more comprehensive and severe than is evident in the conspicuous "dynamics." The likelihood of misinterpreting the patient's illness in this way tends to vary directly with the patient's intelligence and articulateness and with the therapist's talent for eliciting the material which he wants. A boy who "runs amuck," becomes defiant, assaultive, and sexually aggressive in some way, is an easier diagnostic problem if he has an IQ of 90 and uses simple, ungrammatical language. If he is bright and expressive, the chances greatly increase for the therapist's finding valid clinical evidences of classic neurotic conflict and become worse for appreciating that he is psychotic first and neurotic second.

At the age of fourteen Christopher was picked up by the police and referred for psychiatric evaluation after he was found sprinting down the street in the dead of night with no clothes on. He was cooperative and congenial with police officers and the examining psychiatrist. He spoke freely, describing his problems with his parents in revealing detail. His mother was an abnormally seductive woman who had personally bathed him at least twice daily since his birth. His father was a cold, aloof person who had virtually nothing to do with his son, except on those rare occasions when he would feel impelled to do his paternal duty by beating the boy brutally for some relatively minor infraction of a nonexistent discipline.

Christopher explained the combined attitudes of his parents as "a test of my manhood . . . preparing me to enter the lists in mankind's crusade against the forces of femininity."

In a subsequent clinical conference, the expanded history from the parents revealed that his overt troubles began at the age of nine, several weeks after a tonsillectomy. In the ensuing discussion a high degree of significance was attached to the etiological importance of this surgical event as one which had "renewed his castration anxiety." From this came a recommendation for a treatment approach centered on interpreting his nuditive behavior as a defense against castration fear. There appeared to be little question about the validity of the general formulation, but exclusive attention to this detail led to an earnest proposal for outpatient psychotherapy. For Christopher, this would have been like treating a deep abdominal gunshot wound by suturing the skin defect only.

Before it is possible for the patient to contribute usefully to his own treatment, it is necessary first of all for him to recognize that he does have problems and also for him to realize that his therapist knows what these are and which are of first importance. In his *public* appraisal of himself, Christopher had problems; he claimed that he was being prepared to fulfill a sacred destiny. During the course of inpatient treatment the defensive value of this delusion and others serving a similar purpose was recognized and interpreted by his therapist, but not by Christopher. He continued to be exhibitionistic, to regale other patients with intriguing philosophical discourses on the high moral purpose of his actions, and to win a sympathetic and appreciative response from a number of staff women. In time it became apparent that it would be necessary to "interpret his defenses" in a way which would be meaningful to him.

He was told what articles of clothing to wear, when and how to wear them, and when not to wear them. He was also given concrete directions to talk only about work-a-day matters with other patients and staff members and to reserve his philosophical excursions for his doctor.

The problem was reviewed repeatedly with nursing and parapsychiatric staff, and their indispensable assistance in helping to make the interpretation was carefully secured. This was a typical instance of team psychotherapy which, also typically, required a great outlay of energy on the part of the therapist and the entire staff. It entailed an unavoidable amount of unhappiness, error, and disagreement among all of them. Their efforts were eventually successful, however, and in a short time Christopher became severely depressed. A little later he began to experience feelings of depersonalization and derealization, and in the ensuing months it was finally possible for him to make good use of a series of interpretations having to do with unconscious wishes belonging to the neurotic oedipal interaction with his mother and father. But it had been necessary to "control his behavior" before this could be done.

Controlling Behavior

When the idea of setting limits or controlling behavior is introduced, we are apt to think first of clamping manacles on an overtly delinquent, antisocial youngster whose aggressive and sexual actions exceed the tolerance of even a relatively permissive inpatient community. It is not an appealing bit of imagery. For some nonpsychotic delinquent youngsters a psychiatrist can accept that there is sometimes a need for a certain amount of "patterning," i.e., behavior conditioning by the reward and punishment principle. He may also accept without much difficulty, in the case of the neurotic or psychotic youngster, the idea that "Of course, they mustn't be allowed to go too far." These conservative views of the importance of behavior in psychotherapy imply several things which are not true. First, they suggest that everyone understands and agrees that "controls" are important. Second, their very tone shrugs off any question that there would be significant difficulty in implementing them effectively. Third, they relegate the whole issue of wise and responsible child-care practices to the level of homespun homilies, where they enjoy too little respect from professionals. Finally, they imply with a touch of derision that the making of authoritative prohibitions against defensive behavior is moralistic, judgmental, and without proper place in the operational matrix of psychiatry. It is consigned to the province of non-professional adults in general society, and there held in careful exile from the royal activities of more ceremonious methods.

There is also a certain amount of lip service accorded the idea that acting out by children and adolescents may serve as a resistance to therapy, just as it may for the adult. Disagreement is most likely to arise in connection with the best means for treating the youngster who persists in this mode of resistance, despite all efforts to interpret the defensive value of his actions through the medium of words and ideas.

A widespread attitude toward such patients among therapists who limit their practices to the treatment of outpatients is: "His resistance to treatment is intractable. He will have to go into a hospital for safety and supportive therapy. He is not a candidate for intensive psychotherapy." Neurotically stereotyped behavior, whether delinquent or otherwise, also often represents the highest possible level of communication of which the patient is capable when he enters treatment, and therefore the highest level at which the interpretation of defenses and resistances can be meaningfully conveyed to him. The kind of acting out which makes inpatient treatment imperative need not preclude interpretive psychotherapy; it merely requires that one go about it differently.

This view of psychopathology is immensely important in the treatment of the adolescent. As there is no such thing as "*a* delinquent," there can be no specific plan of rational therapy for him. He does not exist. There are helpful principles to be followed in dealing with any youngster whose defenses include delinquent mechanisms, but these will apply to those aspects of his functioning which are of a neurotic, psychotic, or psychophysiologic nature, only if they have been conscripted for part-time service in the ranks of maladaptive character defense. As we proceed to emphasize the importance of controls to the treatment of the *predominantly* delinquent patient, for example, it must be understood that this applies also to the self-defeating character mechanisms of the predominantly psychoneurotic or "schizophrenic" youngster.

This roundabout approach to the problem is for the purpose of clarifying the common misconception that the application of controls is a treatment *technique* and that it is resorted to only when everything else has failed. It is not. It is no more than a matter of being realistic with a juvenile patient who, because of his illness, is not yet ready for the same degree of independence required of the average adolescent.

Permitting the Patient to Feel Safe

For example, in the case of the aggression-inhibited schizophrenic youngster who so fears his own destructive impulses that he scarcely dares to speak, it is correctly observed that improvement will ordinarily be associated with an increase in his "ability to express hostility." A frequent error in treatment is to note this *effect,* i.e., the patient's increased tolerance for his own feelings of anger, and try to apply it as something which will *cause* improvement. We dare not applaud the schizophrenic boy's tentative experiments with feeling and expressing his anger. He is depending upon us to make it safe for him to experiment; this in fact is what made it possible for him to increase his tolerance for "ego-alien" impulses in the first place. Further, the significant failure in his reality testing is the fantasy that his *feelings* of anger alone will cause widespread destruction to the people around him. He is not subject to the delusion that people regard the *acting-out* of anger as a good thing; if he perceives us becoming happy about his acted-out hostility he will rightly suspect that there is something wrong with our reality testing. Firmly directing him *not* to slam chairs against the wall or *not* to shout furious insults at people will *not* "drive him back into his shell." On the contrary, it will make it safer for him to continue to search within himself for a more gratifying, tolerable, and realistic midrange of emotionality. The same principle should orient us to the realistic management of any similar maladaptive character processes which are a part of the patient's defensive system.

Authority in Therapy

The loose transposition of certain principles of dynamic psychology from the office to the ward has led to much confusion for the therapist whose experience has been limited to outpatient work. The matter of authority in the treatment of the adolescent patient is an inflammatory issue. In discussions with colleagues and in the technical literature, we encounter a consistent tendency to treat this idea in a much too concrete fashion. Authority is often discussed as though it were a single thing which the therapist either does or does not impose upon his young patient with little regard to what is being controlled and for what purpose.

Perhaps some of the difficulty lies in our speaking of "control" and "authority" without tying them terminologically to their appropriate functions in treatment. The expression "treating the patient through his behavior" might be a little less provocative to the psychiatrist who is inclined to take up arms and do gory battle with colleagues at the faintest suggestion that a little aggression, properly controlled, can help him accomplish worthwhile aims with patients. The idea itself is easier to understand if one thinks first of several simple and rather basic concepts of dynamic psychology and then begins to apply these to any form of human behavior instead of to symbolic language alone.

For example, if the neurotic adult outpatient suddenly asks his therapist for an aspirin tablet in the middle of an interview, we would immediately think in terms of the manifest and latent content of the request. Manifestly, the patient wants an aspirin because he has a headache. Understanding the latent meaning would require that we know more about this particular patient and his therapist. He may be asking for some kind of symbolic gratification which would represent to him a gift of affection, or he may be unconsciously rationalizing his confusion as resulting from organic pain.

If the same patient is ten minutes late for an appointment, his therapist will undoubtedly recognize a common and often quite meaningful type of outpatient behavior which must be examined for both manifest and latent meanings. If he is usually punctual and explains that he had a flat tire, his doctor will be inclined to accept this at face value. If he has been late several times recently and offers to pass off his tardiness with an explanation that he overslept, didn't notice what time it was, or absentmindedly turned down the wrong street, it is probable that much more attention will be directed to the latent meaning of his behavior. In none of these, however, is it necessary for the therapist to control the patient's behavior, because the terms of the treatment contract have not been violated.

If the patient is an anxious adolescent who has accepted outpatient treatment primarily because of painful symptoms, his tardiness would be dealt with in much the same way. But if he should happen to be a mildly acting-out youngster who was originally referred by the school and parents because of chronic lying and cheating, then it is quite conceivable that his therapist would be more interested in his explanation for the tardiness than in the tardiness itself. If the patient is an adolescent whose illness has required that he be hospitalized under formal protest and who adamantly declines our offer of office-type psychotherapy, these same principles relating to the manifest and latent significance of behavior will still apply. They are as valid on the ward as in the office.

When we ask the tardy adult outpatient why he was late, it is easy enough for both parties to accept that we are not doing this to reprimand him. His behavior has not been unethical or bad. It is examined only because it might lead to his understanding something about himself he was not aware of before. Indeed, the patient is paying the doctor to help him find out about such things. When the ordinarily punctual adolescent inpatient is late for an appointment, his behavior will be examined in precisely the same way and for the same reasons. He will probably claim to be greatly insulted and demand to know why he is being picked on, but for him this is a standard way of beginning a productive interview. The experienced therapist handles it in stride.

But what if the adult outpatient, originally presumed to be neurotic, regularly comes thirty minutes late to his appointment, greets the receptionist with obscenities, throws a chair through the window and threatens to commit bodily assault—and hasn't paid his fee for six months? What is it that his doctor will want to understand about this and to what end? We may assume that he has long since exhausted his supply of insight-producing interpretations with little beneficial effect. The patient's behavior still has manifest and latent meanings, but the therapeutic potential of this knowledge is considerably limited by his inability to abide by the conditions of the treatment contract. He is unable to do this because he is too sick, probably psychotic, and consequently his doctor does not blame him for it. Instead, he has him admitted to a hospital, and there in all probability the patient's treatment will be undertaken by another doctor.

The adolescent who is already in the hospital and who behaves in a similar fashion is not necessarily psychotic. It is much more difficult to excuse him "on grounds of mental illness." To make matters worse, he is not an adult; and to make them worse yet, he is not even a child. If he were thirty years old, his doctor, his family, and the psychiatric staff could appreciate that he is probably psychotic or at worst a "psychopath." If he were six years old, similar behavior would mean to most of us that he is simply a terribly unhappy child. But when he is sixteen years old, raging mad, outrageously manipulative, but apparently not psychotic, he becomes a "vicious adolescent," and we become especially disposed to greet him with massive retaliation.

This word *retaliation* is an anathema in psychiatry, and indeed it should be. Our reactions against any personal tendencies in this direction are powerful, and there are few situations which can force one to such unrealistic extremes of reactive-permissiveness as an encounter with an aggressively or sexually acting-out adolescent.

The humble destination of this necessarily tortuous approach is that it is often necessary to control the adolescent's behavior for a variety of specific purposes and not because it is fun to do so. It is done to keep him from doing great damage to himself or to someone else, to avoid pregnancy, to preserve the intactness of the building so that there will be a place for him to be treated, to keep him within that building. These reasons are not "bad." Nor is it bad to control his behavior in order to make it possible for him to understand something about himself, which he could not do if left to go his own way. It is a measure of psychiatric treatment which is appropriate to his age and his type of illness and especially to the conditions of the treatment contract. Our reaction to our own *unconscious* retaliatory impulses tends to spill over into other aspects of our relationship with him. We hesitate even to ask him why he was one minute late for his appointment, not in fear that he will interpret it as an aggressive act but because we unconsciously fear that this is true. There are many grades of behavior between the routine and the strikingly pathological. The behaviors between these extremes are the most difficult of all to deal with in psychotherapy with the adolescent. They are neither good nor bad to such a degree that one can hardly miss their significance. They always mean something, but it is not easy to tell what it is, how important it is, or how to handle it.

Alex was fifteen years old when admitted to the hospital with complaints of poor school achievement, few friends, withdrawnness, and petit mal seizures since the age of six. The family history and interviews with Alex and his parents quickly revealed that he was an overindulged, overprotected boy whose life had been stringently governed by his parents. His seizures were relatively mild and infrequent, consisting of a few seconds of "absence" once or twice a day. On rare occasions a classmate would refer to one of these episodes as daydreaming, not even recognizing it as an epileptic seizure. But at home it was considered a crippling disease.

Alex was taken to the neurologist once a month without fail, despite the latter's repeated assurances that this was not necessary. The mother applied constant pressure for an increase in the dosage of old medications and for the trial of new ones. She read extensively on the subject of epilepsy and plagued the neurologist with requests that he refer Alex to various celebrated medical centers "so we can get something done about his epilepsy."

In her eagerness to help Alex adjust to his disease, she gave him a liberal education on pertinent social prejudices and laws. He was advised that people would always look upon him as "strange." If he should ever fall in love and want to get married, his fiancée's parents would probably interfere because of their prejudice against the disease and the fear that their grandchildren might be epileptic also. He should never "get a girl in trouble" because law dictated that the child of an epileptic could not be adopted. He would not be able to drive a car. Swimming was forbidden because he might drown during a seizure, and his reasonable suggestion that the buddy system would protect him was swept aside as inadequate. His hope of becoming a physician was dismissed on the grounds that, should he ever specialize in surgery, he might cut a patient's artery during one of his spells. Almost every aspect of his life, present and future, was under his mother's immediate control.

Upon admission to the hospital he was entered into the full activities program. Out of loyalty to his mother he attempted to decline most of these. He quietly observed that when he awoke in the morning feeling "tense," it meant that he would have more spells than usual that day. His mother had always kept him out of school on these occasions. He resisted participating in athletics, crafts, and many other activities on similar grounds. With suitable precautions his doctor gradually tapered off his medications and firmly directed him to full participation in the program, including swimming. Alex protested and tried to refuse, but his doctor "controlled" him.[1] Within six short weeks the frequency of his seizures fell, without medications, to one or two per week. Although his own satisfaction with his improvement was unmistakable, he had excellent reasons for suspecting that his parents would not let him remain in the hospital, and he became deeply concerned about this. He could not acknowledge any positive feelings about hospitalization, but tried to warn his doctor of the danger by boasting, "I can get out of here any time I want to—all I have to do is tell my folks what you're doing to me." His doctor advised him directly against this, but unfortunately it was already too late. Alex had written a letter home informing his parents that all of his medicines had been taken away from him, that he was being forced into school even on his "high spell days," and that he was being made to swim "against my will." The results were exactly as Alex had predicted.

His mother called the director of the hospital and demanded that he be discharged immediately. Although she was temporarily dissuaded, Alex's conflicted feelings about getting better prompted him to make a further test. He taped to the wall of his room a crude finger painting of a naked woman which he had done when he was five years old—one which his mother had long cherished and had sent with him to the hospital as "a little something to remind you of home." A ward nurse intuitively recognized that the picture was serving a cause other than art, and directed him to take it down, an action with which his doctor concurred. Alex promptly mailed it home with a note explaining that he could not keep it in the hospital because the staff regarded it as "dirty." That did it. His parents came in at once and signed him out of the hospital against medical advice.

Alex was in tears. He begged to be left in the hospital and tried, too late, to reassure his mother. His doctor made an heroic effort to persuade the parents to let him remain. At the end of a three-hour interview his mother finally exclaimed during an acute lapse of logic, 'I'm not denying that he's getting better . . . I know he is . . . It's the way you're doing

[1] An intriguing historical precedent for the curative value of authority is suggested in Matthew's account of Christ's faith "treatment" of an epileptic boy: "When they returned to the crowd, a man came up to Jesus, fell on his knees before him, and said, 'Have pity, sir, on my son; he is an epileptic and has bad fits, and he keeps falling about, often into the fire, often into water. I brought him to your disciples, but they could not cure him.' Jesus answered, 'What an unbelieving and perverse generation! How long shall I be with you? How much longer must I endure you? Bring him here to me.' Jesus then spoke sternly to the boy; the devil left him, and from that moment he was cured." (Matthew 17 : 14–18; The New English Bible New Testament; Oxford University Press and Cambridge University Press, 1961)

it that I object to . . . it's better for him to have epilepsy than be treated this way." Then she, too, became momentarily tearful and murmured, "You spend most of your life trying to help them grow up and then they go off and leave you . . . There's no point to it."

She and her husband had been seen regularly as outpatients, but neither this nor the final interview were enough to alter an outcome which, in retrospect, appears to have been inevitable.

From the quantitative standpoint Alex's doctor controlled him as much as his mother had, but there were crucial differences between the quality of these controls. His mother's unconscious aim was to vitiate any of her son's efforts which might have led to his becoming independently capable, self-supporting, autonomous, and eventually able to love someone else. Moreover, her success was assured because the form which her controls took were of *not allowing* him to do things. He could not do what she forbade. He had no choice but to submit, as a child, to parental authority.

The controls which his doctor brought to bear were in support of his *doing* things which most adolescents do, rather than against them. This meant, in the final analysis, that it would be Alex who decided whether he would acquiesce to authority and go swimming as directed. He could have refused this far more easily than he could have refused his mother's mandates *not* to go swimming. Alex and his doctor were both aware of the differences, and his mother became aware of them. That is why she signed him out of the hospital against advice.

If the adolescent patient is sufficiently intelligent, sophisticated, and afflicted with the kind of psychopathology which lends itself to the usual mode of adult therapy, then he may be able to accept the contract which obliges him to frustrate his own defenses. If he *is* able to do this, however, one can only wonder what has become of his adolescence. For the typical patient between the ages of thirteen and sixteen, inclusive, we need not wonder. He can be counted upon to decline disrespectfully the invitation to be a "good patient."

A boy tapes a nude pin-up picture to his mirror and his doctor asks him to take it down. The boy refuses, and the doctor then *directs* him to take it down and follows through until the *order* is carried out. A casual onlooker might suppose that the doctor is something of a stiff-necked prude who is four-square against sex, moralistic in his approach to patients, and blind to the perfectly obvious fact that "all teenage boys like pin-up pictures of nude women." The psychotherapist, hopefully, is capable of a more refined understanding than this, recognizing as he does the conditions which are necessary to an effective interpretation. The pin-up picture is not just a picture, and the boy's act of taping it to his mirror is not *only* for the purpose of ornamentation. He knows that it is normal for the adult to resist certain of these natural adolescent traits; boys usually keep their girly pictures out of sight. He knows that the boy is in the hospital and that relatively strange women, the nurses and aides, will be passing by his room. Also the boy knows that his doctor is equally alert to these realities, and he will be most curious about everyone's astonishingly tolerant reaction to his "perfectly normal behavior."

The behavior may be normal in an abstract sense, as an act isolated from the circumstances in which it occurs, but one simply cannot tell from the nature of the act itself whether or not it is in the interest of this patient's treatment. He is asked to take down the picture just as the neurotic adult outpatient is asked to be on time for his appointment, to pay his fee, or to try to remember something from his past. That the doctor should direct the adolescent patient to do something—in order to make it possible for him to learn more about himself—is indeed abnormal by the usual standards of social intercourse.

So is psychotherapy.

9

DEFENSE, RESISTANCE, AND "MAGICAL" CONTROL

Resistances to Treatment

Although most mechanisms of defense and resistance are used to some extent by virtually all patients, there are significant variations in relative preferences for these which depend upon such things as the patient's illness, intelligence, sex, and age. The mechanism of projection, for example, is prominent in adult paranoid psychoses and rare in the illnesses of childhood. A classic pattern of manic defense can apparently be developed only by a late adolescent or adult patient of high intelligence. Defense by a wider variety of sexual perversions is commoner among men than among women. The anxious, neurotic child of elementary school age is far more prone than the adult patient to cope with anxiety by motoric defenses.

The neurotic adolescent also shows some bias in his unconscious selection of defenses and resistances. In an earlier section some of the latter have been examined from the standpoint of their adaptive as well as their defensive functions. There are also some differences in the form which they take, how they are used in relation to other people, and how reliable and serviceable they are for the adolescent. In a general way they are characterized by instability (a rapid, experimental shifting from one to the other) and crudity, in the sense that their defensive aims are more obviously related to personal neurotic conflict than in the adult.

Displacement. The displacement of instinctual strivings, though not technically a defense, is practiced by the adolescent with desperate abandon. A wide variety of people are passionately loved and hated with little regard for who they are or what they are like.

The "reversal of affect" to which Anna Freud [13] refers appears to be a defensively overdetermined emphasis on the negative valence of the youngster's ambivalent feelings toward the parent(s), as reflected in the pubertal girl's familiar protests, "I don't love him! I don't, I don't, I don't! . . . I can't stand her, I never want to see her again, she means nothing to me!" It is a comparatively feeble mechanism, often enough melting away entirely in the face of a direct, simple confrontation.

PROJECTION. Heavy reliance upon the mechanism of projection is heightened in the adolescent in response to his increased feelings of being "transparent" to others. Changes in body size and form seem to announce to the world that he is experiencing too many "bad" feelings and fantasies and that he is still too much a child to be entitled to these or to handle them with what he presumes to be the safety, dignity, and composure of an adult. Most of his projective efforts do not result in a serious disruption of his interpretation of reality. Much of his angry, indignant complaining about being unjustly accused is more properly regarded as an adaptive exercise of the ego, directed at securing from adults some reliable answers to a number of questions which he has about himself. The same is true of his grandiosity and boastfulness. The evidence for this lies in the ease with which he relinquishes these when they are tactfully challenged by an empathetic adult, and in the grudging but genuine interest and curiosity with which he receives the adult's version of the reality involved.

PSEUDOPROJECTION. Pseudoprojection is an especially useful mechanism which the passive, antisocial adolescent has pretty well perfected during his latency years. All his troubles, he insists, are a consequence of adverse circumstances or of deficiencies in other people. He doesn't go to school because he has a bad teacher who picks on him, and that's all there is to it. It is a particular application of rationalization which is often spoken of, however unofficially, as "externalization."

PHOBIAS. The disappearance of phobias in early adolescence is striking. The preschool child reports his fears with little sense of shame. He is chiefly interested in reassurance and in testing the validity of his fears. The youngster of elementary age is ashamed of his few persisting phobias, but will go only so far to conceal them. According to the adolescent, whether he is sick or normal, his phobias have simply ceased to exist. To him they can be experienced only as utterly disgraceful, and it seems necessary that they be replaced by a rich store of counterphobic attitudes and behaviors. The adolescent boy who voluntarily admits that he is still afraid of the dark is either extremely sick or extremely healthy.

DENIAL. Denial (i.e., of the reality of an indisputable external reality) still makes a regular appearance but is not nearly as popular as it was during childhood and latency. The external dangers which he denied when he was a helpless little child he now faces with courage, defiance, and a strong lacing of counterphobia: "Sure I did it—so what!"

REPRESSION. At puberty there is probably an expansion of the protective coverage provided by the repression of unconscious threats but a diminution in its strength. An emergency moratorium is placed on elective reminiscing. All things of the childish past are treated as remote, irrelevant, and entirely unrelated to psychological events of the present. The explanation for this is self-evident: the adolescent must protect himself from the temptation to remain a child.

The isolation of feelings becomes a more selective process than before. In general, those feelings of dependent need, of loneliness, homesickness, and helplessness, are rather hastily and carelessly tucked beneath the cover of unconsciousness. During adolescence many of these undergo transformations which make it possible for them to be readmitted to consciousness and there to be experienced as having different meanings and purposes in connection with different people. The awful longing for someone to replace the ones who are now irretrievably lost—the mother and father as they were to him when he was a child—is spared from isolation by an unconscious revision in person and purpose. The exquisite aching of adolescent "puppy love," which he readily feels for almost anyone of the opposite sex who happens to be in the vicinity, signals the crucial metamorphosis of love from the filial to the romantic. It becomes a love between peers, now largely free of the taint of incest and childish dependency.

UNDOING. Alleviation of guilt through the undoing of unconscious impulses undergoes a rapid decline in popularity during middle and late adolescence. At this time there is a turning to more circumspect methods for obtaining the urgently needed relief from feelings of guilt. Behaving in a way which evokes retaliation from the outside is one of them [1]. The repeated making of firm resolutions to reform is another which he can usually count upon to provide full, prompt, but sadly temporary relief. The adolescent is generally quite sincere when he declares, "I will never do it again!", even though he has failed to stand by the same resolution many times before.

One of the most effective defenses against guilt for the identity-seeking adolescent is a contemptuous "casting out of the superego," an effort which is as dramatic and shallow as it is arbitrary. "So I'm no good! OK then, I'm bad! My father keeps calling me a slut; I'll just be the same as the name." "I'm going to be a bum . . . If people (parents) learn not to expect anything from me, then they won't be disappointed when they don't get it. (And neither will I.)"

TURNING AGAINST SELF. The handling of aggression by "turning against self" is prominent in the psychopathology of the disturbed adolescent, as it is with child and adult patients. When the small child is filled with anger and hate, we are usually more concerned that he will hurt someone else, a sibling or a friend, and less fearful that he will do deliberate injury to himself. Adults, on the other hand, are more prone to suicide than homicide. The adolescent stands somewhere between them. Clinically, we are probably able to make a better-than-chance prediction about whether or not he will hurt *someone*, but find few reliable criteria for deciding whether he is more likely to hurt himself or another person. A knowledge of the types of pathology associated with nosological categories helps very little if at all. Many homicides are committed by guilt-ridden, self-critical adolescents; and many other youngsters who pass as "personality disorders, antisocial" end by killing themselves.

Making Deals

Because of some of the peculiarities of the relationship which he has with the adult, the adolescent typically inclines to a few patterns of resistance which are distinguished by the extent to which they encourage the therapist into unwitting cooperation with the resistive effort.

Who is supposed to enjoy the greater benefits of psychotherapy, the patient or his therapist? The adolescent can be most skillful at persuading us that we have much more to gain from his treatment than he does. As noted earlier, this is most evident in his recurrent and often supremely subtle efforts to seduce us into making mutual back-scratching deals with him. His strongest bargaining point bears a close qualitative resemblance to the toddler's time-honored threat "if you don't give me what I want, I'll hold my breath until I turn blue." The adolescent threatens to remain sick if we do not cater to his whims or he promises to get well if we do. The proposition clearly suggests that he will improve only as a personal favor to us and that he expects to be well rewarded for his charity. These terms are generally buried in the small print of his communications where they are not easily noticed [16].

Nina, aged sixteen, was referred for treatment because the combined authority of her parents and the juvenile court had not succeeded in curtailing her practice of running away from home whenever she was displeased with the situation there. After some months of treatment she was given the responsibility of pass privileges. She carried these well for about two weeks and then "ran away" to a drug store five blocks away. She returned to the hospital of her own accord in a very short time and greeted her doctor with an extravagant show of spitefulness and defiance:

"No lectures, please! Just tell me whether I get my privileges back or not!"

Her doctor, unwilling to enter the exchange at this level, merely grunted indifferently.

"Well, do I or don't I?"

"I really couldn't say, now could I?"

"Well! Then who can say? Will it take an act of Congress or something?"

"I didn't answer you quite right. I could say . . . I could write down in the order book that it's all right for you to have the responsibility of pass privileges, but I really haven't got a thing to say about whether you can do it or not."

"I can do it if I decide I want to."

"Have you decided yet?"

"Yes! I have! I can!"

"We both know you *can*—have privileges without lousing them up, that is. Is that what you've decided to do?"

"That's what I just said!"

"No, it isn't. It's what you just carefully avoided saying."

"Well, good heavens! All right then. I can tell you one thing for sure. I know absolutely that I won't run away while I'm on pass privileges."

"Well, that's practically a guarantee that you will run away some other time. Anyway, I wasn't talking about just running away—I was talking about fouling them up any way at all. As soon as you stop looking for loopholes in the law, we can get serious about this."

"I can't promise that I'll *never* run away. Right now I don't think I will, but I've thought that before!"

"Now, you begin to make sense. Why did you run away today?"

"I didn't know what would happen. I guess I wondered what you would do."

The transaction was carried out without benefit of extortion. Nina's absurdly imperative opening speech carried an implicit attempt at this, as if she were saying: "This is the big crisis . . . I've got you where I want you, haven't I? You're so proud of me for doing better that you wouldn't dare run the risk of making me worse by denying me what I demand . . . could you?"

These very fantasies, transplanted from the earlier relationship with her parents to the present one with her doctor, were elicited and clarified in the remainder of the interview. Her therapist did not treat it as an all-or-none problem, nor did he force her into the position of having to lie by demanding an iron-clad promise that she would never again do anything "bad." Perhaps most important of all he let it be known, as he had many times before and after this incident, that decisions about her treatment did not pivot on the axis of his narcissim. He was willing to "deprive" her as necessary, even at the expense of whatever burden of guilt his own neurosis might inflict upon him.

The therapist dare not participate in this kind of dealing. Experience reminds us repeatedly that the adolescent's determined haggling is partially intended to establish just how willing we are to sacrifice his future welfare in the interest of our immediate comfort and convenience. He strips us of the comforting illusion that morality and mental health lie in different realms; he also reminds us repeatedly that his treatment must be more by precept than words.

Resistive Fantasies of Omnipotence

Pathologically strong, persistent feelings of omnipotence subserve an especially formidable resistance to treatment. Developmentally, it normally dominates the two-year-old's concept of himself as one who can always get whatever he wants from other people, namely his parents, no matter how big and powerful they may appear. As he grows older and reality closes in on him, proving to him that things cannot be quite that good, a conscious belief in personal omnipotence becomes untenable. It lingers strongly in the unconscious, however, and in times of emergency, as in front-line combat, the normal person will temporarily recover this feeling of indestructibility and total power through a highly selective regression which abets the familiar denial: "The others may be killed, but not I."

A child whose early life experience has been reasonably satisfied is able to relinquish the delusion. If he has had too little indulgence or too much of the wrong kind, he is left with a greater than average need to believe that he can compel others to fulfill all his wishes as quickly as they arise. To accomplish this he invokes the magical manipulations of the two-year-old: demanding, throwing temper tantrums, seducing with charm, threatening, or, if all else fails, by "revising reality" in a way which will make it seem that he has achieved his ends even when he has not.

Age and experience enable him to refine his methods somewhat, but their aims and basic nature remain the same. It is in this pattern that the sick adolescent, and particularly the delinquent one, compulsively and unconsciously attempts to evoke from us the same kinds of responses to which he has become so accustomed in the past. Qualitatively, his behavior toward his therapist is a form of "acting-out in the transference," but it is probably best not to describe it this way because the expression suggests that a verbal interpretation of the *meaning* of the behavior will enable him to abandon it. It will not.

Regarding the chronically, characterologically delinquent adolescent who demonstrates the problem most clearly, there are several concrete and very common treatment principles which should be examined more closely. The fundamental resistance to treatment is his fantasy that there is no treatment. Doctors and nurses are only giving something to him or withholding it from him, and he is only succeeding or failing in getting it from them. In the case of the "confirmed" delinquent (meaning the one whom we do not know how to treat), it is impossible to do anything affecting him without his believing that he has compelled us to do it. This helps to explain his curious insistence that we deal with him by the talion principle. He can predict our actions if they are vindictively motivated [16]. The idea that he can foretell the future "proves" the fantasy that he brought it about *as he intended*. Being unable to "predict" brings him dangerously close to reexperiencing the impotence and desolation against which his delusion of omnipotence is protecting him.

Jess, a sixteen-year-old boy, had been in almost constant conflict with the juvenile authorities since the age of seven. He was admitted to the intensive-treatment adolescent ward in the hope that some way could be found to help him. After several fairly quiet days of casing the ward, he became defiant, profane, and uncooperative. He insistently demanded to know what would happen if he should break up furniture, run away, or assault another patient or a member of the staff. It was explained to him as emphatically and concretely as possible that his question was unanswerable, and every reasonable effort was made to help him resist the immense pressure to test for one. He wanted to know about the adult closed ward and wondered what a person would have to do to "make you throw him into the seclusion room."

Attempts to interpret the manipulative, controlling aim of his behavior fell on deaf ears. He became increasingly aggressive, and it was finally necessary to put him in the seclusion room on the closed adult ward for his own sake and for the welfare of other patients and staff. There he felt safe. He was totally controlled and protected by forces from the outside. He was fed, cared-for, and catered-to as he had never been when he was an infant. His doctor expressed regrets about this development and explained, in effect, that "we can't get much accomplished while you're in here . . . I am really very sorry that I had to have you secluded like this."

Jess was genuinely astonished: "You didn't put me here. I made you put me here and I can make you keep me here."

The illusion of omnipotence can be maintained only by repeated proofs. Some of the technical and vernacular terms referring to the means by which these proofs are secured include *manipulation, magic, conning* (i.e., *swindling*), and *trickery*. In practice they take many forms, ranging from the very gross to the minutely refined.

Management of Some Common Adolescent Resistances

Magic

The consequences of a successful interpersonal manipulation often appear to have been brought about magically because the process causing the effect is not readily apparent. In the *Oxford Universal Dictionary* the word *magic* is defined as "the pretended art of influencing the course of events by compelling the agency of spiritual beings, or by bringing into operation some occult controlling principle of nature . . ." In the magical control of one person by another, the "controlling principle of nature" is the remarkable effect which one person's feelings and unconsciously motivated behavior can have upon those of another person.

Magic, as used clinically, refers to the toddler's belief that certain effects can be caused without logical implementation. The magician points his finger at an empty hat, and for no apparent reason a rabbit appears; the magical effect depends upon our not seeing how the rabbit was put there and is achieved even though we know intellectually that there is a natural explanation for the mystery.

Children learn quickly that there are a certain number of inherently simple and insignificant acts which are capable of eliciting cataclysmic reactions from otherwise powerful and imperturbable adults. For example, what is to him an unpretentious bowel movement on the living room carpet can work emotional miracles with his parents. A little later in life he learns that a few short, phonetically simple words can also accomplish marvelous and predictable effects in other people without benefit of mechanical aids.

The process is qualitatively the same whether it occurs among people in an ordinary living situation, between the therapist and his patient in individual psychotherapy, or between a group of hospitalized adolescents and their supervisory ward staff. In program treatment on the ward the practice of manipulative "magic" is in many ways supported and reinforced by certain characteristics of groups.

Obscenity as incantation. Of the many forms which magic may take, profane and obscene language is one of the most difficult to deal with in residential groups of children and adolescents. It is not at all uncommon for the most bristling obscenities to become deeply entrenched in community tradition.

There are several explanations for the psychiatric staff person's readiness to permit hospitalized youngsters to substitute "f—— you, nurse" for "good morning, Miss Smith." (Experienced workers will appreciate that this is not an exaggeration.) The psychiatric staff person enjoys viewing himself as objective and nonjudgmental. He also "understands" that this type of deviation from the norm is to be expected in mentally ill persons, especially if they are children or adolescents. Further, being surrounded by an abundance of flagrant pathological behavior sharply defines his professional status. Friends and family will marvel at the kind of thing he has to put up with in his line of work and will commend him for his patience and understanding. Without realizing it, he may also derive a great deal of vicarious pleasure from the young patient's uninhibited acting-out of a primitive drive derivative which he himself has long since abandoned. By not looking at this practice from the patient's point of view, he remains blissfully ignorant of the fact that he is being thoroughly manipulated. He calmly reassures the patient that "I have heard all those words before. They don't bother me. You're not impressing anyone." The youngster knows better. We are all shocked to some extent by obscene language and especially so when it is levelled at us with aggressive intent. We seldom, if ever, use such language ourselves in the presence of patients. Some of us never use it at any time or under any circumstances, and the rest of us use it only in the most limited and carefully defined social situations. The patient is keenly aware of all this, which helps to explain the characteristically smug smile with which he greets our composed admonition that "you don't bother me with that kind of talk."

In the therapeutic community the citizenry should not be issued permits to use this very potent instrument of manipulation. Stopping it, once it has begun, is only a little more difficult than preventing it in the first place. In either case strict prohibition must be augmented by concrete proof that, although the words do have a certain impact on us, we are willing and able to speak them ourselves if there is good cause for doing so.

Lonnie, a fourteen-year-old boy, possessed a rich and ready vocabulary of obscenities. He was admitted to a children's psychiatric ward and while there wielded considerable power over its affairs. In response to an emergency call his therapist appeared on the ward one day to find Lonnie holding a half-dozen full-grown nurses and attendants at bay. They surrounded him at a respectful distance as he swung a metal-filled stocking menacingly overhead and assailed them with a relentless barrage of obscene language. Psychologically, it was he who was surrounding them. His doctor moved in quickly and swept Lonnie into a side room with terms of command which were more thunderous than articulate. Still quite drunk with power, Lonnie turned on him with a shout: "Get out of here you . . ." (obscene synonyms for *feces,* for one who acts out his oedipal strivings, and one who performs fellatio—all utterable but better left unprinted here because they *do* carry a certain emotional charge even when used in an objective context).

His doctor interrupted him with "You can say those things *to* me but not *at* me. And if there is some question in your mind about this thing, let me clear it up for you right now: You are right! I don't like to be called a . . ." (He then proceeded with direct quotations of the expressions and words which Lonnie had used.)

The shocker was shocked. Lonnie turned pale and tremulously wrapped his pillow around his ears. He wept in genuine distress: "Please don't say those words anymore. They're awful . . . I hate to hear you say them."

After this he became much quieter and rationally conversant. His resistance had collapsed when his doctor demonstrated that he knew "how the trick is done." He did not swear *at* Lonnie—he simply *quoted* his own words back to him. His action, though aggressive, was not destructive. It was aimed primarily at counteracting Lonnie's "black magic" so that treatment could proceed. In fact, had the therapist allowed himself to engage in a destructively motivated exchange of "dirty" insults the immediate effect might have been much the same, but the long-range consequences could well have been irreparably damaging.

This specific approach to the problem cannot be prescribed as a technique. It is something which one might do with helpful effect only if he is keenly aware that the patient, mostly out of fear, is fending him off with real desperation. Any attempt to practice it as a technique without this quality of appreciation would be correctly perceived by the patient as an angry counterattack.

SPELL OF MEDUSA. Seductiveness, which in itself occurs in great variety, is another form of adolescent sorcery which gives comfort to the patient's fantasies of omnipotent control.

Sonja, thirteen years old, had the physical appearance and manner of a much too sophisticated young woman. She was admitted with a history of sexual promiscuity, although it was revealed later in treatment that she had never had any sexual experience beyond a little calculated necking. Short of this she had done everything imaginable to create the strong public impression that she was, as described by her mother, a "hopeless nymphomaniac." This is the rather common syndrome of *pseudopromiscuity.*

Her mother was an inhibited and prudish woman who seemed devastated by her daughter's behavior, but was inadvertently encouraging it in many ways. At the time of Sonja's admission it was recognized that her alleged sexual misbehavior had, in part, served well for repeatedly manipulating the mother into a position of strategic disadvantage. Because of this defensive, characterological "set" her doctor advised that she should say nothing to other patients or staff members about her alleged sexual activities. She was firmly encouraged to reserve these matters for the work of therapy. This was a well-intended but unsuccessful effort at prophylaxis. Within a few hours after admission Sonja was industriously publicizing her mythical sexual adventures far and wide, and had already taken to slapping the boys affectionately on the buttocks as they walked past her. She also favored slinky clothing and an exhibitionistic gait and posture. Her appearance and behavior contributed to a poor caricature of a certified public voluptuary.

Initial efforts of the staff to curtail this behavior were ineffectual. Anxious, tentative suggestions that she change her dress or pull her skirt down over her knees while sitting elicited nothing more than a smile of secret wisdom. Her therapist hesitated for several days, hoping that she would be able to bring some of this to her therapy interviews, but she had no need to. In a subsequent session he questioned her directly about her seductive behavior. She protested ignorance and sat quietly in wide-eyed innocence. She coolly observed that she couldn't imagine what he was talking about, so he told her in calm and matter-of-fact tones: "I mean telling the other kids about your having sexual intercourse, and how you put your hand on a boy's behind when he gets near you, and the way you sit with your legs spread apart when some of the boys are around so they can see up under your skirt." The magic was undone by this simple translation from the abstract to the concrete. Sonja burst into tears and wept for a long time, pouring out feelings of depression, loneliness, and of great resentment toward her mother for forcing her to "act like a grown-up woman instead of a thirteen-year-old girl."

THE HYPNOTIC EYE. In the course of individual psychotherapy there typically develop instances of covertly controlling behavior which are not as easy to identify as the cruder efforts. The mechanism, however, is essentially the same.

Dr. D, an unusually perceptive resident psychiatrist, complained in supervision that his efforts with a fifteen-year-old boy were "all hung up on a strong negative countertransference—for the last three weeks I've hardly been able to stand the idea of even seeing the kid."

He went on to explain in a ruminative fashion that his patient was "behaving himself all right . . . isn't causing any trouble or being unreasonable about anything. He's cooperative in the office . . . if anything he's talking more than ever before about . . . He just irritates me, and I don't even know why . . . sits there and looks at me and I get madder and madder for no good reason. He gives me the feeling that he's running the whole interview somehow or other. Maybe he does it by being so cooperative—he just sits there staring at me and agreeing with everything I say."

The supervisor, noting several casual references to being looked at and stared at, asked for more information about this. Dr. D continued, "nothing special about it, he just stares at me . . . keeps his eyes fixed on me all the time and never looks away. Well, he looks so comfortable about it, as though he's staring right through me . . . can tell exactly what I'm thinking and what I'm going to say next. When I look away and then look back, he's still staring at me."

By this time Dr. D had brought himself to the point at which he was more than ready to make sense of his supervisor's observation: "Apparently the boy thinks he has a hex on you. From what you've just said, maybe it would be more accurate to say that he *does* have a hex on you." With this Dr. D was able to confront his patient with their shared, previously unconscious fantasies about the aggressive, controlling power of the "stare." The patient's aggression was thus rendered ineffective in the same way that a card trick ceases to be amazing when one learns how it is done.

THE INVISIBLE BLUFF. For reasons having to do with the psychological work of his age, the adolescent keeps his perceptive apparatus sharply tuned to the strengths and weaknesses in the adult's defensive system.

He has an uncanny talent for assembling subliminal clues about his therapist and for interpreting and applying them to optimal advantage.

Dr. A, another gifted resident psychiatrist, sought consultation with a sense of uneasiness similar to Dr. D's. He complained of a vague feeling of dissatisfaction with the third psychotherapy interview which he had just completed with Max, a very bright sixteen-year-old delinquent boy.

"As far as I could see, it went very well. He said he was very glad to have me for his new doctor because some of the other kids told him I was the best one on the staff. I let him know that I really could not commend him on such crude flattery and wondered what he expected to get in return for his kind words. He laughed very nicely and said he guessed it wouldn't work to try that kind of thing again. So I called him on that one too, tried to get across to him the idea that I'm not at all entirely immune to manipulation. I assume he could drop me into the corner pocket most any time he wants to, and told him so. After that he sobered up, and we just talked for a while about his family, his father's work, and things like that. It was all very pleasant, but by the end of the interview I felt like taking a swing at him, and I don't know why. I felt so guilty about it that I almost gave in when he asked if he could make a telephone call to his father."

The source of Dr. A's unreasonable anger became apparent in the following exchange with his supervisor:

"There's an explanation somewhere in there. What else did he say during this delightful conversation?"

"Well, mostly about his father's work. He has a very good position with (an important agency of the Federal Government). He has to travel a lot, goes to Washington once or twice a month, things like that."

"Any other details about his work or about those trips to Washington?"

"No, just that he goes there on business. Oh, Max said he was going there next weekend to visit some friend of his who is a big shot in one of the other bureaus. Max has met the man. That's why he said he wanted to call his father—to send his regards to this other man."

"What bureau is he a big shot in? Did Max say?"

"No, just that he had something to do with immigration."

"Oh. Oh my! Dr. A, brace yourself. To your colleagues and friends you are a respected visitor from South America, but to Max, it appears, you are to be dealt with as an undesirable alien whose application for American citizenship *could* be looked upon with disfavor by his "influential friends in high places!" See how? He starts the interview with a transparent ploy, quickly concedes to your superior grasp of manipulative strategy and to your authority, then slides into the breach with a magnificently tactful offer to help you get your citizenship. All you have to do is be reasonable about a few little things."

Dr. A returned immediately to the ward to complete the unfinished interview with Max. A short time later he reported back that Max had confirmed everything by "denying it absolutely. He was kind enough to assure me that he did not regard me as inferior to himself just because I have a darker complexion. He generously granted that my abilities as a physician make me an exception to the general prejudice against foreign doctors. Speaking personally, he would like to see me become an American citizen, and that if he ever has a chance to help me, he would be only too glad to do so!"

"What did you do?"

"I acted out. I gave him hell. I told him he was in a terrible position to condescend to anyone . . . to close his mouth and stay in his room and think about what he was trying to do until I send word down that he can come out. I know that wasn't the right thing to do, but I am awfully mad at him!"

"Some punishment wouldn't hurt him; he's earned it. The trouble is he's probably sitting down there now taking great delight in the fantasy that you are holding him incommunicado to keep him from having you deported. I'm not sure what's best to do about it. You might consider giving him a point for getting you sore, then offer him a chance to test out his power. Invite him to write his father, or his friend in Washington, *against* you. I think he can enjoy his delusion only as long as he doesn't have to put it to the test. Tell him to get it over with for his own sake. Call his bluff."

TOKENS AND TALISMANS. There is no visible end to the guises in which this brand of magic can appear. Although the props change from time to time, it was only a few years ago that many delinquent boys favored "levis" with broad black belts. Such a youngster typically provided an accurate index of the degree of omnipotence which he was experiencing at any given moment by the level at which he wore his belt. When feeling irrationally powerful, his trousers would dangle precariously from his greater trochanters, traversing the symphysis pubis, while on his more sociable days he would be modestly belted around the waist.

In these illustrations nothing has been said about the treatment significance of the instinctual components of this kind of behavior. The pleasure aim is abundantly present but remains either inaccessible or functionally irrelevant to therapy until the patient can appreciate that his doctor is able to recognize and frustrate his controlling efforts. The therapist is obliged to dispel the youngster's belief that he has certain secret and magical powers which will enable him, at any time, to compel his therapist to do his bidding.

A facial expression, a tone of voice, a bent cigarette dangling from the lower lip, a hand signal, or any other conceivable though frequently unperceived behavior can support this fantasy. In manifest content an action may be innocent enough, but the meaning ascribed to it by patient *and* therapist can amount to an impregnable resistance to treatment. This matter rates the most careful consideration because it presents so many delicate problems in treatment. The adolescent's outstanding flare for provocation helps explain the earlier observation that so many people, though strongly attracted to the abstract subject of "adolescents," are most loath to endure the presence of live ones.

Essential Fallibility of the Therapist

Because they tend to bring out some of the worst in us, as well as the best, we are in constant need of defending ourselves against either over-reacting or under-reacting to them. We become too much involved, too sympathetic, or affectionate; or we retreat to a defensive position of cool detachment which is no less revealing to the patient than its opposite. We become unreasonably angry and find ourselves retaliating or attacking in the name of treatment, or we react against these strivings with fatuous permissiveness.

The therapist of adolescents is constantly in jeopardy of being suspected by the patient, a colleague, or most importantly by himself, of "acting-out in the counter-transference." It is well enough to explain the need for undermining the patient's delusions of omnipotence in the interest of treatment, but the fact remains that many of the things the therapist must do to accomplish this savor unwholesomely of aggressiveness and seductiveness. Certain questions hover perpetually. Will not the patient misinterpret our motives by the manifest appearance of some of these actions? "You're mad at me . . . you hate me!" How can the therapist be sure that he is acting primarily for his patient's welfare rather than for his own feelings? What does the patient receive in return for what is "taken away"? Reassurance about these questions can be found only in results. Does the patient get better or worse? Theoretical explanations offer little consolation.

Eissler [8] and Hendrickson [16] have emphasized the importance of constantly surprising the delinquent adolescent as a means of neutralizing his fantasies of omnipotence. This is unquestionably necessary and effective, but it is probably unnecessary to *plan* such measures in advance. As it usually turns out the delinquent is repeatedly surprised when his behavior is dealt with justly and realistically, because this kind of response is not what he has learned to expect from others. His life experience has prepared him otherwise. In this same connection some question must also be raised about Eissler's view that it is essential for the therapist to appear omnipotent to his delinquent patient. This could be desirable if it were possible, but it is not. Any effort to represent ourselves as infallible is destined for failure. A patient's delusion of omnipotence is, after all, a sometime thing. The delinquent youngster does not always feel this way himself, but it is true he must always feel that *someone* is omnipotent. It is when he is most beset by a sense of degradation and impotence that he will most urgently need to regard his therapist as all-powerful. But it is a delusion either way, and he deserves from us a credible demonstration of reality rather than a confirmation of his pathological reconstructions of it.

Perhaps the most useful generalization about how one actually proceeds to weaken his patient's delusions of omnipotence, without pretending to them himself, is to permit himself to reveal, with tact and purpose, a liberal sampling of his own strengths and weaknesses. Although we cannot possibly know everything, our prospects in most instances are quite good for being at least a little wiser, smarter, and considerably more realistic than our patient.

Being realistic and honest, oddly enough, can also become too artful. It ought not be practiced exclusively for its own sake. Successfully diagnosing and curtailing the delinquent's attempted manipulations amount to a demonstration of tactical superiority which will inevitably bring the therapist pleasure. It does not help to try to conceal this fact behind a rationalization. The patient will always suffer a loss in self-esteem each time he finds that his therapist is capable of being craftier and more cunning than he. If the doctor is motivated primarily by the wish to out-maneuver, he will succeed only in enhancing the patient's feelings of impotence, which are at the basis of his need to feel omnipotent, and thereby compel him to rely more heavily than ever on the latter.

Although it is often necessary to "out-smart" the delinquent youngster, it is not necessary to withhold a reasonable expression of critical appreciation for his manipulative virtuosity. Even as he frustrates an attempted swindle, the therapist may use the incident to demonstrate some of the advantages of a direct, as opposed to a devious, approach to people. In other words, as Juracsek has said, "In psychotherapy you do not take something away without also giving something back" [23].

Sam was a severely disturbed and delinquent fifteen-year-old boy who suffered the consequences of a lifetime of extreme emotional deprivation. He was unable to read, had no better than scapegoat status with others of his age, and could ward off his overwhelming depression and sense of worthlessness only through his manipulative control of other people.

Most of the patients and staff sensed his insatiable need to be a troublesome "itch" and were able to tolerate him fairly well, but at times his behavior would exceed their limits of tolerance. On one such occasion he had to be seen by his doctor for refusing to get up in the morning, for refusing to attend school, for insulting several members of the nursing staff, and for perpetrating a general program of passive obstructionism. With his doctor he was at first obnoxious and defiant and then coldly proceeded to promise eternal "good behavior" in trade for the right to sleep in fifteen minutes later than the other patients. His doctor jousted with him for a few minutes, in the course of which he secured Sam's promise to get up fifteen minutes earlier than the other patients, in exchange for which he would not have to guarantee to do any more than his "very best" to stay out of trouble. Sam realized a split-instant too late that he had been "had." He was very dejected.

"You tricked me into that. It's no fair."

"Yes, I did. I tricked you instead of letting you trick me. You knew that you were trying to trick me, didn't you?"

"I didn't try to trick you! I just offered a trade!"

"But I didn't accept it. Then I offered you one, and you accepted it and came out on the short end. I out-smarted you."

With injured professional pride Sam retorted, "You're older than I am . . . and you're a doctor!"

"That's right, and what's more I didn't really trick you . . . and I didn't get tricked. I did in a way, but it wasn't for keeps."

Then, relying on the weight of adult authority instead of manipulation, he went on to explain, "You don't have to get up fifteen minutes later or fifteen minutes earlier. Just get up when the other kids do; we're about the same place we were before you started all this stuff."

"Boy, you really cut me down!"

"What do you mean, I cut you down?"

"You never give me a chance. Every time I try to do something, you cut me down to nothing."

"You mean I want you to get up and go to school so that you can work hard and get an education for *me?* Does that make sense to you? Anyway, what's this *always* business? You've outsmarted me lots of times, and you will again, I'm sure. But I wish you wouldn't. It never gets you anything you can really use. It just makes you feel worse in the long run even if you do get a little kick out of it for the moment."

Sam became less resentful, and more cooperative and friendly. Then in an abrupt non sequitor he respectfully invited his therapist to join him in a game of table tennis and feigned perplexity when the invitation was declined. His doctor was genuinely amused and also appreciative of Sam's ingenuity: "Well, it's a very shrewd move on your part, Sam, but you know that I wouldn't have a chance of winning a game of table tennis against you."

"What's the matter—can't you stand to lose?"

"I don't *like* to lose, but I can stand it. The thing is that I don't think that you could stand for me to lose right now. I don't think that you could stand to beat me at anything for a while yet. I'm afraid you'd make too much of winning a simple game of table tennis. You know, like you were winning an unconditional surrender from the whole world."

Although there were many things which he could not understand about the world of reality, Sam understood this freakish confrontation perfectly. In this exchange the therapist fulfilled a vital treatment obligation by frustrating an attempted manipulation which would have nourished the patient's highly resistive fantasy of being "in control." At the same time he complimented Sam for his quick, clever thinking and for his truly fine ability as a table tennis player.

Nondelinquent Manipulation

It is probably not too helpful to think of manipulation, i.e., what Erickson refers to as "making other people," too generically [11]. We do know that pathological manipulation is a desperation measure resorted to by the individual who does not feel himself worthy enough to deserve the good feelings of another person. He has to *take* what he feels will never be given. Any one who grows up loses something in the process. He will attempt to recoup some of these losses in his normal adult life, but what he "manipulates" for is a gratifying emotional response from another person, and he expects to get it because he feels himself to be a good enough person to deserve it. The chronic, full-time manipulator has pretty much abandoned hope for winning and making pleasurable use of this affectionate, respectful response from others. In place of this forlornly abandoned goal, he substitutes the manipulative process itself.

But seldom does the adolescent patient of any category aim exclusively for one or the other of these goals. By definition, the psychoneurotic delinquent has by no means given up hope of enjoying mutually affectionate relationships with others. Indeed, the ideally healthy adult will surely find that added to the enjoyment of good emotional returns from other people is the bonus pleasure in being the kind of person who *can* get it, use it, and return it. The neurotic delinquent is not as desperate as Sam in the example above. He attempts to manipulate and control his doctor to a certain extent, but with a much greater interest in obtaining responses which will convey something about the doctor's feelings toward him. He is not so much interested in the process of winning as in "being liked" and in becoming "able to like." Clarifying this lesser confusion of aim and goal in psychotherapy with the neurotic delinquent takes place in the following instance at a somewhat higher and quieter plane than in Sam's case.

Induced Feelings as Clinical Data

Terry, a sixteen-year-old girl, was admitted for treatment because of severe anxiety, depression, school truancy, and intractable defiance of her parents. After some rather difficult months of inpatient treatment, she began to gain ground. She became attached to her therapist, and considering the frozen, silent, angry quality of her past relationships with adults, she was able to do surprisingly well at accepting her therapist's prescription to exercise at being courteous despite her contrary inclinations. Although this required great effort on her part, she began to make a conscious effort to have occasional friendly conversations with several nurses whom she considered "hateful." She worked harder on school assignments and rather rapidly relinquished other passive-aggressive behaviors which had previously seemed too much a part of her character to be abandoned so quickly and completely.

Several weeks after the beginning of this striking improvement, she modestly requested pass privileges. She did not try to bargain and appeared rather to be most earnest about wanting to do well with the increased responsibility while enjoying the satisfactions of greater personal freedom.

Her therapist detected in himself a notably unconflicted wish to grant the request, which he openly interpreted *to her* as an unrealistic degree of optimism on his part. He explained to her that he could not understand why he should be so eager to comply with her request, when only a few short weeks before she had promised nothing but trouble. She was not angered by what appeared on the surface to be an unreasonable suspiciousness, but neither was she able to contribute much toward answering the question. He then asked her to join him in reviewing some of their preceding and current fantasies about the transaction.

"When you were thinking about asking for privileges, did you expect much argument from me?"

Turning her face, she smiled involuntarily and replied, "No . . . I thought you'd give them to me."

"You thought I would give them to you . . . that you had earned them? Something like that? But this is a pretty big step for you, and I wonder why you didn't expect me to go pretty slow with it. I always have before with lots of other things that weren't nearly this important to you."

"Well, I've been doing a lot better, and I think I can handle them all right."

"Yes, I think you've been doing much better, too, and that's partly what worries me. I think you really could do well with this privilege, but is that why you've improved so much? Maybe that sounds like a stupid question to you, but that's one way this kind of treatment is different from other things. Sometimes I have to be just as interested in why you're good as in why you're bad."

"Well, I know what you mean, but I wasn't being a good girl just so I could get rewarded . . . But I sure wouldn't get any more privileges if I kept on the way I was going before."

"That's true, and I'm convinced. I'm sure you didn't start getting better just to get privileges. The trouble is that no matter what your reasons were, I'm just too eager to reward you for doing better. Maybe it's my problem, but on the other hand, maybe we'll never have any idea about what's going on if we just go ahead and start you on privileges now."

"But I don't see what's wrong with trying it. I really have been doing better, and I'm feeling lots better too. What would be wrong with trying me on outside privileges?"

"There could be something to lose by trying. Serious harm isn't what I'm worried about. Loss is what I'm concerned about. Loss of a chance to find out some things that might not seem too important to you right now. Like why are you so much better, and why am I so pleased about it, and what's the connection between the two things? There is a risk in all this. The happier I get about how well you are doing, the harder it would be to back up in your treatment, like removing your pass privileges. I can look up ahead and almost see that. What would happen? Can you imagine how you'd feel?"

"I'd be furious!"

"It would seem like a punishment, I'm sure. Like taking something away from you for being bad . . . like giving something nice to you for being good. What do you think?"

Terry smiled knowingly and studied her hands for a long moment, then answered, "Well, I'll be afraid to ever ask for anything again. I won't even feel like it's right to ask."

"No. Now that this is out in the open, you should be freer to ask for things, and I should be much freer to say No."

She laughed in spite of herself and did not repeat the request until after she had separated it a little better from the general fantasy: "If you like me, you will give me anything."

This had not been an intended attempt at manipulation, nor was it primarily that even at an unconscious level. She was mostly seeking a tangible demonstration of respect and liking from her therapist, but in line with the long-established pattern of relationship with her parents, she unconsciously sought this in the form of a reward for good behavior. Both she and her therapist held somewhat higher expectations for her than this, i.e., that she be enabled to find some satisfaction in her own improved abilities, rather than expecting to be paid off immediately with a lollypop or a penny for committing good deeds. She was able to reveal that she had fully expected to have her request granted, and, in time, to appreciate that her confidence was based upon what she could well have expected from her parents in a similar situation. This would not have come to light had her bid for privileges been granted first and reviewed afterward.

Terry also acquired some additional understanding about the purpose and operating mode of psychotherapy. This was demonstrated partly by her therapist's clinical use of certain feelings which her request had *induced in him.* Introducing his own feelings demonstrated several very useful things to her, most of all that feelings are not too dangerous to talk about and that they do have some specific, predictable effects on other people *now*. They exist not in vitro but in vivo. By telling her about his impulsive, immediate wish to comply with her wish, he was not making a haphazard confession of a neurotic countertransference. Rather, he noted that her genuinely endearing, puppy-like approach to making the request had sharply evoked feelings in him which were specifically related *to her*. They were more marked and of a different quality than the run-of-the-mill countertransference anxiety and reluctance which he always felt about "denying" anything to a patient. His reactions, in short, were valuable clinical data which he capitalized upon as an important step in helping her to recognize her reflex-like approach to getting things from other people. It was as if she were saying each time: "I am good and sweet, for which you should give me something good. If you don't, it will mean that you don't love me, and I will be hurt and angry and will make you feel so guilty you'll have to appease me. Then we'll start all over again."

Sense of Identity as Resistance

CHARACTERISTICS OF SENSE OF IDENTITY. What is ordinarily spoken of as one's sense of identity is not amenable to clear definition. In general, it is a perpetual and powerfully influential complex of ideas and feelings composed of all that a person consciously knows and unconsciously senses about himself. It includes one's conscious conception of the physical boundaries of his body and that all-important sense of physical and psychological separateness from all other people. In normal development this profound feeling of autonomy is elaborated, reinforced, and threatened to some extent by everything which happens within one's perceptual sphere. It includes all currently conscious and unconscious ideas and feelings which have any potential for eliciting feelings of pleasure or pain. All latent and immediate memories of the past, the emotional impact of present experiences, fantasies which anticipate the future, the quality of one's instinctual needs, the mechanisms of defense, and even symptoms make their own characteristic contributions to one's sense of identity. This is equally true whether the net effect of all these forces is psychologically normal or psychopathological. The mentally ill patient's sense of identity includes some general and particular conceptions of himself as being mentally ill. His sickness has become a part of his "self."

One of the outstanding characteristics of a person's sense of identity is the immense vigor with which it resists any change in its status quo. Although one may sincerely wish to be different, perhaps more mature or emotionally healthier, the prospect of realizing such a change will inevitably threaten the relative feeling of comfort which is provided by a stable, though "sick," sense of identity. The hope of being liberated from all the bad and painful things of the past is bound tightly to the fear that this might also result in the loss of all that was good or, if not intrinsically good, at least reassuringly familiar.

There is probably no fear equal to that of losing the sense of identity, that feeling of being someone separate and particular. By comparison to this danger some of the more specific aberrations of the self-sense, e.g., "confusion of sexual identity," are of secondary importance. This can be demonstrated by comparing the appalling agony of a patient in "catatonic excitement" with the comparatively mild discomfort of the "well-adjusted" adult homosexual. So vital is the individual's need to sustain a reliable composite picture of himself that he will, if his deficiency is great enough, automatically paint into it anything which becomes available to him, no matter how terrible, humble, or useless it might seem to a normal person.

A psychotic eighteen-year-old boy was admitted to the closed adult ward after killing his "stepmother," the fourteenth with whom he had been placed in the course of his life.

History revealed that he had suffered nothing but deprivation and neglect from the day of his birth. He had not learned to read or to achieve otherwise in school. He had never had friends or jobs and had not even been delinquently "antisocial."

During the year prior to admission, he developed the idea that "I am the other people," meaning all the people he had ever seen or heard about. He also came to feel that his most recent stepmother had been "spreading lies about me being the devil . . . turning all of the girls against me . . . against all of the people who are me."

Finally he killed her with a shotgun blast in the chest so that "they would have a chance to make up their mind about which one I am."

The examining psychiatrist began the initial interview with an explanation that he understood the reason for the referral. In response to this the patient appeared to pull himself together; with an air of dignity and solemn pride, he answered, "Yes, I guess I'm the one who did it, all right."

His action had been determined by many forces within himself, but it seemed clear that at least one of these was a compelling urge to carry out a definitive action, one which would reassure him of his own distinctive existence. Following the murder he was no longer "all the others" but "the *one who did it.*" This same peculiar sense of new-found pride and contentment is commonly encountered in psychotic adolescents who have committed homicide or some other momentous deed.

"I CANNOT CHANGE YOU." The fact that a painful symptom can become an important part of the patient's sense of identity presents a familiar problem in psychotherapy. For the adolescent especially, his consuming awareness, first of the struggle he is having in becoming a particular kind of person and second of his fear of being changed in any way, can bring our treatment efforts to a flat halt if not dealt with adequately. Like Quasimodo, he will tend to cling to the perverse satisfactions of remaining a "king of fools" rather than risk losing even these in a wild gamble to become a real king (i.e., autonomous).

In the course of successful psychotherapy with any adolescent, there comes a time when it is necessary to tell him directly and literally that we cannot change *him.* He will continue to recognize himself as the same person he has always been. He must remember that the aims of treatment are that he feel better, condemn himself less, like himself more (and therefore others as well), be less destructive to himself and others, and live more effectively.

The acutely decompensating psychotic patient seems to experience his illness as something terrible which is happening *to* him. The neurotic patient may complain bitterly about the discomfort and waste of time involved in the performance of compulsive rituals or about having to live in an almost constant state of anxiety, but we often find upon closer examination that the patient is also saying, "but that's the way I am and have always been . . . I cannot conceive of being otherwise." A psychoneurosis, in other words, almost always proves to be a little more "characterological" than it seemed at first.

When the adolescent patient is asked to relinquish a resistive defense which is standing in the way of his progress, he will respond with a perplexed and barely articulate complaint that to do so would be dishonest —an act of pretending to be something which he is not. He will also sense in it an invitation to betray the people (parents) who in some obscure manner *wanted* him to be the way he is. Associated with this will be the fear of losing those elements of his identity which were acquired from his parents, which loss would in turn mobilize the depression and anxiety attached to the ever-present dread of losing the parents themselves.

Victor was admitted to the hospital at the age of fifteen with a long history of running away from home, school failure, and minor delinquencies. Some of his mother's most fundamental feelings about him were reflected in her harsh and sadistic treatment of him during his childhood. When he angrily threatened to run away at the age of five, she forced him to pack up his suitcase and ordered him to "go find yourself a new home. . . . If you don't need me, I don't need you."

His father found him sitting by the road a few blocks from home several hours later, weeping and frightened. His mother greeted him with tears of joy and for a day or two thereafter overwhelmed him with affection and attention. Victor and his mother reenacted this little drama many times in the years following, and always according to the same script.

Several months after admission to the hospital he ran away, stole a car, and drove it to another city. When he was returned to the hospital, it became apparent, as it usually does in such instances, that his fantasies about the runaway included that of being rescued by his therapist as he always had been by his mother.

In this behavior Victor achieved another temporary answer to an eternal question. The runaway was not only an effort to master the repeated trauma of acted-out rejection by his mother but also a ritual attempt to resolve a lifetime accumulation of unsettled feelings about how worthy he was of being affectionately regarded and wanted by her or anyone else. However, in thinking of this as an attempt on his part to test for the probable outcome of the highly ambivalent relationship with mother, it is easy to neglect his need to keep this question forever unanswered. In other words, finding out whether he was "acceptable" or "rejectable" had become less important to him than continuing forever to be the kind of person who looks for the answer over and over but does not ever expect to find it. The big question had become less of a dilemma than a way of life, a perverse but available substitute for an unattainable satisfaction.

The young patient has the rather remarkable fantasy that we, because of our great powers as psychiatrists, will actually be able to make him into a new person. The fear is often unconscious, and even when conscious it is very difficult for him to put into words. The therapist must sense its presence, ferret it out, and deal with it. Overcoming this resistance is difficult enough when only the patient believes that he can be changed, but it will not be dealt with at all if the psychiatrist shares this quaint delusion. Its presence as an active hindrance to therapy is often signaled by the patient's angry protest that "no one can change the kind of person I am. I'll never be any different—there's no point even trying!"

Terry, whose case was discussed earlier in this chapter, progressed to the point at which it became possible for her to accept some of her therapist's directions on faith. She was asked to make a deliberate effort to give up the pouting, snubbing, hostile silence which she characteristically assumed in the presence of women staff members.

It was explained to her that this was a necessary prelude to her learning more about how and why it had become so important for her to do this. She was forewarned that the effort would be difficult, perhaps interesting in a way but not pleasant. She worked very hard at her assignment and with the continued support of her therapist succeeded well. But after several weeks of being courteous and friendly in her public manner with others, she reported, "I don't know how long I can keep this up . . . I . . . I . . . I miss myself . . . the way I really am . . . It doesn't seem real."

She was able to continue with her character exercises, however, in spite of the increased anxiety, depression, and feeling of unreality which it caused her. No longer protected by her fragile but functional facade of anger, she was finally able to recognize that there were some other feelings involved in her previously undiluted "hatred" for adult women. She began to distinguish them as individuals, instead of lumping them together as "staff," and to develop for them some realistic likes and dislikes which were much more rationally related to their individual attributes.

As she came to find more pleasure in her own friendliness and in theirs, an oppressive feeling of guilt gradually overtook her. This was in contrast to her earlier view of herself as a cold, conscienceless creature who cared for no one, not even herself. She had difficulty finding words to describe this sense of guilt because it seemed, at first, to be a new sensation: "I feel like I'm bad . . . very bad . . . I never had it before. Last night I started to get mad at Miss Wilson because she wouldn't let me go to the snack bar for a milkshake. . . . I stopped it, but then I couldn't think of anything else to say, and then she got all confused and couldn't think of anything to say either. . . . Then all of a sudden she changed her mind for no reason at all and said she wanted one, too. So we went upstairs together, you know, for milkshakes. She started teasing me that I'd get fat, and then we both teased back and forth, and it was . . . well . . . I don't know . . . it was fun. It was more fun than I've had for as long as I can remember. But when I got back to my room, I felt terrible. She had as much fun as I did, I guess. I don't see how she could . . . because if she knew what I'm really like . . ."

At this point she trailed off, and more weeks passed, interspersed with brief but discouraging relapses, before she could approach some of the guilt-laden fantasies about "what I'm really like . . . I don't deserve to have friends." These were mostly in connection with a group of not-too-unusual feelings about her parents. Patches of light began to fall here and there on her near-total amnesia for almost everything which had happened to her before puberty. Through this and some of the other agencies of psychotherapy, she came to know, after a few more months of work, that her self-condemnation was more than she deserved. When the feelings of guilt had increased at puberty, in response to intensification of the old feelings toward her parents, she spared herself by resorting to a "casting out of the superego." Her latent capacity for feeling tenderness and affection for other people—frozen in the crisis of early adolescence—thawed in the course of therapy and became available to her once more. Although they were still frightening, they had at least become partly pleasurable, and perhaps best of all they held the all-important promise of an increasing tolerance for such pleasure in the future.

She was no longer totally ashamed of being a girl. She underwent many improvements, but, in her words, "I haven't changed a bit since I've been here. Things are better; I guess because I've gotten a little older."

In treating the adolescent patient we attempt to do many things which will strengthen his sense of being someone special and hopefully of being someone whom he and others will be able to recognize as more worthwhile than worthless. Accepting him for treatment, and maintaining him there despite all of the trouble he creates, is the first and perhaps most important contribution to this end. The aim is also supported by our holding solid expectations of him which are realistic, i.e., which we believe he can attain, but which are considerably more than he has ever been able to expect of himself.

His sense of worth is further served by our teaching him, and finding ways in which he can be taught, new skills and knowledge that to an extent are compatible with his abilities. We resist the temptation to infantilize him by doing for him the things which he is capable of doing for himself, and avoid saddling him prematurely with more responsibility than he can carry [16]. In the psychotherapy process his sense of self is strengthened by our insistence that he examine himself in order to learn something about what he is made of or, at the very least, to learn that he is made of something.

We openly respect and support his every effort to feel better and to do better; just as openly we criticize him when his efforts fall short of his abilities. In doing less than this the therapist would be validating the youngster's picture of himself as infantile, dependent, and irretrievably sick.

PART II INDIVIDUAL PSYCHOTHERAPY

10

INTERPRETING REALITY TO THE ADOLESCENT

The things which are implied by the words *psychotherapeutic* and *psychotherapy* do not always go hand in hand. The former is a gratuity, the beneficial consequences enjoyed by a person as a result of an experience which was not necessarily intended to help him psychologically. A certain amount of good hard work is therapeutic for most of us, but, theoretically at least, we have better reasons than this for working.

Psychotherapy includes anything which a person does, whether purposely or inadvertently, while intentionally striving to create conditions which are expected to have a favorable influence on the outcome of a patient's mental illness. It is also necessary to stipulate that psychotherapy takes place between a therapist and a patient in order that people not become too confused about whether they are in therapy or just living. That is, a psychiatrist is not "treating" his own child when treating him with paternal solicitude, nor is he "treating" the resident psychiatrist when supervising him, even when the results of these efforts happen to be emotionally beneficial.

Most of the things which are effective in psychotherapy are familiar to the practicing clinician by their technical names: catharsis, abreaction, suggestion, and insight, for example. And yet there is probably not a single therapeutic force operating in psychotherapy which is not also at work in the everyday lives of people everywhere. Psychological therapists have been able to develop scores of techniques, but no new therapeutic forces. The various technical systems of therapy are often represented as therapeutic specifics, either for mental illness in general or for one of its subtypes. This is due chiefly to the therapist's natural need to enhance his own self-esteem by emphasizing all the things about his work which are different, difficult, mysterious, and hopefully beyond the grasp of the nonprofessional. Unfortunately, it is a need which has created within psychiatry a serious bias against any measures which appear commonplace, with a resultant loss in our therapeutic potential which at times verges on the tragic.

This is also why it is so important to better clarify our criteria for distinguishing between the therapist and the nontherapist. Although the ways in which they influence other people emotionally are qualitatively the same for both, the difference between them is that the psychotherapist makes a conscious effort to study, understand, and apply the same therapeutic forces which the layman uses more automatically and to other purposes. In this sense the therapist who can take a clinical view of his work (i.e., that its principal task is the treatment of sick people) will be better able to appreciate that a willingness to use every available therapeutic force—the ordinary as readily as the esoteric—will do no serious damage to his professional identity; at the very worst it will only tarnish his public image a little. Careful consideration of some of the discrepancies between the private and public images of the therapist and his work is a useful avenue of approach to the problems involved in treating adolescent patients.

The mental picture most likely to be elicited by the word *psychotherapy* includes a doctor and his adult patient sitting in an office talking with each other. The patient is doing most of the talking and the therapist is listening, interrupting only occasionally to ask a brief question or to clarify something which is uncertain, to give a little reassurance or to interpret some aspect of the on-going emotional transaction of which the patient is unaware. This goes on for set periods of time and at a fairly definite frequency, ranging from perhaps once a month to several times a week. The physical setting, timing, the assigned roles of the participants, and the conditions set forth in the treatment contract all contribute something to the process of psychotherapy, as do the words and reciprocation of feelings which are exchanged during the interviews.

In some ways this picture is too comfortable, complete, and overdrawn; in others it is decidedly incomplete. As our specialty has developed, however, it has somehow become the prototype of ideal therapy, the reference point against which all other treatment measures are gauged. Although it is understood that approaches other than this are needed for many patients (indeed, for most of them), the concession is often made in a spirit of philosophical regret and resignation. We are very much inclined to feel that our therapy can be truly dynamic only in this setting, from which it follows that other approaches should be conceived of as inevitably less-than-ideal modifications of classic therapy. Experience with the intensive and extensive treatment of many different kinds of adolescent patients suggests that this is not an entirely fruitful point of view.

Some Adventitious Effects of Interpretation and Insight

The stability of this picture is maintained by a general agreement that there are certain activities which properly belong to it and certain others which do not. Psychiatrists have long recognized that although there are many beneficial influences operating in psychotherapy, the one among these toward which he takes the most proprietary attitude is the acquisition of insight. Traditionally, the patient is assisted to an increased awareness of himself in two ways. First, he attempts to abide by what is known in psychoanalytic therapy as the "basic rule," meaning that he will try to speak as openly as possible about whatever enters his mind without selection and censorship. The second factor is provided by the therapist, who attempts to infer certain probabilities about the patient from the latter's verbal productions, and then to explain, clarify, or interpret these to him at appropriate times.

The things which are interpreted will have to do with wishes and defenses which unknown to the patient are greatly influencing his feelings and behaviors. It is expected that by becoming aware of the psychogenetic origins of painful symptoms and constricting defenses, he will be better able to appreciate the irrational nature of the frightening childhood beliefs and feelings which underlie them. He will recognize them as emotional anachronisms which have persisted into his adult life, and in doing this he will be said to have acquired improved insight. This, in turn, is meant to enhance his position for coping with the ill-effects which these old influences are exercising on his contemporary life. It is hoped that this liberated energy will then become available for a more flexible and productive reinvestment in what is often spoken of as the adaptive work of the ego. This very brief and oversimplified review is introduced here as a background for considering some of the variations in theory and application which may be of importance in psychotherapy with the adolescent patient.

The fact that a good effect is achieved by an interpretation, i.e., by the insight which it induces, tells us very little about why this is. It is usually assumed that it results from the patient's having learned more about himself, which in turn improves his ability to tolerate and manage that which was successfully interpreted. But in practice there probably is no such thing as a pure interpretation, meaning that the therapist cannot make such an observation about a patient without doing certain other things at the same time—things which may be helpful, hurtful, or simply ineffective. These are the *adventitious effects* of the interpretation. The therapist often provides them without realizing it, and their import to the patient's treatment is often far greater than the interpretation by which they were conveyed.

A patient is often deeply moved by the interpretation of an instinctual wish which, judging by his reaction, is presumed to have been quite unconscious to him. He sometimes confirms this expressly with sincere statements to that precise effect. He may then continue to expand and elaborate on the theme with further highly relevant memories and feelings from his own experience, from which we assume that he is not just being agreeable in the interest of resistance. That is, he gives a much fuller response than might have been unwittingly suggested to him by the therapist. As far as we can tell, he has enjoyed a genuine increment of self-understanding. Following this it is not unusual to note some improvement in his sense of well-being, his attitude toward therapy, and in his total adjustment.

This sequence of events reasonably suggests that the insight *caused* the improvement, but this is not necessarily so. In the typical interpretive transaction other things occur which can, and frequently do, account for the positive response. These do not argue against the validity of the new insight; they only place in question the common assumption that increased self-understanding must have been the force responsible for the improvement. There are emotionally potent influences which, acting quite independently of the content of an induced insight, frequently bring about these beneficial if somewhat extraneous effects of an interpretive effort.

THE HERETICAL ADOLESCENT. As a militant antitraditionalist the adolescent is exceptionally active in contesting some of psychiatry's most-cherished postulates. He is loath to share our convictions that we know just what we are doing and how we are doing it. As far as it is safe to generalize about such a thing, the adult neurotic patient is far more willing than the neurotic adolescent to accept professional authority in theoretical matters. The adolescent asks too many embarrassing questions either verbally or behaviorally, and by his suspicious nature is indisposed to accept even the most sophisticated formulations if they do not ring with truth.

He understands too quickly, for example, the therapist's reasons for leaning so heavily on physical props and ceremonies to do his work. He recognizes almost immediately that certain techniques of psychotherapy provide the therapist with the maximum opportunity to be intelligent and ingenious. Often enough he is so impressed by the method and the subject matter upon which it concentrates that he hungrily incorporates it into his own defense system. He becomes more of an understudy than a patient and with diligence and enthusiasm turns the extraordinary psychodiagnostic talent of his age to everyone but himself. For his own part he is quite capable of probing the shallows of his psyche for tasty fresh information about his putatively unconscious wishes and conflicts, but will do this only as long as it does not significantly interfere with his view of himself or his way of life. Psychotherapy can be a fascinating hobby, in other words, if it costs him nothing. These are a few of the reasons for drawing attention so closely to the adventitious effects of interpretation.

INSIGHT AS A SOURCE OF IMPROVED SELF-ESTEEM. There is still some controversy about the therapeutic efficacy of the insights, i.e., their content, which is achieved in analytic types of therapy. Some psychoanalysts feel that their technique is greatly overrated as a form of treatment, and are inclined to regard it primarily as a research instrument. This growing disenchantment does not stem from any revision in the fundamental principles of analytic psychology. If anything, it results more from a greater appreciation for the remarkable power of unconscious drives and for the immense force and tenacity of the defensive activities by which they are modulated and directed. It has become increasingly evident that the acquisition of insight about previously unrecognized needs does little to diminish their strength. Realizing that they exist may improve a person's ability to "just live with them," but this in turn suggests only that one defense has been substituted for another. That is, in becoming aware that he wants certain kinds of gratification which are not compatible with the dictates of his conscience, or with the personal standards which he has tried to live by for many years, the patient's decreased anxiety may be at the cost of some loss in self-esteem and heightened depression. These, however, might then be counterbalanced by his sense of satisfaction in *knowing* more about what he is like, even if the knowledge does not do him great credit.[1] Or the loss might be compensated for by his assigning a higher moral value to the need, thus permitting himself a somewhat greater latitude for self-indulgence than before, e.g., "I have this neurotic hostility problem, so you will understand why I just told you to go to hell." An increase in self-esteem may also be achieved by the successful deprecation of a drive derivative: "I no longer found it necessary to play the piano after my masturbation conflict was analyzed."[2]

THE ORACLE EFFECT. We are greatly assisted in drawing inferences about the nature of the patient's psychologically dangerous wishes by our understanding of the *universality* of certain strivings and wish-fear complexes. The patient has had no opportunity to examine and treat great numbers of people psychiatrically. To him his wishes are unique, and our ability to divine them on what appears to be the flimsiest of evidence is in itself a vastly impressive phenomenon. It is as though we can read his mind, are infinitely shrewd in our understanding of people, or so intimately attuned to him that he can conceal very little from us. If the

[1] It must be confessed that one occasionally finds it difficult to endure the smugness of a colleague's "more-insightful-than-thou" attitude.

[2] These are not fictitious whimsies but direct quotations of statements which were made in complete seriousness.

therapist searches intently, he will commonly find that the patient has been more affected by his own revised view of the therapist—as an omniscient revealer—than by what has been revealed. The effect is cryptic and easily missed. As a rule all eyes are focused on content, a condition which facilitates the patient's displacing his feelings of astonishment, respect, or fear of the therapist onto the newly revealed fantasies.

In the adolescent patient we find many times that the universal wish-fear complexes were barely, if at all, unconscious. It often comes out that he has regularly, consciously indulged himself in the frightening pleasures of highly variegated sexual and aggressive fantasies, but has found protection from the guilt, anxiety, and shame which they might cause by excluding them from his conception of himself. He has treated them as though they are transient, alien intrusions, silly ideas, intellectual ruminations, crazy thoughts, which pass through his head but are not *really* his. This is a perfectly normal defense which need not be illuminated interpretively unless it also supports painful symptoms or self-defeating behavioral defenses. However, when it is deemed necessary to do so, the effect on the patient is often dramatic. He cannot help but feel that we are terribly wise and understanding, which in itself strengthens our potential for appearing very reliable, trustworthy, forgiving, accepting, and benevolent. Being told that he feels guilt about sexual feelings for a parent, even if he was already conscious of it, has the effect of overwhelming his denials in fantasy. Moreover, not realizing that we have learned that such feelings are universal among people, he is likely to feel that we have supernaturally divined what he has long regarded as his own unthinkable, unfathomable secret. He has been touched by a healer!

Interpretation as reassurance. Another adventitious effect can be illustrated by a simple analogy. A child in normal development suffers transient phobias. He is afraid of shadows in his room and is also unduly susceptible to other illusions. A chair in the darkened corner becomes a crouching monster; a tree branch silhouetted against the moon outside of the window, a vampire bat or more likely—with the current generation's burgeoning interest in paleontology—a pterodactyl. By trial and error the parent finds that there are two general ways of quieting and reassuring the acutely frightened child. He may go into the youngster's room and turn on all the lights, thus dispelling the shadows and demonstrating that the chair is really just a chair. The child recognizes that he believed falsely and is reassured, even though he does not understand why he *needed* to misinterpret reality. This is one mechanism.

The parent may achieve equally good results simply by going into the child's room without turning on the light. He need not remain there long and he need not come in every night, but his occasional appearance at times when he is needed often has a remarkably therapeutic effect. Commonly enough the illusory monster is the child's disguised and projected concretization of certain fears which he has about his father. When father actually appears at this juncture and reveals through his gentle and reassuring manner that he is not *all* monster, the child is greatly comforted even though he has developed no insight into his defensive phobia formation. The need to misidentify shadows has been somehow diminished. His perception of the irrational character of his fears comes about very effectively without even as much as an illumination—or a clarification—of his phobic misperception.

INTERPRETATION AS CORRECTIVE EMOTIONAL EXPERIENCE. One quickly learns that every measure which he hopes will be therapeutic is double-edged and that it is very hard to know which way his efforts are working. For example, one of the most potent forces in the treatment of the adolescent is that which operates through sharing aloud with him some of the guilt-laden feelings and fantasies with which he has had to live in frightened, closed-off silence for so many years. There are several things which contribute to the usually salutary effect of this measure. The confessing of his dreadful secret is a partial atonement because it causes him painful embarrassment. Sometimes the relief which he experiences by this mechanism is so great, and so transient, that we have to direct him to stop confessing. We make clear to him that we are not much interested in symbolic atonement which only lends support to his rationalizations for doing it again or to some other resistance. He is often inclined to construe our kindly, objective acceptance of neurotic causes of undeserved guilt as justification for continuing behavior which he *ought* to feel guilty about. It is true that the therapist's benign attitude toward almost everything which the patient brings into therapy can be more frightening than reassuring, but even so it is often the latter with the adolescent.

On the other hand, many of his painful revelations about himself are followed by a useful, therapeutic improvement in his mood and a waxing enthusiasm for learning more secrets. In discovering that his therapist does not respond to him as he had expected, he begins to enjoy the benefits of what Alexander has called "the corrective emotional experience"[2]. The therapeutic effect is brought about by the patient's appreciating, in close relationship to another person, that his frightening wishes and fears are greatly exaggerated. His *emotional* belief in them diminishes, perhaps not so much as a result of his understanding how they originated as from learning that they can be brought to the level of *shared awareness* with another person and can be talked about, felt, and reexperienced internally without being realized externally. He develops a genuine belief in the difference between thought and deed and learns also to discriminate more realistically between the moral and practical import of different kinds of deeds.

THE PLEASURE OF SELF-SCRUTINY. Even as he is finding that he can speak of his innermost thoughts without doing real damage to himself or to his therapist, he also begins to appreciate that there is a certain pleasure in this process. He finds that the expense of a little pain is more than justified by the dividends which it returns. But at the same time the way is smoothed for increased intellectualization, rumination, and for working at fulfilling his personalized concept of his role as a patient, which he and his therapist are actually delineating very specifically. The therapy process, though painful in some ways, may provide so much covert erotic pleasure for both patient and therapist that it becomes an end in itself and, thereby, perennially nonprogressing. Something which started as psychotherapy evolves into a legal enough but essentially supportive aim-inhibited perversion of treatment.

THE PROHIBITIVE EFFECT OF INTERPRETATION. Whether accurate or not, an interpretation can also work a predominantly prohibitive effect. A guilt-ridden, delinquent boy may abandon almost any kind of highly valued antisocial behavior if, for example, it is interpreted as having an unconscious relationship to his masturbation. Believing as he does in the existence of the unconscious and the wisdom of his therapist, he may respond to the interpretation, whether it is valid or not, with the idea that giving up some manifest delinquency will prove to the therapist that he has stopped masturbating. Indeed, the therapist may sharply inhibit any of a patient's activities, from piano playing to excellent school achievement, by vigorously interpreting them as derivatives of forbidden sexual or aggressive impulses. This inhibitory effect does not depend upon the accuracy of the interpretation's specific content.

INTERPRETATION AS A MANIPULATION. The well-intended interpretive effort sometimes elicits a disturbingly paradoxical response when it is perceived by the patient as an attempt to manipulate his will and undermine his autonomy.

Jack, a sixteen-year-old inpatient, had a lifelong history of school difficulties. For him, going to school amounted to a passive, infantile submission to the stringent and unrewarding demands of parents who valued his achievements too highly. Much time was spent in psychotherapy in examining those past experiences and feelings having to do with influential connections between his feelings about his parents and those about school attendance. He gradually developed a new appreciation for experiential determinants of an adjustment deficiency (school refusal) with which he himself was quite dissatisfied. For a time his school work improved, but then quite unexpectedly he retreated to his previous resistance to school.

When this was examined with him, it developed that he had come to regard the good results of these interpretations as meaning simply that he had again been manipulated into a submissive position. No matter how he looked at it, he was still able to regard therapy only as a seduction, a form of treachery, a way of compelling him to act out his unrecognized wishes to be passive, controlled, and completely at the mercy of an adult person. Attempts to interpret *this* reaction were similarly misconstrued by him. He agreed that it was all true, but no matter what was said or done, it would still end by his yielding his will to another. Finally his therapist said to him, in effect, "All right, there doesn't seem to be anything I can say or do to convince you that doing well in school is something that you should want for yourself, and not just to satisfy me. I can't make you go to school, or at least I can't make you learn anything there, so I'm not going to try to go through the motions. It's up to you now. But I owe it to you to make one thing as clear as possible. By not going to school you are working against yourself, and you're doing it for reasons that we can both understand, for reasons that really did matter a great deal when they got started in you ten or fifteen years ago. But now these reasons are real only in the way you feel about them. By not going to school you may disappoint me some, but you won't cause me enough worry to make it the kind of revenge you'd maybe like it to be. And even more important than that, since I'm not getting anywhere with this business anyway, I have no choice but to leave it to you."

When all pressure and support were removed, Jack decided to resume school.

SOME COMMON MISAPPREHENSIONS. The adolescent frequently shows a remarkable tolerance for an intensive probing into his deepest and most carefully guarded sexual and aggressive yearnings. This may be because he feels relatively little guilt about them, or perhaps because talking about them with an avidly interested listener is a sexually pleasurable experience, or because his recitations are so intellectualized and barren of immediate feeling that they cause him no distress whatever.

What is taboo for one youngster will be far less so for another. The depth of a searching exploration cannot be readily determined by the content of *what* is uncovered. The youngster may earnestly accept with relative ease a valid interpretation relating to shockingly aberrant sexual wishes, only to dissolve in tears, anxiety, and embarrassment when confronted with the observation that he seems to be troubled by feelings of tenderness and affection for one of his parents. A simple affect, in other words, is often more offensive to the adolescent ego than is the raw instinctual drive from which it was derived. As this is less likely to be the case with adult patients, we sometimes find ourselves emphasizing the wrong syllable with the adolescent.

Tacit encouragement to the acting-out of antisocial impulses is another possible consequence of the ill-conceived interpretation. This danger is similar to that which Adelaide Johnson [22] warns against in connection with taking a history from the adolescent. Asking him, for example, whether he has ever had sexual intercourse may mean to him that an affirmative reply is *expected,* thus pushing him to act in a way which will justify such an answer. Similarly, interpreting his anxiety as arising from unrecognized hostile and aggressive wishes toward a nurse may be regarded by him as a friendly bit of advice about how he might relieve his anxiety, i.e., by verbally attacking the nurse.

One of the worst and least recognized of the many possible antitherapeutic consequences of an interpretive effort is the slowly corrosive effect which it may have on the patient's attitude toward his therapist. Understanding as we do that he cannot help resisting any tendency to change in himself, we can also appreciate that he will either purposely or unwittingly strive to maintain his personal status quo by devaluating the therapist. One of his most subtle and effective ways of doing this is to bait a trap with choice bits of highly suggestive but inconclusive psychological data and then to wait for the verbal interpretation which will correspond verbatim to his own private prediction. "I knew you were going to say that!" is his triumphant though often unspoken fantasy. In simpler language, *he leads us on to state the obvious.* When succeesful in this his respect for the therapist will gradually ebb, to be replaced by feelings of smugness, omnipotence, and contempt. But, unfortunately, in trapping his therapist into doing his bidding, he has once again trapped himself into the impossible position of having no one to rely upon *but* himself.

Behavioral Interpretation

Theoretically, it should be possible to point out to the patient the irrational nature of his reactions and to encourage him to examine his memory for psychogenetic determinants which can be meaningfully related to the present. Practically, this seldom works well as the first step in dealing with conflicts which have been compromised characterologically. This naturally applies regardless of the primary diagnosis. No patient is without some character defenses. As Hendrickson has put it: "there is no superego so punitive that somewhere in it you cannot find a hole big enough to drive a truck through" [16].

Being directive and analytic. The neurotic or even the normal child who attempts to refuse school may understand perfectly a rational "interpretation" of the reasons for his reluctance, but usually he still will not go unless he is told to. This is because he does not *want* to go. Most practicing psychiatrists have found that ordinarily the most effective approach to the treatment of the school refusal syndrome includes sending the little patient to school *first,* and talking with him about his internal conflicts afterward.

If an adolescent boy prefers stealing cars to suffering the anxiety which he would experience if he did not steal cars, he will probably not be helped by interpretation alone. The general principle is the same as in the treatment of addictions and perversions; it is virtually impossible to treat a chronic alcoholic successfully in a tavern.

With regard to neurotic character elements in any adolescent patient, and not meaning just with the antisocial youngster, the therapist imposes upon him not the too-demanding burden of correcting his reality misinterpretations by himself but, as Eissler has pointed out, the reality itself [9]. The therapist relies upon his authority as a physician and an adult to demonstrate how certain things must be. Being directive is not the opposite of being analytic. Far from excluding each other, these two general measures of therapy are often crucially dependent upon each other, especially with the legally dependent patient, e.g. a juvenile, or a "committed" adult. Sometimes the most effective interpretation of a defense is a simple and heartfelt "No" or "Don't do that any more, you hear?"

A newly admitted fifteen-year-old delinquent boy was directed by his therapist to keep his shirt tucked in, to have his trousers cleaned and pressed, and to request the barber to trim off his redundant half bale or so of "tough" cascading curls and sideburns. He desisted strenuously. No one could tell him what to do. He regaled his doctor with impressive accounts of his gang fights, playing "chicken" in speeding cars, and other daring feats of courage. Following a prolonged verbal struggle, he angrily did as he was told. He underwent a startling personality change with these sartorial and tonsorial revisions. Before the change he had contemptuously refused to participate in football with the other boys because it was "wasted" (i.e., chicken, square, effeminate). Afterward he confided tremulously that he felt like a fourth-grader and dreaded the very thought of having to face the other boys in his shorn condition. He was terrified by the idea of playing football with them because he feared he would be "mashed into the ground." It was the beginning of much better things for him. The therapist must often play Delilah in the "delinquent Samson syndrome"; i.e., evict the magical strength to make room for real strength.

It would have done no good at all to confront this boy with a verbal explanation of the defensive value of his hard-boiled pose, because he was too hard-boiled to be impressed. The therapist's words were: "Stop the arguing and get your hair cut, keep that shirt in, and get those cruddy pants to the cleaners." This was the verbal component of the interpretation. The patient's acquiescence to it was equivalent to the Ideal Adult Neurotic's thoughtful reflections on an interpretation which has just been made to him. The boy's literally expressed feelings of immaturity, passivity, and fear of physical injury reflected the same type of insight which the adult neurotic finds concealed beneath his essentially autoplastic defense.

The difference between these two instances, strangely enough, is not in the fact that the adult neurotic was willing to accept the interpretation whereas the delinquent boy was not. The fact is that the boy did not really have to get his hair cut, tuck in his shirt, or anything of the sort; no one held him down or threatened him with any other dire consequences. His doctor simply told him to do it, and he meant it. The boy did it, and did not really *have* to do it. The real difference is in the treatment contracts. The adult patient has agreed to examine himself without the pressure of direct authority, and the adolescent has tacitly requested that he be required to look inward only after having been allowed a face-saving show of resistance. The doctor's harsh words were not as cruel and aggressive as they sounded, although sometimes it is only the doctor and patient who realize this.

There are limits to each person's capacity to tolerate his own aggressive strivings, and most of us must settle for approximately the same standards which are adhered to in public school teaching, football coaching, or child-rearing. It is perhaps unfair to demand more than this of ourselves in treating this disturbed adolescent; but to offer him any less verges on psychiatric malpractice.

EGO EXERCISE AS A PREREQUISITE TO INSIGHT. In the various case illustrations used here, it is evident that this rather aggressive-appearing approach to the interpretation of character defenses applies only to certain patients and at certain times—usually in the earlier phases of treatment. There are a few youngsters who require very little authoritative direction at any time in their treatment. The majority do require it early in treatment, but progress to the point at which they can participate more independently and profitably in a comparatively conventional type of "office psychotherapy." There are usually some transitional stages between these two extremes. The adolescent patient must test enough to be sure that he can trust his doctor before he abandons his treasured character defenses, and of course the therapist must respond to these tests in ways which will justify the patient's trust. A castaway does not let go of his life-saving bit of flotsam until he is sure that his would-be rescuer can swim well enough for both of them.

Then, too, like any other person, the adolescent often has difficulty understanding why he should relinquish a familiar pattern of behavior which he consciously regards as normal. His doctor may recognize it as maladaptive defense, but he can only see it as "the way I am."

When he has come to appreciate that his doctor is more often right than wrong about such things and has begun to nurture a faint, ill-defined hope that things can be better for him, he will be ready to accept distasteful treatment prescriptions on faith. His doctor will offer him what sounds like highly arbitrary advice and he will accept it, not always because he understands the reasons for it but because he has learned from experience that it might turn out well for him. He becomes willing to set for himself a rigorous regimen of "ego calisthenics," a conscious and purposeful exercising at doing certain things differently, as illustrated in the case of Terry (p. 161). His efforts in this direction correspond very closely to the adult neurotic's attempts to surmount his own unconscious resistance to change, and to penetrate and revise defensive processes which are participating in the maintenance of his symptoms.

Other Aspects of Interpretive Therapy with the Adolescent

Handling those unconscious instinctual strivings which are the raison d'être of neurotic symptoms or of pathological character defenses presents many problems which are different than the ones associated with the interpretation of the defenses which have been raised against them.

What does the therapist do, in other words, with that which has been uncovered?

The great fluctuations in the effectiveness of repression and other defenses during puberty and adolescence add new significance to the idea of "individualized therapy." We are accustomed to thinking of the psychiatric patient as having a relatively fixed set of instinctual strivings which are opposed or modulated by the acquired prohibitions of conscience and by a reasonably stable, if abnormal, system of ego activities. With respect to the strengths of these conflicting forces, the adult and child patient are, as a rule, somewhat better stabilized than the adolescent.

Because of this the psychiatrist who sees many adolescents finds himself facing each new patient with no particular, preconceived interviewing plan in mind. There are, of course, a number of rather well-defined syndromes of adolescence which can often be identified by history alone and which will suggest that one general approach or another would be most likely to yield the greatest understanding of the patient with the least discomfort to him. Many other youngsters come with histories offering very few clues of predictive value. This is particularly true of acute disturbances in puberty. The youngster who comes to the clinic with a malignant-sounding history is far more likely to turn out to be mildly neurotic than the adult who is referred with a similar history. Conversely, a relatively benign history, such as a slight drop in school grades, frequently accompanies the youngster who turns out to be much sicker than the adult patient with a comparably "mild" background.

Directness in Interpretation

Psychotherapy with the acutely disturbed early adolescent often necessarily begins during the initial evaluation interview. What the therapist does with respect to the interpretation of unconscious wishes depends upon many variables which, as a rule, he will have to respond to more swiftly and decisively than would ordinarily be required with the child or adult.

Vicki, aged thirteen, was referred with a history of deteriorating school performance and inability to maintain friendly relationships with her classmates. She was of low-normal intelligence, and had never been a good scholastic achiever. However, she had managed to do reasonably well in a special education class until the age of ten. At this time she had gone to a fly-by-night circus which was located several blocks from her home. While wandering around looking at the sights, a Negro roustabout coaxed her into his trailer and raped her. A friend of her family saw the man take her into the trailer, but instead of intervening directly he called Vicki's mother on the telephone. By the time the sheriff made his appearance, the rape had been completed. The man was arrested and imprisoned, but Vicki, because she bore no "marks of struggle," was held morally responsible for the episode by both of her parents. Up until the time of referral, three years later, whenever Vicki misbehaved her mother would remind her of the catastrophe: "Do you remember what you let that man do to you that summer? That was a terrible thing you did!"

It was evident within the first few minutes of the interview that Vicki was a rather simple girl who, though profoundly and chronically anxious, was not psychotic. She was understandably reluctant to talk about the rape incident but worked up to it because she realized that it had something to do with the merciless anxiety which she was suffering.

She gradually offered tiny bits of expressly "denied" information which, when pursued further, led swiftly to some of the more deeply seated sources of her symptoms. She knew, for example, that there was more than maternal solicitude behind her mother's constant, accusatory reiterations. "She likes to talk about it, or something . . . I don't know why she keeps talking it up all the time. She don't want me to forget it."

She did not attempt to persuade the psychiatrist that her nervousness had been caused by the fear and shock of the rape. On the contrary, she was eager to "enter a plea of guilty" for herself. It proved unnecessary to make the kind of interpretation which is sometimes offered in this sort of trauma situation. She acknowledged having been frightened by the attack, but with a visible increase in anxiety and shame she further volunteered quite openly that she had partly enjoyed it. She found herself unable to repel the insistent memories of the incident. She indicated that during waking hours her mind was filled with recurrent, obsessional ruminations about it, and even though these caused her much guilt and anxiety, she also appreciated that they were a source of pleasurable excitement for her.

The entire community knew of the episode, and she was occasionally teased by her classmates. On several occasions she had been crudely propositioned by some of the older boys in the school. Even though she "needed to be accused," there was no indication that she had provoked the other youngsters into performing this service for her. She counterattacked, concentrating her attentions on the several Negro children in her classroom. She upset her parents and the teachers with many wild stories, most of which centered about her alleged involvement in knife fights with Negro boys. In these fantasies she would always emerge the victor, having succeeded in wresting the knife from one of the boys and "cutting him with it."

During the first interview she also complained of chronic insomnia. She would lie awake at night fearing that she would die suddenly of a heart attack or "would get a stroke and lose my brain." When asked if she also had the other (i.e., pleasurable) thoughts about the rape while lying awake, she confirmed this and quickly acknowledged that these thoughts aroused her and were closely associated with her fear of dying or of "having a stroke." The doctor then postulated that, under the pressure of these very strong feelings, she probably had sought to relieve her tension in some way, whereupon she became startled and hastily replied, "Sometimes I lie awake all night and can't get no relief, so I go get a glass of milk to quiet down."

Her doctor, who by now had become her therapist, explained, "I wasn't exactly thinking of that way of getting relief from those feelings . . . I imagine you know what I'm talking about."

She did and promptly gave a history of having practiced compulsive, ungratifying masturbation ever since the attack. She was next confronted with her knife-fighting fantasies and, also in conjunction with these, her theretofore unconscious wish to "cut off his thing." She had suffered much guilt over this wish. On many past occasions she had expressed excessive concern over the fact that her assailant had been imprisoned: "They took away his most important thing . . . his freedom."

In immediate association with these fantasies there came elaborations on the fear that she would lose her mind, that masturbation, paradoxically, would "drive me crazy . . . but keep me from losing my mind." Then she began to detail some of the remote past experiences with her parents and siblings which attested to the severely depreciated status which came of being a girl.

There were practical reasons why it was not feasible to plan long-term, intensive psychotherapy for Vicki, but it appeared likely that this would have been neither desirable nor necessary anyway. Her mother was seen in several consultations, and although she did not really understand why she should stop accusing Vicki of complicity in the rape, she did seem to sense that there was something wrong about it and agreed to stop.

Vicki was also seen on two more occasions, during which she both demonstrated and reported a marked improvement in symptoms. She also suggested by diplomatic indirection that, because "I sleep good now," it really would not be too important that she return regularly. The fact that her improvement continued indicated that it was more than a flight into health.

There are several features about Vicki's problem which made it possible and worthwhile to conduct what might appear to have been a dangerously swift and radical exploration of her instinctual wishes. In the lower socioeconomic class of which she was a member, the prohibitions against premarital intercourse, pedophilia, and rape are much less stringent than in the higher classes. Even though the mother had her own neurotic reasons for unconsciously pushing Vicki into further sexual adventures, it would not have been too surprising in any case for members of her family and the community to indict her as they had. They assumed that she had enjoyed the attack, and their direct accusations had "helped" make this interpretation to her. She was, moreover, a psychologically uncomplicated girl who was accustomed to blunt talk and to concrete terms for describing instinctual actions. She required very little help in recognizing some partial origins of her symptoms in her scarcely disguised fantasies of talion revenge against men (meaning, of course, specific men in her life) and in her pervasive feeling of sexual, anatomical inadequacy.

Ellipsed Interpretation

THE ADOLESCENT'S NOT-SO-FREE ASSOCIATION. This much directness and speed in therapy with the adolescent are the exception rather than the rule. In the following case similar wishes and defenses were approached more deferentially than with Vicki. Many of the same problem areas, however, were dealt with just as thoroughly—though somewhat more obliquely—through allusion and the judicious use of some specific connotations of selected and well-timed words and phrases. The verbal nexis of the interpretation was ellipsed, in other words, because its content was understood without having to be stated explicitly.

June was an intelligent, pretty, thirteen-year-old girl who was seen in psychiatric consultation several days after an apparent suicide attempt.

Her father was a small-business executive who suffered chronic, moderately severe alcoholism. His drinking had resulted in many job changes, but he had always managed to land on his feet financially. Her mother was an attractive and highly competent woman who had worked during the day for the several preceding years in order to supplement the family income and save for the future. The fact that her husband worked nights and she during the day could not be explained entirely by the fact of economic necessity. Their other motives for avoiding one another were quite unconscious to both of them, however.

According to the mother's history, June had been unremarkable in her general development. "She was a delightful child for the first eleven years, but she's made up for all of that in the past two." She seemed genuinely interested in June and was eager to do the right thing, but a quality of aloofness was revealed in her persistently competent, reasonable, and somewhat clinical description of family problems.

She reported that "June and her father were very close when they were younger, but something has gone wrong. They seem to resent each other terribly. He is displeased with everything she does, and she can't speak to him at all without shrieking and then running from the house." She emphasized that June had been an excellent student until the semester preceding the onset of her acute illness, at which time her grades had fallen off to an average level.

The incident which prompted referral had been touched off by a violent argument with her father about a television program which he considered "too indecent" for her to watch. The next morning her mother made temporary arrangements for her to live with a young aunt in a nearby town and also helped her to get a part-time job in the municipal library to keep her busy.

Her immediate supervisor on this job was an eighteen-year-old visiting college student from Italy, to whom she soon became strongly attached. Later developments revealed that there had been nothing improper in their relationship. The young man was pleasant to her but respectful of her age and, presumably, to the dictates of his own conscience. They chatted occasionally on the job and during the lunch hour but never met outside of work.

There was no trouble until June was brought home to prepare for the next semester of school. Almost immediately upon arriving home she went to the bathroom and inflicted a number of slightly deeper than superficial lacerations on both wrists. She then rushed screaming into the living room where both of her parents were quietly reading. Although hemorrhaging rather conservatively, she commenced flailing her arms about with such abandon as to cover the greatest amount of territory with the least amount of blood.

Her terrified parents rushed her to the hospital emergency room. As her wounds were being sutured and dressed, she explained between shaking sobs that she wanted to die because she could not stand the thought of living without Michael, her librarian friend.

The parents were advised to seek immediate psychiatric consultation and they did so. In the meantime, despite her wounds, June managed to fire off five urgent letters to her aunt. In all of them she implored her aunt to intercede for her with Michael, to understand that she could not live without him and that she was already "dying" and needed "help . . . help . . . help!"

From the history provided by the parents, Dr. L, the examining psychiatrist, was at first inclined to regard June's illness as an "acute dissociative (hysterical) reaction" but had occasion to question this impression shortly after the beginning of the interview. Although more controlled and trying hard to be cooperative, June was trembling visibly with anxiety. Far from being autistic and preoccupied, she seized hungrily upon Dr. L's every word, even though her responses were at times general and evasive and at others frankly irrational and incoherent. Surprisingly, she made no demands at all and seemed rather to be waiting for someone to tell her what to do. She volunteered no information about Michael, and when asked about this, she was strangely indifferent to the whole subject.

"But I thought that's why you cut your wrists—because you loved him and couldn't be with him."

"I never said I loved him!"

Dr. L again reviewed the history, along with the five letters to the aunt which had been hastily recovered by the parents, and found that there was indeed not a single reference to "love."

"Then I don't understand this. You tell me about it."

"There's nothing to tell. I needed to be with him, that's all, and if I couldn't be with him, then I needed to be dead."

"What did you need to be with him for?"

"To keep from being dead."

Attempts to explore her fantasies about the episode yielded little information. She made no attempts to dramatize her suicidal gesture (which might, of course, have resulted in a tragic *psychological accident*—the actual death which she had not really intended). She could say only that "dying" would enable her to return to the library and remain there, forever, with Michael. She appeared to be thoroughly serious about this, and could give no assurance that she would not harm herself again when asked directly about her intentions. On the other hand she made no threats, seeming instead to regard a possible recurrence of this sort as something which would either happen or not happen, quite independently of her own volition.

When Dr. L began to ask about her family, June could scarcely control her rage. Time and again she spat out words of hatred, disgust, and contempt for her father. In contrast, her eyes filled with tears whenever she mentioned her mother, and she became incoherent while trying to explain the guilt which she felt for having "let my mother down" in some inexplicable way.

"I can only make it up to her by dying."

"Make what up to her? What is it you've done to her that you should kill yourself for?"

". . . the way he's treated her . . . you can't understand! I don't know!"

"Maybe you know more than you think. He treats her badly because of you? If you were dead, they would be alone together, and you wouldn't interfere with them anymore. Is that it?"

"No, that's not it . . ." She seemed genuinely mystified and asked, "Where did you get that idea?"

"From you. I think that's what you were saying."

"No, it isn't. He disgusts me. My mother hates him, too. Everything would be all right if he were just dead."

Following this many other details of her relationship with her parents were filled in. There was also a careful examination of the pros and cons of admitting her to the hospital for protection and possibly for intensive, long-term inpatient treatment. At first she heatedly resisted the idea, but then began to ask questions which concluded with an inverted, ill-disguised request for admission. When this was pointed out, her mixed feelings about future planning came into the open. By the end of the interview her anxiety about treatment plans had increased markedly, in sharp contrast to her earlier indifference to the future. At the same time her general level of anxiety had decreased. Although much more comfortable and rational, she remained realistically worried about what would happen next. Drawing from their earlier, rather detailed review of her fantasies about suicide, Dr. L explained the danger of her belief that she could "die without really dying," emphasizing her defensive disavowal of any personal liability for self-destructive behavior.

"Your ideas about this are very mixed up. You have ideas about what it would be like to be dead, but you don't know, really, what it would be like."

She then replied seriously, "No, not really. Do you know what it would be like?"

"No, I don't. No one knows for sure. It's probably like being deeply asleep, but that doesn't matter right now. One thing I do know about it, though, is that once it happens there's no way to change it back. A person *can* make it happen. You could make it happen to yourself. You might not really know whether you want to or don't want to, but if you do the wrong thing you could make yourself *dead* anyway. You don't know what's safe and what's dangerous, so don't do any of them . . . that's what I want you to know."

She accepted all of this very soberly, then wondered if she were to return for another interview or come into the hospital. For a number of reasons, not all of which have been clarified here, it was decided that she would stay at home and return for another outpatient visit in a week.

On the second visit she was more composed and in better spirits. She continued to be extremely anxious about the question of entering the hospital, now openly expressing her wish for admission, but more with an air of teasing and coaxing than in desperation. There was further talk about her family, but this was much the same as it had been in the first interview. She volunteered some information about school and described what sounded like a rather gay and girlish social life. She made a casual reference to her boy friends and alluded to having had a few sexual experiences of an unspecified nature. Dr. L was impressed by her decidedly precocious show of savoir faire, and pressed for details about her boy friends and her activities with them. She promptly confessed, with mixed shame and defiance, that she had really had virtually no experience at all.

"I'm not that kind of a girl!"

"What kind do you mean?"

"That kind—you know! Necking and things like that."

"Why is it that you're not that kind of a girl? Because you think it's bad, or because you just don't like to neck . . . play around?"

"I hate it! It's disgusting! Boys are disgusting!"

"So many things are disgusting to you. Is necking disgusting to you the same way your father is?"

June made no immediate verbal reply to this. She looked vaguely startled and thoughtful, then her body stiffened and one leg jerked involuntarily sidewise. At the same time she slid down in the chair, bringing the hem of her skirt to midthigh, and rotated herself slightly in Dr. L's direction. She appeared unmistakably excited but at the same time appeared quite unaware of this.

"I don't have any secrets . . . I don't know why I said that, because I wasn't thinking about anything in particular. Some of my girl friends giggle about their secrets . . ."

After saying this she again sat up in her chair, crossed her knees, and smoothed down her skirt, all quite automatically.

"Everyone has secrets, June. You have them, too. Maybe I'm asking too many questions, too fast. Do you have any idea why I'm asking all these questions?"

"No. I don't."

"Then I'm glad I brought the subject up. You've had a lot of trouble lately, haven't you? Lots of hate and disgust, and terrible ideas, and ideas that don't make any sense. You know what it's all about?"

"No."

"All of these questions I'm asking have something to do with those things. Do you believe what I'm saying to you?"

"Yes."

"You believe very easily. I've asked you some pretty personal questions. You haven't told me yet what you thought about my reasons for asking them."

"I didn't know. I guess you're interested."

"In what?"

"Well . . . in helping me with my problems?"

"Or maybe just interested in some of the answers to the questions, don't you think? Tell me, do you like coming over here to talk with me?"

"I don't want to keep coming back here forever, if that's what you mean. It makes my mother miss work, and I miss school, and if the kids ever found out about it . . ."

"I know, but that isn't what I asked. I asked if you liked coming over here to talk with me."

"Well, it's not fun."

"Meaning that it's partly fun? But that's not why you're coming here. And you're right, it's not supposed to be all fun, just for the sake of fun. You're not a very happy girl. Sometimes you're very unhappy. Talking about some of these things can be fun, but some of it is no fun at all."

"I know."

On the third visit there was a striking change in her appearance. On the first two occasions she had been dressed attractively but conservatively, a little younger than her years. This time she was dressed beyond them. She wore high heels and a tight sheath dress. It was evident that beneath the latter she had taken great pains to make the most of her youthful assets. Her makeup and hairstyling were appropriate to her age, however, and she did not affect pseudomature speech or mannerisms. She had made herself more attractive than the occasion required but was pleasant, friendly, and appropriately tense.

She spoke even more freely than before. Her manner was chatty and casual sounding, and much of the information which she got across about herself was indirect and not quite consciously intended. Little effort was required of Dr. L to draw her attention tactfully and reassuringly to the half-recognized fantasies behind the words. She told how she and her friends got together after school to gossip and play records. They usually went to Sally's house because there was a recreation room over the garage, where Sally's parents seldom bothered them. When boys were also present, Sally's mother would stop by every hour on schedule, smile briefly into the darkened room, and retreat.

"Why do you always go to Sally's house?"

"Because of that . . . We always know when her mother's coming up to the room. She makes lots of noise on the way."

"It sounds like they're in favor of whatever's going on."

"No, it's just that her mother understands her. She trusts her."

"Well, that's unfortunate, but go ahead and tell me the rest of it. There are boys there with you and your girl friends, and you have parties. Is that it?"

"Sure we have parties, but we don't do anything bad!"

"Do you mean you don't, or they don't, or nobody does?"

"I don't! Oh . . . sometimes the other kids neck—but not me! Sally does. It's disgusting. She and her boy friend flop out on this big couch they have there and make a big show of it."

"And you just watch?"

"Well, I don't exactly stand there and stare!"

"What's everyone else doing while Sally and her boy friend are necking on the sofa, or whatever?"

"I don't care what Sally does. She can do anything she wants to. I could just sit there and read a book, sometimes."

"That's pretty casual. I'd think you'd have some feelings about it all. Somehow I get the idea that some things are going on there that give you a lot of feelings, the excited kind. You don't like to talk about them, naturally."

"Nothing goes on! What could go on? Just tell me what could go on!"

"The way you tell about it makes it sound like someone's having sexual intercourse."

"Not there! My gracious!"

"All right not there, somewhere else."

"I hate those words . . . those ones you said."

"They aren't the nicest, but I don't know what else to call it. Do you?"

"No, but I don't like to think about it."

"Course not. But can you think about it? Do you know what it is?"

"I know what it is!"

"Is it that you can't *stop* thinking about it?"

"No . . . that's nothing to talk about anyway. You should just call it *loving* . . . that's what we call it. We've got different words for different things."

"Like what?"

"Oh, just words. You know, like *silly* . . . *queer* . . . *goofy* . . . just words we use for different things."

"Those words you said aren't all the same kind. *Silly* and *goofy* are nothing special. *Queer* means something different to lots of people. How do you and your girl friends mean it?"

"I know what *queer* means. Everyone knows that. It's like *sweet* and *fine*—they mean different things, too . . . A *sweet girl* is a girl who doesn't do anything with a boy, and a *fine girl* means that she's really fine for a boy when she's with him. This is a joke we have."

"You don't seem to think it's very funny."

"Not now. I laugh when I'm with my girl friends. At least I *think* it's funny . . . a little."

"Do all of your girl friends know what it means?"

"I think so. They think it's funny . . . but they act kind of queer sometimes."

"There's *queer* again. How do you mean it this time?"

"Not that way!"

"What way? You don't have to know *everything* in the world, June. You act like you don't know what it means."

"What does it mean?"

"Tell me what your idea is about it."

"I don't know. I know it means something dirty."

"Well, I don't know about dirty. It means homosexual."

"That's an awful word too! But I don't know what it is!"

"It's men who love men and women who love women."

June jerked upright in her chair and became a little incoherent. "I knew it! I knew it!"

"Knew what? It's not quite as simple as I made it sound. You look shocked. You're probably making too much of it. Not everyone is "queer" just because they played around a little, especially when they're your age. Who are you worrying about? One of your girl friends . . . someone you know? Are you worried about yourself?"

"That's Meg—she's queer."

"You looked kind of shaken up for a minute. You're all right now?"

"Sure. Meg's only thirteen years old. She's half a year younger than I am."

"Is she a friend? Do you like her?"

"I feel like you're trying to make me confess something!"

"I'm sure you do, but I'm not. I'm trying to give you a chance to unload some things that are bothering you a lot. It's not quite like confessing."

Again she was approaching tears and looking vaguely perplexed. "But I really don't have *any*thing like that on my mind!"

"I know you don't, and you do, both at the same time. Maybe we're not talking about the same thing. Think about this. What if you could make your mind work like a moving-picture projector, so that it would show all of your thoughts and daydreams on the wall up there, where we could both see it. Would you switch it on?"

She was thunderstruck. "Do you have a machine like that!"

"Good lord, no! There's no such machine and never will be. I said if there were something like that, would you be willing to have all your thoughts shown so that somebody else could see them?"

She covered her face with her hands, blushing brilliantly. "No, oh no!" She recovered quickly and lashed back, "What about you! Would you do it?"

"Certainly not. I'm like other people. I have lots of thoughts I'm ashamed of. I always have had and always will have. But you say you don't have any."

"I have them, but I didn't even know what you meant until you said that about . . . showing them up on the wall."

Following this she bounced one heel rhythmically on the floor and tugged absently at the collar of her dress.

"What are you thinking about?"

"Are you reading my mind?"

"No, I am not reading your mind! Now, think back, and please try to get this straight. We were talking about your thoughts . . . thoughts that you don't like to have, and you sometimes think you haven't even had, yet you've had them. Do you follow me?"

"Yes."

"Then right after that your mind wandered away, and you got kind of tense. It didn't take a magician to see that you were thinking real hard about something."

"It wasn't about anything like that. I was just thinking about how much I hate . . . Oh, my father was disgusting yesterday. I don't ever want to get married."

"How so?"

"I can't even stand to have a boy touch me!"

"Some special boy friend?"

"One, sort of. His name's Jim. He's real nice . . . not like some boys. Before that I used to go with a boy named Danny, and he was . . ." She made the guttural sound of disgust.

"Disgusting?"

"Yes. He always tried to pet with me. I didn't mind too much if he'd just kiss me once or twice, but then he'd try to put his hands on me. But Jim's not like Daddy at all . . ."

"Daddy?"

"What?"

"You said that Jim wasn't like Daddy."

"Did I? . . . I did! . . . I can hear myself saying it still . . ."

She became wide-eyed and vague. Her eyes filled with tears, and her voice suddenly became strained and remote. "I love him so much . . ."

"Who, June?"

"Dandy . . . Daddy . . . Danny. I mean Danny. He was so nice, except for that stuff he tried to do . . ."

"You're not very sure who you're talking about?"

"I know! I know! Let me think a minute!"

She again became distracted, but this time more bemused and less troubled.

"What are you thinking about?"

"Some things . . . nothing . . . never mind!"

"I guess you are, and I think that's good . . . probably. Look, there's no point trying to talk about everything all at once, and anyway some things will probably never get talked about at all."

"I know. I don't need to say anything right now. I know what you're talking about. Oh, by the way, my mother wonders if we could come back in the morning next week instead of the afternoon?"

"We can work that out. I'll talk with her about it."

"I don't think I'll have to come into the hospital. One of my girl friends said if a person thinks he's crazy, then he really isn't. Is that true?"

"You're still worrying about that?"

"Not so much. There are a whole lot of dances this fall, and I want to go to them. Some boys have asked me already. If I came into the hospital I couldn't go to the dances . . ."

June's mother reported briefly following this interview that things were much better at home. "She seems like a girl all of a sudden, she's started calling me Mother again. She even said a few things to her father last week without screaming at him. She's sleeping much better . . . do you think it's really necessary for us to keep coming back?"

"Yes, for the time being. We haven't even decided yet whether she should continue as an outpatient or come into the hospital. I imagine you've got some questions about this. Have you been talking them over with Miss W (her case worker)?"

Discussion of ellipsed interpretation. The ellipsed interpretation is one which the therapist provides no more than the least number of words or the least complicated action necessary for conveying the sense of some observation about the patient. Conversely, he avoids making too much of his ingenious observation by omitting intelligent elaborations on the theme, no matter how proud of them he might be. For the adolescent patient especially there are often a number of distinct advantages to leaving many things implicit, unstated but understood.

At the end of successful psychotherapy a patient must leave with the feeling that he has improved largely through his own efforts, which in fact would be the case. In saying more than is absolutely necessary about what he observes, the therapist is boasting of his cleverness, superior wisdom, and judgment and is asking the patient to praise him for these. For an adolescent the sage interpretation, like the very best advice, is a musty dry mouthful to swallow. The choice of metaphor is intentional. A person can always more easily and effectively incorporate into himself the desirable attributes of another person under conditions which permit him to do this actively, rather than passively. The important thing, after all, is that the patient recognize certain things about himself, not that he be unnecessarily reminded that we saw it first and only then helped him see it.

But without words of confirmation, how does the therapist know when his adolescent patient has enjoyed a beneficial increment in self-understanding? There are those typically indescribable ways of suspecting when this is taking place. At various times we are able to recognize this in the patient's startled reaction, pensive silence, anxiously abrupt denial, or perhaps in a manifestly irrelevant subject-change which still includes a veiled confirmation of the accuracy of an intended interpretation. Often enough the adolescent patient will deny, disparage, and resist each and every one of his therapist's speculations about him, only to reveal in his overall behavior that these things have meant a great deal to him. In other words, he will let us know in one way or another how well and usefully he has been able to appreciate something about himself which we have tried to make it possible for him to see.

In talking with June about her feelings for her father, Dr. L noted the repeated and passionate exclamations of disgust. When she repeated this word with special vehemence while describing her necking with boys, he simply asked if she were using the same word to denote that her feelings in these separate situations were identical. He did not *tell* her that her feeling of "disgust" for her father was a reactive defense against quite opposite wishes or that they were being reexperienced by her in normal sexual play with boys. He did not have to say much about her irrational need to "atone" for having in some mysterious way betrayed her mother. He needed to *say* very little about any of these things because, as June tacitly expressed it, "I know what you're talking about . . . I'll be back next week . . . I'm still a little crazy but I don't need to come into the hospital. I'll go to dances and talk with you about it."

There are other reasons for leaving the content of this kind of exchange unspoken. June's immediate reactions indicated that the business of self-revelation should proceed at a certain rate. She and her therapist both realized that some of the things which had only been touched upon could be returned to as necessary, and if necessary, in the future. The adolescent, unprotected by an official treatment contract which specifically rewards self-criticism, is especially susceptible to feelings of humiliation and disgrace. What we regard as useful, though painful, self-understanding, he will tend to perceive as a personal attack. June, even as she began to learn some new things about herself, was spared the pain of having to hear the "charges" read out loud.

Perhaps an even more important advantage of the ellipsed interpretation is that it helps to avoid the *spoiling effect* which verbal description will invariably have upon those transactions which are essentially emotional in the first place. This point may be clarified by noting that the most meaningful exchanges in human relationships take place by way of glances, physical pressures, and poignant silences. Adolescents often discuss with each other their techniques of kissing and caressing, partly to increase their skill for stimulating a better response from the next partner but also as a defense against consummation. They talk about "it" partly to keep from doing it and also to substitute for doing it. This analogy between certain aspects of romance and psychotherapy is chosen deliberately. Both relationships, if carried out properly, are more feeling than philosophy. Too many words can convert either of them into a sort of intellectual chess game, which is a superficially colorful but emotionally drab imitation of the real thing. This objection might be designated more simply as "defense by intellectualization," which does have the advantage of placing the blame on the patient but which does not show how the therapist has contributed to it by revealing his own skewed interest in the wonderful workings of the intellect. A practiced stance of intelligent objectivity may also conceal another cryptic resistance which is suggested by the romance analogy. Lingering too long in the realm of instinctual wishes can quickly become a highly eroticized activity in its own right, even though it is consciously designed to improve the patient's insight. There is no serious objection to the therapist's finding some satisfaction in the romance of psychotherapy—the work—if he is able to appreciate that this is entirely different than romantic psychotherapy.

Dr. L began to sense that he had moved too far in this direction when talking with June about her sensual feelings for her father. He identified her involuntary motoric thrust as a welling-up of sexual excitement which he had helped to induce by his leading questions and speculations. A direct explanation of his error would probably only have excited her further. In the following exchange he let her know elliptically that he had erred, why he had erred, and that in the future he expected better than this from himself and from her. Her transient, partial loss of impulse-control forced him to question his own motives for having led her so far in this particular direction. He raised *this* question openly, directing it to himself as well as to her, and established that both of them understood that—although talking about sex can be fun—it is not their primary reason for talking about it in psychotherapy. He corrected their shared tendency to instinctualize a process of therapy. When she returned for the next hour, she was attractively dressed in a way more appropriate to her age, but at the same time was less seductive and more controlled toward him. Even so she was able to speak more freely than before about these same matters. She felt safer.

Supervisors occasionally advise the therapist-in-training to offer the patient direct reassurance to allay the anxiety which is engendered by increased instinctual feelings which occur "in the transference." Saying to the patient, "You seem very frightened by these feelings which you are having for me. You needn't be afraid . . . I am not going to have intercourse with you," leaves something to be desired. Again, it implies that the problem is entirely the patient's, and it also suggests that the therapist has given some sober consideration to the possibility of actually seducing his patient. That he will not exploit the patient is another one of those things which, if it is true, is so true that it need not be said. If it is true and the therapist says it anyway, then his patient will suspect that he is either reassuring himself or being insufferably pompous and patronizing.

Another disadvantage to too much foraging among the instincts is that the patient may interpret this, as noted earlier in connection with history-taking, as a "sanction" for acting out these wishes. Depending upon how he is approached, the patient may find reason to believe that he might please his therapist by bringing him reports of *real* activities of the sort which they have both enjoyed talking about so much [22].

Finally, there is that tendency of the adolescent to be strongly attracted to life's more melodramatic aspects. From many sources of public information and sometimes from his own therapist, he can find the raw materials for a view of psychotherapy which will favor his turning the serious business of purposeful self-scrutiny into a silly imitation of living. The characterologically hysterical girl is a good case in point. She will often relish an opportunity to play the role of a mink-clad debutante who is stopping by for an hour on the couch. These spellbound girls have observed that patients in television plays are almost always wealthy, bright, adorable, blameless, and suffering very little from their tightly circumscribed amnesic disorders of single-trauma origin.

Sometimes we help our patients forget that the most worthy aim of psychotherapy is to leave it feeling better, not to feel better by remaining in it.

The theoretical purpose of the analytical interpretation is to help the patient understand how, and why, he protects himself from becoming aware of certain unconscious wishes, what they are, and how they affect his life. In general, his need to keep them out of mind stems from the loss of self-respect which would result from his acknowledging them as belonging to him. The question frequently arises as to how the patient can bear to face up to these things now, in treatment, when it has been so necessary to turn from them in the past. How great is the danger of "removing" his defenses? What does he get in return for what is lost?

There are some current ideas about these questions which are probably overrated. In the first place it is very difficult to remove a person's defenses *by intention.* It is just as hard to harm a patient in this way as it is to help him. It is true that very sick patients will frequently become worse in the course of psychotherapy, but this is often because of influences which act independently of the much vaunted bursting through of unconscious wishes and fears. These acute intercurrent psychotic episodes, so often ascribed to injudicious interpretation, are probably triggered much more frequently by such things as (1) the intensification of sexual and aggressive feelings which is inevitable in the extraordinary intimacy of the treatment relationship; (2) the fact of the patient's being hospitalized, which can in itself induce him to retire his own controls and become sicker; (3) circumstances in his environment which in some other way have increased the force of his forbidden wishes and fears or have diminished the effectiveness of his defenses; or (4) his misconstruing the therapist's motives for talking about such things at all. It is vanity for the therapist to exaggerate the potency of the interpretation itself, and foolish of him to neglect the other, less evident agencies which can influence the patient even more powerfully.

Therapeutic Value of Interpretation

Palliative replacement therapy for chronic deficiencies—relation to interpretation. Many apparently trivial matters acquire critical importance in the inpatient treatment of the adolescent. These are things which (1) help him to strengthen his adaptive resources, (2) weaken those maladaptive defenses which we believe he is able to relinquish without suffering a damaging degree of disorganization, and (3) provide much of the answer to the question about what the patient receives in exchange for the defenses which have been weakened or removed during the treatment experience.

Increasing numbers of psychiatrists seem to be abandoning the idea that insight is notably therapeutic in itself, except in the limited ways previously mentioned. In the course of intensive therapy the alcoholic patient may, for example, acquire a deep appreciation for certain determinants of his abnormal thirst for intoxicants: the unsatisfied longing for mother, for the breast and milk, warmth, pressure, and for that psychological enigma which we refer to as "love." These are things which he did not have enough of and which, in this hypothetical case, he perpetually strives to recover in different forms. His is an emotional deficiency disease. Knowing what caused his need does not repair the deficiency any more than understanding the pathophysiology of itching diminishes the need to scratch. This is also true to a greater or lesser degree of all kinds of mental illness. The more conventional concepts of causation in neurotic illness do not stress this same kind of deficiency.

In a classic formulation of a boy's oedipal neurosis, for example, the greatest importance is attached to his erotic strivings for his mother and to his fear of retaliation from father. Most people in our society grow up in a family which provides the conditions necessary to the development of an oedipus complex. The normal individual lives through this phase of psychological development in a way which enables him to care about other people, get married, have children, and work. From this we assume that there was something different about the neurotic patient's childhood experiences with his parents. As ordinarily considered, the patient was unable to "resolve" his oedipal wishes and fears because of insufficient or "improper" fulfillment of still earlier wishes, e.g., those relating to anal sensations or to the mouth-tactile-thermo-pressure longings of infancy. Ultimately, these disturbances are then explained as having resulted from a very early and persistent distortion, or deficiency, in the feelings of the parent(s) for the child. It is in this sense that the neurotic illnesses, etiologically, are also deficiency diseases. They are probably no more amenable to change in psychotherapy than the "functional" psychoses, but because they are less severe, or less obviously so, we can more easily get away with claims of having brought about great structural change in the neurotic patient.

There are some tight limitations girdling our efforts to provide "replacement therapy" for deep-reaching psychological deficiencies. The hypothetical "end-organs of the psyche" which have been so impaired become less and less responsive as the individual matures. To complicate matters further there are a number of highly influential social values which also restrict the permissible routes for administering replacement agents. Neither bottle-feeding nor a good mothering experience will cure the emotionally deprived adolescent. This is another way of saying that his unfulfilled needs of the present are no longer identical to their origins or, allegorically, that the effects of an avalanche are not reversed by returning the first fallen pebble to its initial position. At his age it is misleading to think of his dependency needs as "oral"; if they were still this, they could be gratified easily. The dependency of the infant is simple in comparison to the "dependency needs" of older children, adolescents, and adults. The fulfillment of these is correspondingly complex, especially in that full gratification at these ages requires the very careful nongratification of the primal biological longings.

It has been repeatedly implied that the adolescent will not accept direct instillations of affection, interest, help, or sympathetic understanding. This is not really true. What he cannot accept is a simple-minded adult's condensed and abstracted version of these things. These are psychological poison to him because he correctly interprets them as misguided efforts to assuage his infantile hungers. For him digestible replacement agents must be things which are appropriate to his age—things which he can *privately* experience as reflecting another person's feelings of interest in him and affection for him.

For example, he suspects we are interested in him if for no better reason than because we put up with all of his nuisance and nonsense and because we "keep picking" at him to do what is good for him while opposing what is bad for him. He is not blind to the fact that it would be much easier for us not to bother with him at all. By appearances alone he furiously resents our refusal to permit him to enter young manhood without finishing school or acquiring some skills which will improve his ability to take care of himself. His confidence in our high regard for him increases further when he sees that we not only are capable of putting up with *his* anger but that we are also sufficiently secure in our total feelings about him to tolerate *our* anger toward him—even when he gives us good cause to be angry. He appreciates being expected to do things which other people, including himself, have supposed him incapable of doing; and he also appreciates the opportunity to express his gratitude through complaints and protests.

It is quite true that most technical measures of therapy are effective only if therapist and patient mutually enjoy liking and respect for each other. However, the psychological process of liking someone cannot be prescribed, acted, or acquired by design. It is not the same as sentimentality, and it is not real if it must be planned, publicized, or talked about in detail. The adolescent who is realistically disciplined, or controlled, will be the first to recognize and respond to such measures as acts of interest and affection. He will almost always find it much easier to take than for the therapist to give.

SUMMARY: INSIGHT AND CHANGE. After these things have been appreciated, it is feasible to consider the therapeutic value of the intepretation and of the insight which it induces. Insight into either wishes or defenses is helpful only in the extent to which it is experienced in the present, in reality, in relationship to a contemporary person. The average adult continues to change a little bit throughout his entire life in the reciprocating influences between himself and others. He acquires some insights and undergoes some "structural change." It is intended that the psychiatric patient will experience more of these changes, and faster, in relationship to his therapist. In facilitating his increased understanding of himself, through verbal interpretations as well as by the many other influences which are brought to bear on his life, we simultaneously provide him with other things which are not significantly related to the content of the new insight. He looks upon his therapist as a wise person, as one who understands things about him which he himself did not even suspect. The therapist is someone who can be depended upon, whose values make better sense to the patient than many of his own, and who is more knowledgeable about practical things. Although the patient's old feelings, wishes, and fears are reexperienced in relationship to his therapist, they are not consummated in fact. He finds that his weaknesses are not exploited and his strengths not allowed to atrophy. It is impossible for the therapist to make an interpretive observation about his patient without implying advice and direction at the same time. He inevitably communicates something of his own opinions, of the values which he attaches to anything within the sphere of human affairs. The galling fact that these judgments are sometimes inferior to his patient's is usually therapeutic for both. He is someone to lean upon when the patient is unable to find this with anyone else. He will listen and, even more important to the adolescent patient, he will talk with him as well.

These are consolations which inevitably carry with them certain threats, but in discussions among ourselves we have become accustomed to hearing only of the threats of "being in therapy" and of the pain and sacrifice which it requires. The willingness to seek help is regarded as evidence of maturity. This is felt to be especially true of the psychiatrist, who is in the enviable position of being able to claim only the loftiest of motives for seeking personal treatment—to learn more about himself in order to become a more competent therapist. Very little is said of psychotherapy as a respite from the routine and tasking obligations of being an independent adult; as an arrangement which offers a reliable and accepting person to replace the parents whom he can no longer turn to as he did when he was a child. Little is said of the patient's satisfaction in finding himself genuinely liked by someone without having to "like him back," and in being able to like someone while protected by a special contract from the dangers and demands which are inherent in a mature, reciprocating love relationship between adults.

Because the standard circumstances of adult psychotherapy do not provide such covert protections for the adolescent he must make his own. He is so desperately aware of his need for help that he dare not call it by that name. He must represent it to himself and to others as an abominable infringement upon his personal rights by a meddling adult. He doesn't understand about "transference." When he becomes angry with his therapist he really thinks he's angry at his therapist, and he also acts like it.

He seeks a great deal more than self-understanding.

11

DEPARTURES FROM CONVENTIONAL VIEWS OF THERAPY

Testing for Facts, Attitudes, and Values

The adolescent keeps his eye on the therapist and looks for any values, attitudes, and ideals that might be adaptable to his own system. As noted earlier, these can be of service to him only when he is able to conceal from himself the fact that he has "copied" them; he must think of them as being his own, as having arisen spontaneously from within himself. Like us, he enjoys learning but despises being taught.

The guile with which he seeks satisfaction on countless points of confusion about what kind of person he should be is a means which is justified by this end. He pursues a similarly circumspect course in his quest for believable facts and information which he needs for developing the body of knowledge and values which will soon become such an important part of his adult identity.

He is greatly troubled by the vast disparity between his sexual-physical maturity on the one hand and his ignorance of the world on the other. He has the looks of a matinee idol and the savoir faire of a seven-year-old on the threshold of his first birthday party with girls. By his own admission he is easily a far more knowledgeable and skillful tester of reality than the wisest adult alive. How, then, does the unimpeachable expert on everything manage to ask a question about anything?

A fourteen-year-old boy in outpatient treatment came to one of his appointments with an acute situational problem which he introduced casually enough.

"I finally decided to give that girl a break . . . Took her to the movies last Friday."

"How did it go?"

"OK. Nothing special. You know how it is."

"Not really. I wasn't there."

"Well, she's a nice kid, but sort of dumb."

"How so?"

"Oh, just sort of a dumb kid, that's all. Actually, she's kind of stupid . . . well, I had my arm over the back of her seat—not touching her . . . exactly—and she got all nervous about it."

"Maybe she figured you were going to try to make out with her?"

"That's just what she thought! She said kids aren't supposed to make out[1] because they might catch a disease."

"What's she mean by that? Was she talking about catching a cold or syphilis or something like that?"

"I think so. Syphilis is what she made it sound like, but I wasn't about to ask her. She thinks you can catch something like that, oh . . . necking, like."

"How old is she?"

"She's only about thirteen, I think, but she *looks* older."

"Well, she's still pretty young to know everything. Maybe her parents or her family doctor told her it's possible to get syphilis by kissing somebody who has it."

"Her family doctor?"

"Or somebody else. But maybe they didn't tell her it just doesn't happen to kids who date the usual way, with kids they know. A person can't get it from someone else unless the other person has it—it doesn't spring up out of nowhere. Even then he wouldn't be very likely to get it from kissing anyway. It's one of those things there's not that much reason to worry about."

"I don't think she knows that; she's still pretty young. Of course, I'm not much older myself, but at least I know a few things."

Deep-seated, crippling neurotic fears about feelings of tenderness for other people are reactions which the adolescent is likely to cover with a disarming display of worldliness and sexual bravado.

Woody was a tall, good-looking, seventeen-year-old high school senior who had cultivated an impressive continental manner. He was referred for psychiatric evaluation after it was learned that he had "seduced" a

[1] In current usage the term *make out* does not mean what it did twenty years ago. It is a point of semantic confusion which has struck consternation into the heart of many a contemporary mother—a fact which perhaps explains its one-generation evolution in meaning from the frankly salacious to the merely naughty. It is somehow important that all such matters sound as bad as possible when uttered by the adolescent.

sixteen-year-old girl whom he had been dating sporadically for the preceding several months. There were several good reasons for his entering psychiatric treatment, but with regard to the referral complaint it was evident that he was as much the seduced as the seducer. He gave no resistance to describing the affair, explaining casually that he had "laid her a couple of times" and was worried for a while that he might have "knocked her up." He expressed relief that "she finally had her period," following which most of the trouble blew over. His laconic, cryogenic handling of the pertinent anatomy and physiology tended to divert attention from one glaring omission. In his thorough discourse on her reproductive apparatus, he had neglected to mention the name of the girl who owned it or any of the feelings which he and she might have about each other.

"You didn't tell me the girl's name."

"Oh. Susan. Sue is what they call her."

"What do you call her?"

"Huh? I call her Sue. Why?"

"Why not? I was just wondering if there was a girl attached to all those organs you were talking about. From the way you told it, I couldn't get much of an idea what kind of a girl she is. Do you like her?"

"Like her! What do you mean? Yeah, I guess I like her all right. What are you asking me that for? Why wouldn't I like her?"

"You told me you laid her, but you didn't tell me you liked her. There's a difference."

"Well sure, I like her—better than most. I don't date very much."

"I got the impression you do. You mentioned earlier that you run around quite a bit."

"That's mostly with some of the guys I know at school. Oh, we go over to a dance every now and then . . . pick up some broads . . . things like that."

"You don't usually ask girls for dates ahead of time?"

"I don't go for that . . . stuff. You know."

"No, I don't."

"There's something the matter. They see you driving around town, they think you're the coolest citizen in the county. Then you go out with them and you can't . . . well . . . you can't just sit there."

"Why, what's the matter?"

"You don't know what you're supposed to say. They think you're so great . . . Hell, I don't know!"

"You'd just as soon they don't find out what you're like? What you think you're like? Is that what you mean?"

"That's what I mean. I don't even know what I'm supposed to like them *for*. It's real easy to lay them, but I never know what to talk about. They might find out—you know—like what a jerk you are."

For the adolescent to admit to any doubts about the validity of his own facts, attitudes, and values is a most quisling approach to the task of developing an identity. He speaks with absolute authority on all issues and brooks no rebuttals, or at least not publicly. It is sometimes several days or more before we recognize that *on his own* he has, by sheerest coincidence, acquired a new attitude which corresponds with blueprint accuracy to the one which we had vainly asked him to consider just a short time before.

Gwen, fourteen years old, waged a major campaign against attending an optional but highly desirable group activity, a trip to a local carnival. Although her refusal was accepted by her therapist without special comment, she was unable to drop the subject, and angrily announced in every corner of the ward her absolute refusal to attend. She made such an issue of it that it became necessary for her therapist to search for what was really troubling her.

After dragging across a few red herrings, which failed to distract, she finally came to the point with a passionate objection to being "forced" into public association with the Negro attendants. She rushed onward in her denunciation of the Negro race and finally, revealingly, declared that "no white girl could sink any lower than to be seen in public with a colored man." In context with such holy indignation, "colored man" was an oddly ambivalent choice of epithets.

Further exploration revealed that her racial prejudice had a solid basis in the socioeconomically depressed and despised status of her own family and in her personal feelings of sexual guilt. Although these matters were dealt with in time, an equally important issue took precedence. Although her diatribe had been intemperately dogmatic in content, her voice and gaze betrayed her uncertainty about this attitude. As the smoke cleared away, she remarked sullenly, "You don't agree with me—you think I'm wrong to feel that way."

This observation, though accurate, was partly a projection. Her therapist took this opportunity to confirm quietly her suspicion that he did not agree with her personally but regarded this as no barrier to their continuing to work on a problem which didn't seem to make very good sense to her either. He commented on the unexplained intensity of her feeling and suggested that it might have to do with something more important than skin color. This led her to a preliminary examination of some of her feelings of being sexually debased and of deep shame for the black reputation which she had acquired in her own neighborhood. She accepted this without comment and returned quietly to the ward. On the following morning she was waiting at the ward door to inform her therapist that she had attended the carnival and had especially enjoyed the company of Mr. Y, a Negro, "Because he's not like the others."

A Special Use of the Transference

The adolescent's transference can be used to foster a particular developmental process which will work best when it is not interpreted. Fraiberg [12] comments that the adolescent crisis occurs when the youngster replaces the incestuous love object (parent) with a nonincestuous choice. She follows Katan in observing further that the postpubertal phase of adolescence, which is distinguished by the youngster's having "removed" most of his love interest from the parent to another person [24], makes possible the development of the "transference neurosis." This, she notes, is an entirely different state than prevails with the pubertal child.

The therapist of the adolescent can greatly abet this normal process by simply being someone other than his young patient's parent. The youngster who has been unable to direct his erotic and loving fantasies to someone outside of the family will find a rich opportunity to do so in the extraordinarily intimate treatment relationship.

One gets the feeling at times that this gratuitous effect is one of the most helpful of all the treatment forces for a number of pubertal and midadolescent girls. So many of them are referred for treatment after they have become unable to tolerate the intensified wishes toward father which accompany the onset of puberty. For a while the young girl with this kind of problem can hardly speak of anything but her hatred and disgust for him. In this early phase of psychotherapy she treats her therapist as a sympathetic confidante. A little later she becomes sulky, petulant, and defiant with him, just as she was toward her father, and soon after this is vehemently but somewhat anxiously protesting these feelings of anger and disgust for her therapist exclusively.

It is perhaps here that the popular counsel against interpreting the positive transference is meant to apply. A minimum of formal treatment effort is required of the therapist at this point. The most important thing is that he continue to exist and to see his patient. She may be disturbed and defensive in reaction to her own feelings about him, but he is still a much safer "object" than her own father.

Occasionally she may need an extra boost through this crisis with some glancing references to her irrational defensiveness and its origins. "Well, I seem to be disgusting you just as much as your father used to, and you're so convincing about it I almost believe it, but not quite. I know you like me—what's so wrong with that? And while we're on that subject, I have to say I don't find your father quite as horrible as you describe him."

At about this same time she will also become involved in a passionate romance with some boy of her own age, usually one who is an impossible candidate for a consummate love relationship. This is puppy love and it is not a joke. All the torments of feeling are gradually diverted to this saintly Abelard of a boy friend. Her anger, previously aimed at father and therapist for being so disgusting, acquires some additional targets and a new rationale. She accuses her therapist, teachers, nurses, or any other available adults of trying to break up her romance. She carries on as though we condemn her utterly for daring to love someone else, and in the name of humanity we are truly obliged to accord her a merciful measure of disapproval. To do less than this is to slight the importance of her "affair"—to treat it as an insignificant girlish crush. She deserves the tribute of being denied her demands for full and libertine access to the company of her boy friend. It is a demonstration of our respect for the sincerity and validity of her feelings for him. These prohibitions, of course, also serve a genuine practical purpose. The need to prove that her love is for someone else may be great enough to force her into proving it concretely by acting it out sexually. Adequate prohibitions from responsible adults will usually substitute for this admirably by supporting the fantasy "I love that boy so much, I've really got them worried . . . their concern proves that I love him, I love him, I love him!"

This love is soon replaced by another one, and then still another. After a year or two of this she usually persuades herself that it really is possible for her to love someone else and that the associated sexual feelings are not so dreadful as she had once, defensively, wished and feared they would be.

Her angry disgust with father (and therapist) fall away and are gradually replaced by more tolerant attitudes. With all this new-found worldliness she becomes a little condescending and scornful. Her references to father now suggest that he has suddenly aged about thirty years, and she assumes a pitying attitude toward the waning of his youthful vigor and strength. Her mother, whom she had perceived a few months earlier as a raving beauty, seems to have grown gray and withered. The therapist meets a similar fate in her fantasies, although his official status as a non-incestuous love object does not yet require that he be rendered a doddering old man. He will still be needed as an occasional reference point for a while longer.

This particular phase of treatment can be most difficult for parents to tolerate, and often it is more of a strain for the therapist than he would care to acknowledge. Adolescents, with their rather contemptible pride in their own youth, begin to feel sorry for us, and we, for our part, are at least a little resentful that they should desert us, after all we've done for them.

PREFERRED SEX OF THE THERAPIST. There are probably no useful generalizations about the eternal question of the preferred sex of the therapist. There are advantages and disadvantages to the patient's having a therapist of the same or opposite sex. Although it may be a matter of personal prejudice, it has often seemed that Katan's "removal" process for the adolescent girl is facilitated by her having a man therapist. It should follow that boys would do better with women therapists, but experience suggests that this is less likely to be the case. Social and individual conscience-prohibitions are much stronger against mother-son than against father-daughter incest, which is convincingly reflected in the fact that the latter is acted out far more frequently than the former. The commonly presumed reason for this, to the general effect that the boy has more to lose in consequence of his incestuous wishes, need not be elaborated here. Even at a prosier level of reflection we can appreciate that the adolescent boy's endeavor to prove himself a young bull would be seriously hampered by his being placed in a subordinate position to a woman therapist. And the woman therapist, because of some of the same attributes which attracted her into such an ambitious profession as psychiatry,[2] may be relatively intolerant of the boy's efforts to assume a dominant position in relation to her.

In any event, the sex of the therapist is far less important than his individual character. During evaluation and planning for treatment, many adolescents will say this directly when asked about their preference for a man or woman therapist. "I don't know . . . it doesn't matter that much . . . just so it's someone nice . . . actually, I don't want either one . . ."

Therapeutic Value of High Expectations

The greatest single environmental force in a youngster's development is the collective *expectations* of the people with whom he lives. There is a certain perverse logic in the fact that this force, being of the first order of importance, is also the last to be given serious theoretical consideration in the work of psychotherapy. It is somehow looked upon as commonplace to the point of being vulgar.

Sanctions for superego lacunae. To align this idea of the therapeutic import of positive expectations with prevailing concepts, it might be paraphrased as a comprehensive group of attitudes which the therapist holds toward his patient and which he unavoidably communicates to him. Positive expectations provide sanctions for ego and superego matrices. As a psychological *process* which occurs between people, it is identical to the one delineated by Szurek [31] and Johnson [22], where it is used with reference to the providing of sanctions for superego lacunae.

The difference between the two processes lies in their precisely opposite effects on the outcome, moralistically speaking, of a youngster's personality development. The parent, by inadvertently revealing some of his most deep-seated feelings about his child, unwittingly encourages the youngster to favor certain ways of managing his own wishes.

[2] In fairness to distaff psychiatrists, no great claims are being made for the secure masculine identification of the men who enter this field, either.

Glenda, aged twelve, was referred to the clinic when it was learned that she had been having sex play with her pet dog for many months. As her mother reported, "I finally discovered that this is why she's been spending so many hours up in her room with that dog. I was suspicious for a long time, sometimes I stood outside of her room and listened, and it *sounded* like there were some funny things going on in there. Maybe it wasn't the right thing to do, but I finally decided I'd better see what it was all about, so I looked through the keyhole . . . I couldn't believe my eyes . . . I went back downstairs and thought about it, and thought about it, and I just ate my heart out for a week wondering what to do. I guess I hoped she'd realize she was doing wrong so I wouldn't have to say anything to her . . . but anyway, I thought it would be best to wait a while and give her a chance . . . but it didn't work. I checked up on them several more times just to make sure, but it was still hard for me to believe it was really true. Well, that's when I decided the thing had gone on long enough, so I went in there and beat her within an inch of her life!"

Glenda's mother had been a very shy and isolated girl in her early life. She recalled that during her elementary years she had suffered from a severe dog phobia. This fear "reversed" at puberty and she became intensely interested in animals of all sorts, which led to her keeping a number of dogs and cats as pets. Her preoccupation with zoology "didn't leave me much time for a social life." But her own mother encouraged the interest and commended her for devoting her time to studies instead of wasting it foolishly on boys.

It was otherwise with the mother's sister who was two years younger. She had always been thought of as the black sheep of the family, so regarded because of her indifference to studies and her allegedly promiscuous behavior with boys. Glenda's mother recalled having been bitterly jealous of this sister and admitted that she was still deeply resentful of her because "she was never punished. My mother hated the things she did, but Nan was always her favorite anyway."

At the conclusion of the interview Glenda's mother blandly inquired, "Now, what should I do about that dog? Should I let them spend so much time together up in her room, or would it just be best to have him destroyed?"

It had not occurred to her that there might be a more conservative course of action than the extreme measures which she proposed.

At one point in the evaluation interview with Glenda, she burst into tears and wailed, "I don't know whose fault it is. I don't know what my mother wants me to do!"

Without realizing it, Glenda's mother, though a stable person by outward appearances, was helping to maintain this adjustment partly by continuing to "live out" some of her own childhood conflicts through her daughter. In this rather typical example the girl was unconsciously expected to behave in ways which would provide vicarious satisfaction of the mother's unfulfilled and unsettled sexual and aggressive wishes.

SANCTIONS FOR EGO GROWTH. This same mechanism operates also in the growing child's unconscious choice of preferred mechanisms of defense and other measures of adaptation.

Many grade school children are referred to guidance clinics because of low scholastic achievement and aggressive behavior with classmates. Such a youngster will often externalize the cause of his trouble, protesting that he is doing poor school work because his teacher is no good and that he gets into fights because other kids are always picking on him. When the parents of such a youngster are seen, they are usually found to be using identical words to defend identical explanations.

In normal development a vast variety of major and minor ego lacunae, ego assets, and superego assets are similarly sanctioned, along with the superego lacunae. The final effects on the child attract little clinical attention unless they include behavior which is illegal, immoral, or otherwise unhealthy.

A junior medical student (who was not a psychiatric patient) described to colleagues a difficult problem which he had in learning to perform lumbar punctures.

"I never could work with my hands. Long as I can remember, I'd always find a way out of doing any work with my hands. Last year, when I found out I was next on the list for a lumbar puncture, I panicked . . . I knew I could never do it . . . I couldn't think of any way out, and I got so miserable just thinking about it that I got to wondering *why* I couldn't do it. It didn't stand to reason. My father was a master carpenter, an old school cabinetmaker. He started teaching me carpentry before I went to school, and the more I thought about it, the more I remembered. Well, what he gave me was a graduate course in cabinetmaking. Every time I'd so much as cock a hammer to hit a nail, he'd snatch it out of my hand and show me the *right* way to do it. He did such a good job of showing me, I got damn few chances to hit a nail. By the time I got to kindergarten, there was no doubt in my mind . . . I was no good with my hands. The night before I was supposed to do my first puncture, I went up to the anatomy lab, when no one was around to take the needle out of my hand, and I put one of the articulated skeletons off on the floor, and I did lumbar punctures right-handed, left-handed, and standing on my head. I burned a picture of that spinal column into my head that will stay there the rest of my life. The next day I didn't even see the patient's skin . . . just the vertebral processes, the meninges, and the spinal canal. No trouble. No trouble ever since. I still can't hammer a nail, but I can do a lumbar puncture blindfolded."

This student's father, in trying to teach his son too much, and too quickly, had seriously impaired his confidence in his ability to work with his hands. Unintentionally, he had sanctioned an ego lacuna. However, he was also the kind of man, as the student commented a few moments later, who was not inclined to let anything get in his way once he had made up his mind to do something. By his own example, rather than by teaching, he had also encouraged the development of this particular ego asset in his son. He was an intelligent, ambitious man whose own hunger for higher education had been frustrated by financial problems. Although proud of his trade he wanted none of his children to be craftsmen. He got this message across to them in spite of his apparent eagerness to teach them his skills.

Whether the outcome of a parent's child-rearing efforts is predominantly delinquency, symptom formation, character neurosis, or normality, it will inevitably be found that *unconscious parental expectations* have played an overwhelming causal role. These expectations are enforced by the parent's power to confer or withhold the loving acceptance which is, to the child, as important as life itself. As long as he holds any hope of earning it, he will do anything to please the parent who has it to give.

Children are relatively immune to an elder's earnest little lectures on right and wrong and on the kind of a person we want you to be when you grow up. These ritual pep-talks serve another purpose. If they do not square with the expectations which the parents unintentionally reveal by nonlanguage signals, the youngster may be confused and upset, but will usually dismiss what he is *told* in favor of what he *understands*. Like his parents, he becomes adept at parroting the proper words and ideas, but he will not betray their deeper wishes. He will give them what they mostly want.

Personality of the therapist. These expectations are communicated just as effectively and inadvertently with respect to normal adaptive personality processes. This is why psychotherapy cannot be taught as a system of techniques which can be relied upon to transcend the impact of the therapist's own personality on the young patient. The adolescent reads us too well. He can be counted upon to respond far more to what we expect of him than to what we *say* we expect of him. In therapy there is no value in telling him that he must not drive the family car if he is then sent home on pass to a father who has repeatedly boasted, "That boy drives like a devil. He can corner a car at seventy without losing the shoulder . . . but some day he's going to kill himself if he doesn't take it easy."

Nor will the therapist help the youngster become more independent and self-determining if, without realizing it, he is deriving too much satisfaction from the patient's flattering dependence upon him. Few of us would challenge the notion that the psychotherapist often has some very special problems of his own in this general area. He is, naturally, deeply interested in psychopathology and in dynamic personality processes. Indeed he could not be a psychiatrist if he were not. This professional asset becomes a dismal liability, however, when his fascination with these things overpowers his determination to free the patient of their harmful elements as swiftly and fully as possible. The psychotherapist is under obligation to consider this an occupational hazard, one which he must guard against consciously and continuously if he is to avoid sanctioning continued illness in his patient, and thus encouraging an interminable course of nonprogressing therapy.

A boy who continues to fail in school because of an unconscious fear of surpassing and thereby destroying an envied sibling must be approached from at least two sides. Helping him to understand the origins of his need to fail can be most helpful to him, but his identity as a proved failure, and the character processes which preserve it, will require much more active management. It will not be enough for the therapist to remind him that, "it's also important for you to do your school work," while neglecting to inquire about study habits, attentiveness in class, completion of assignments, and other details of the real business of the day.

On the other hand, the compulsive, perfectionistic youngster will have to be approached with an equal degree of determination applied in the opposite direction. Interpretation alone will have little effect on his rigid scheduling of work, the much too cruel demands which he makes upon himself, the passive-aggressive aim of his superior achievements, and similar. For him, also, a realistic application of authority and discipline will often constitute the only meaningful, effective behavioral interpretation of the defensive aspects of his approach to school.

Intensive Infrashort Therapy

As mentioned earlier there are occasions when the diagnostic interview with a particular youngster unexpectedly develops into an extremely intensive course of therapy. Although it may all take place during a single interview, one lasting for perhaps as long as two or three hours, it is not necessarily any less intensive or effective than many months of treatment for another patient. In such cases, however, it is obviously far more difficult than usual to draw believable inferences about the means by which the therapeutic result was accomplished. As a rule one can recognize at the completion of one of these unplanned sessions that virtually every known force of therapy has entered into the process. The fact that *something* important has happened can seldom be demonstrated to the satisfaction of others; it is a subjective judgment which the therapist makes mostly on the basis of his having been emotionally moved himself by the experience, and only to a much lesser extent on an eventually favorable outcome which might well, indeed, have been merely fortuitous. Because of the very brevity of such a transaction many of the most therapeutic events which take place in it are necessarily extraverbal, ellipsed, only implied, and glancingly touched upon, but nevertheless—in some unexplained manner—deeply and mutually understood by patient and therapist alike. Surely there is no experienced clinician who has not handled such cases many times, particularly if he sees many pubertal and early adolescent patients. It is not surprising that we hear so little about them, however, because of our conditioned tendency to equate effective therapy with long-term therapy, and also for the very simple reason that it seems almost impossible to describe with words something which takes place largely outside the dominion of verbal language. It is worth attempting, nevertheless, in order that we not despair unnecessarily of accomplishing something worthwhile with the patient who, for any of a variety of reasons, does not appear to be a candidate for any treatment beyond that which can be provided in one or two outpatient visits.

Drew had just turned fourteen when he was referred by his natural father and stepmother for psychiatric evaluation. They complained that he had been failing in school for the past eighteen months and had become increasingly withdrawn during the same period. For several weeks prior to referral, he had been virtually mute. Although he attended school, the teachers reported that he seemed totally preoccupied in class and was accomplishing nothing. They referred also to his glassy-eyed look. His stepmother complained particularly of his passive noncooperation in performing routine household chores and of his apparent lack of feelings about anything or anyone.

His natural parents were divorced when he was four years old. He lived alone with his natural mother for the next eight years, and it was evident that he had suffered greatly in this relationship. His mother suffered a chronic, remitting psychotic illness. At times she had violent outbursts of temper and threatened to send Drew to an orphanage. At other times she was excessively solicitous and seductive toward him. His feelings for her were, of course, intensely ambivalent, but they somehow managed to survive together until he reached puberty, the changes of which were totally disruptive to the pathological but still workable balance of their relationship. After a stressful series of court actions, he was transferred to the custody of his natural father.

His stepmother, though a hysterically neurotic woman, tried very hard to be a good mother to him. She expected too much of herself and slowly became discouraged and angry when things did not work out as idyllically as she had hoped. He was too "detached." He would not "respond" to her. She could not "get through to him," and within a short time she came to dread being alone in the same room with him. Drew's father was a well intended but rather passive person who managed to skirt the family crisis by increasing his working hours.

During the first evaluation interview with Dr. N, Drew looked depressed but was otherwise emotionally unexpressive. He responded to all questions with a dreamy, indifferent head gesture. His first several efforts to speak ended in complete "blocking." Dr. N began to review aloud what he knew of the history, asking questions, interjecting guesses and inviting replies as he went along. He picked details not only from the history but also from what little he had already learned of the father and stepmother. He regularly referred to his own surmises about Drew's ideas, fantasies, and feelings, which were drawn from little more than the faintest flickering of facial expressions, change in bodily attitude, and other extraverbal routes.

"After your parents were divorced, you and your mother lived alone. I've talked with your father and stepmother, and I have some ideas about it all, but not too much . . . mostly general things with no details. Can you remember back to the time when your parents got divorced? Maybe you can't, because when I just now asked you about that, your whole face flattened out, as though you've found a way to keep from getting hurt all over again by what happened then. This is starting in the middle instead of the beginning. Did your folks tell you why they brought you over here today?"

"Yes . . . to-to-to . . ." He was unable to go on.

"To help you with your problems? That's what the kids are usually told . . . it's true . . . but usually nobody has much idea what those problems are. I'm trying to figure out whether you can tell me about them, or could tell me about them if you wanted to, or if you want to but just can't. I think you can't right now but maybe later. It'd probably work best if I'd just do some guessing—OK? There's not too much to guess on, except these few things I've heard about. How you feel now is important—looking at you, I'd say you feel terrible. You feel this way most of the time? Real sad or something like that. Can you tell me?"

Drew shook his head 'no,' glanced at Dr. N, and then dropped his eyes in a faintly thoughtful frown, all of which suggested that his reply was more than evasive compliance.

"I guess not, or at least now now. Maybe that's the way you used to feel, but it got to be too much . . . this happens to people. They have to quit feeling . . . but maybe the way you are right now is even worse —not feeling anything at all—with nothing hurting and nothing feeling good—with nothing but two or three daydreams that keep going on in your head. They probably aren't any fun either, but at least they don't bother you. Is this about right, or am I way off?"

He bobbed his head in a distinct, wondering affirmative.

"You feel nothing, is that what you mean?"

"Yes. I don't feel. No . . ."

"But you used to . . . feel a lot—feel too much. Is that right too?"

"Yes."

"Can you tell me what it was like then . . . anything what it was about?"

He looked momentarily troubled, but this quickly yielded to the previous masklike expression.

"I'll keep guessing and talking. It's better than both of us sitting here. You tell me if I say the wrong thing. When you were younger and living with your real mother . . . I don't know how much anyone has told you about her, or how much you've guessed about her, but this is no time for secrets anyway . . . from what I've heard it sounds like she was sick, you know, mentally ill. You probably knew that."

He nodded "yes."

"It doesn't sound very good. There's one thing here about a time when she whipped you with an electric cord and said she was going to send you away to a prison for boys. That's when you were about six or seven years old . . . remember that? I guess you didn't, until I reminded you about it. Those were a lot of years, and not very good ones, I'd guess . . . Can you remember much about them or is it a sort of blank . . . everything gone?"

"Blank."

"Completely? Can you remember anything from then? You don't have to tell me what you do remember if you don't want to, but it's important for me to know if you *can* remember."

"Not much. Hardly anything. Just a little."

"You look like you're thinking about one of them right now, something you can remember. There are some reasons why it might be good if you'd tell me what you can remember. You don't have to, but I'm asking you for a reason—what I think is a good reason."

"She gave me . . . she gave me . . . she gave me . . ." He blocked again, and the skin around his eyes and over his cheek bones turned a vivid, bluish red. His eyelids glittered with tears, but the rest of his face remained masklike.

"That's what I mean . . . You started to say something you remembered, but it's easy to see it made you feel awful. You shoved it away, and now you look like you're feeling nothing at all, again. Try to tell me, do you know that you started to feel something?"

"No . . ."

"You said no but not very certainly. Maybe you're not sure. The way I can tell is because your eyes got red and wet, and to me it looked like you were almost crying, but I don't know why. Maybe because you started to feel sad, or mad? You started to say she gave you something. A while back I said something about how she was mentally sick, and it could be that you thought I was criticizing her or saying something bad about her. I'm just guessing again, but maybe you started to tell me about something nice she did for you, to let me know that she wasn't all sick. Living with her wasn't all bad. It *has* to be true that she was good to you sometimes . . . I know that. What did she give you that you were thinking about a minute ago?"

"Christmas. Some Christmas. Back then . . . it was a toy monkey with real fur . . ." His head jerked involuntarily in a gesture of disparagement, and a tear spilled from each lower lid and ran down his cheeks. His face was still expressionless. Dr. N had to resume Drew's part of the interview, as he was unable to continue.

"It's not much, a toy monkey . . . not really . . . but it was a lot then, and sometimes it still seems like a lot. That's because—I don't know how to say it best—it's not just a toy monkey, but it stands for things that make a big difference to you. You don't like to cry, do you? It's embarrassing all right, but I still think it's better than nothing."

A fleeting expression of curiosity and perplexity passed across his face.

"Maybe you can't tell? Well, you're crying; at least you've got some tears there. Didn't you know you just lost a few tears? They're on your cheeks now."

Drew touched his cheek and then looked unbelievingly at his fingers. He saw that they were wet, then dropped his hand and shrugged briefly.

"Well, I didn't know that at first . . . I thought you knew you cried a little bit there for a second . . . you don't seem to be used to it . . . has it been a long time since you cried?"

"I'm not crying. I never did. I've seen other people cry. This is the first time I ever . . ."

"You did, but you don't remember. It's like a lot of the things you've forgotten. Well, at least I'm glad to see it's possible for you to feel something. Maybe you don't have to be so scared of it now—having some feelings, at least while you're here in the office talking with me. I wish you'd take a chance on it, trying to remember some of the things you haven't been able to think about for a long time . . . take a chance on it if you can."

"What? What things?"

"I don't know exactly what. Let's see, thinking about the last year, or the last two or three years or maybe longer—before you came to live with your father or stepmother. You told me one of the good things—a Christmas present she gave you. Do you still have it?"

"No."

"What happened to it? Do you know?"

"I don't know."

"You're thinking about it . . . maybe you can remember. You had the toy monkey for a long time, I imagine. You were a little boy then, so you probably took it to bed with you, and carried it around sometimes. Little kids do that. Do you remember?"

"I didn't do that. It was on a shelf . . ."

"Why? Try to explain it to me. What was it one the shelf for?"

"She kept it there."

"Who is 'she'? I know who you mean, but it would help if you'd just go ahead and tell me."

"She said it was there to keep it clean, so it would stay nice."

"That's the reason she gave? It's a reason. It doesn't make much sense but it's a reason. Maybe there was another reason that you knew more about than she did. It's not very easy for you to tell me who 'she' is, is it?"

"No . . . my mother."

Now there were no tears, and his face was barren of feeling.

"Do you see her now, anymore, since you left there? Do you get any letters or telephone calls or visits or anything like that?"

"No."

"What happened to the toy monkey when you left there? Did you bring it with you?"

"No."

"You remember now? Did you get rid of it or something?"

"I cut it up with a butcher knife in the middle of the night. I got out of bed when she was sleeping and got up on a chair and got it off the shelf. Then I stuck holes in it with a knife and squeezed out all the stuffing on a piece of newspaper. Then I went down in the basement and put it in the fire and watched it burn up."

"Was that after you found out about going to live with your father?"

"I don't know . . . Yes."

"You cut up the toy monkey . . . you remembered that. Do you remember how you felt then? It sounds like you were mad . . . real mad. Did you plan it ahead of time, or just get mad all of a sudden in the middle of the night?"

"I don't know if I was mad. I thought . . . well . . . I can't remember how old I was then."

"That was a couple of years ago. You were about eleven or twelve years old. Why? You started to say something about why you cut up the toy monkey, then you stopped and wondered how old you were then. Why is that? Are you thinking that you were too old to have the thought —whatever it was?"

"I thought if I cut up the toy monkey she would die."

"I see what you mean. But she didn't die, did she?"

"No. Not yet."

The interview went on for about two hours, and Drew gradually became more articulate and relaxed, but was still excessively composed and inexpressive. With more of this same kind of leading, touching, retreating, gentle urging, and knowledgeable guessing, Dr. N was able to carry Drew through a tortuous and at times peripheral exploration of many things which he had not been able to tolerate consciously for a long time. Drew was able to sample feelings from the extremes of the fused love and hatred which he felt for his mother, of the overwhelming sense of loss which came with the consummation of the literal rejection which he had so long anticipated, and of the persistent dread and guilt connected with his wishing and fearing that his furious destructive fantasies might actually destroy her. He was helped to acknowledge the almost total renunciation of feeling which he had resorted to in defense against a sense of desolation which he could not live with. These things were "updated" to the present as much as possible in an effort to show him that they were running his life.

Before the end of the interview he was able to remember some of the actual circumstances and feelings associated with his father's desertion. He had little difficulty in consciously formulating the dormant wrath and resentment against the stepmother for stealing his father away, and he feared that she, too, would retaliate against him. He fought her with passively aggressive measures even as he tried to protect himself by outward compliance. In her great eagerness to do her duty as a mother, he found a weakness which he could not resist exploiting. He frustrated her by failing wherever she wanted him to succeed and by succeeding where she expected him to fail. The fact that he never caused her the "big trouble" she expected was more difficult for her to accept than his refusal to do the little things she expected. These elements of the relationship with the stepmother developed against a background of mistrust and tortured ambivalence which he had acquired and transferred from the long past experience with his natural mother.

His stepmother's affectionate overtures also frightened him because he had learned not to touch or be touched. Having absorbed much of his psychotic mother's angry and sadistic feeling for him, he was able to deny having lost her by intensifying his own cruel, hateful feelings for himself and by compelling others to do the same. He despised and injured himself. He provoked his stepmother into rages which she herself could hardly bear, even though he withstood them extremely well.

He forced his father to whip him for laziness, and his disgrace deepened even further when his school grades fell from average to failing shortly after the change of custody. Although these things were touched upon in a single, relatively brief interview, Dr. N had little idea about how much it might mean to Drew, how much it might help, or if it would help at all, and if it did help, why? These hopes and misgivings were openly aired in the "therapeutic monologue" which terminated the interview:

"You haven't even asked me why I wanted you to talk about all these things in the first place. It could be you just don't care, but my guess is, you know the reason for it all as well as I do . . . maybe even better . . . anyway, I'm glad you haven't asked me because I don't think I could give an answer . . . how to say it? Maybe you have a little better idea about where you stand now, and that *might* help . . . just how, I don't know, but it might . . . You've got a lot of hate and things, sadness too, that you can't help having. I can understand that, you can, too, but one of the worst things about it all is, well, there's no place to put the blame. Your mother is sick, very sick . . . That might not make you feel any better about it, but for whatever it's worth let me tell you this: She couldn't help the things she did, the way she felt . . . maybe you can. And one thing more: If there is someone to blame, that someone isn't you. You've been hurting yourself a lot and you don't deserve it, it made a certain amount of sense then, but a lot less now . . . You keep her feelings inside of you because it's a way to keep her. Fourteen years isn't old enough to go on your own as much as you'll have to, Drew, but there isn't much choice, is there? I think your father and stepmother will help you as much as they can, but it won't be possible for them to know enough about it to do the right thing always. If these things are going to be done, you'll have to do most of them yourself. I'm not sure that you can do it, but I think maybe you can. Now, do you sort of understand what I'm talking about, or what . . . ?"

"I understand."

Drew's parents readily agreed to the recommendation for a private boarding school. It was made clear to them and to Drew that this should have a fair trial but that Dr. N would be readily available for further consultation should the need arise. Geographical problems precluded outpatient visits, and it was felt that this particular type of placement outside of the home, even without psychotherapy, held more promise for Drew than would outpatient treatment with his living at home. The decision was largely intuitive, as there was little objective evidence which could be invoked to justify the plan.

No word was heard from the family for almost two years. Then the stepmother called to report that she had once more become deeply concerned about Drew's condition. In the interim history over the telephone she reported that they had gone through with the school placement as planned. Since then, Drew had "gotten along beautifully." His grades went up to honor-roll level and stayed there. He was popular with his classmates and well liked and respected by the teachers; he had developed some strong interests in athletics, electronics, and geology. During the first summer vacation he got a job in a fruit orchard, where he worked hard and was able to save enough money to buy a secondhand car. The old tensions between him, his stepmother, and his father still persisted but to a lesser degree. Although they all kept a respectful distance from each other, Drew's external manner was at least a little friendlier and more cooperative.

His second year in school went equally well as did the second summer vacation. Then, toward the end of the vacation, his natural mother died. It was Drew's reaction to her death which had upset the stepmother and prompted her to call Dr. N again.

"He didn't even care. When they called and told me she'd died, I didn't think I'd be able to tell him about it, but when I finally got up my courage, he just shrugged it off . . . he wouldn't even go to the funeral. When his father and I were getting ready to go to the funeral, he was flopped out on the sofa listening to rock-and-roll and reading some paperback. I could have throttled him. It's still like that. She died three weeks ago, but you could never tell it by looking at him. Not a word, not a tear—just nothing! Maybe there's something wrong with me, Dr. N, but is that normal? Isn't he supposed to have some grief?"

Dr. N naturally had some ideas about Drew's reaction and because of these was apprehensive about seeing him at this particular time. However, the stepmother's feelings were so strong that it appeared likely that she would force some kind of damaging crisis unless helped. Dr. N advised her to tell Drew about their telephone conversation and to explain her reason for having called. He also urged her to ask him if he would be willing to come in for a return visit, for her sake if not for his own. She did this and then called back for an appointment, indicating that he had appeared indifferent to the idea but had agreed to go along with it.

Drew was interviewed first and, as it developed, rather briefly this time. The reasons for the referral were reviewed. He was keenly aware of his stepmother's deep concern about his lack of feeling, but he correctly regarded it as her problem.

The change in him was striking. Although his emotional expressiveness fell somewhat short of effervescence, he was at least articulate and significantly more tolerant of his own feelings than he had been two years before. He groused about his stepmother's interference: "She clucks around like an old hen." He was a little sheepish about the distress which he was causing her, but as one might expect, he was by no means entirely unhappy about it. It was soon evident that this was an emissary referral—that the acute problem was less Drew's than his stepmother's. Dr. N debated briefly about whether or not to approach the matter of the natural mother's death at all but finally decided that avoidance of the issue would make it even more conspicuous.

"But what about your mother's death, Drew? I'm asking more because I'm interested than worried. Your stepmother seems to go pretty much by what she can see and . . . well . . . I guess you know she's just not able to see into you very far."

Drew squirmed uneasily in his chair and made a minimizing body gesture, but said nothing.

"We don't *have* to go into this, but why not? It was almost two years ago when you were in here last, and that's a long time. Give me some idea, will you, if you can remember some of the things that we talked about then."

"I remember, all right."

"Oh. You've done some thinking on your own since then?"

"Yeah."

"Well, I guess that's all I really need to know to satisfy my curiosity. About your mother—you've been doing your grieving on your own . . . when nobody would know about it? Late at night . . . in bed?"

Drew nodded his head briefly, and then the tears came in profusion. He buried his face in his hands and wept quietly for several minutes. When he was finished, he yanked a handkerchief from his pocket and blew an appropriately raucous note of manly apology for his outburst.

"Are things going pretty well otherwise?"

"Real good. I got my driver's license this summer, put my old junker into pretty good running shape, too."

"Will they let you have it up at school?"

"They'll let me keep it up there, but you can't drive around town. I can drive it home on weekends now and then. I'm not that hot on the idea of coming home, but . . ."

". . . it makes a very nice drive?"

"Yup."

"Well, then, you'll let me know if anything comes up that I can help with?"

"OK. Thanks. So long."

Dr. N saw the stepmother briefly after reaching an essentially tacit understanding with Drew that attention would be focused on her worries rather than on his. She had privately withdrawn the referral complaint even before entering the office.

"I know he feels bad about his mother, but I just can't stand the way he acts sometimes. You'd think a big good-looking kid like that would be old enough not to hang around the house all the time. Oh, he's all right when his father's around, but when his father's gone, I just can't stand to be in the same house with him. If he comes in the front door, I go out the back . . . I can't even get to sleep at night till I'm sure he's asleep. I don't know what's the matter with him, anyway, but I've got to do something to get my mind off of him. Well, he goes back to school next week, so things will settle down then, I guess."

Some passing thought was given to advising her to seek outpatient treatment, but it was decided against mostly because of her desperate need to ascribe some of her own frightening wishes to him. Her seemingly total "rejecting" attitude toward Drew troubled him very little, because he sensed much more clearly than she that it masked some strongly positive feelings which, though not exactly maternal in nature, were still complimentary to him.

It is almost embarrassing to report this kind of case. At the time of initial evaluation Drew was regarded as "too sick" to tolerate and profit from intensive inpatient treatment on the Adolescent Service. He probably was. There were indications for separating him from his home and providing him with some type of residential care, and yet a state hospital program did not seem appropriate to his needs. The evaluation interview, as so frequently happens, rapidly evolved into about two hours of short-term, intensive psychotherapy. At one point or another, virtually every force of therapy had entered into an infinitely complex transaction between a psychiatrist and his patient. What might have seemed at times a reckless plunging into the deep unconscious, and which was exactly that on some points, did not precipitate further psychotic disorganization. It had, if anything, an opposite effect. On the surface the closing phase of the first interview and most of the second interview included little more than a few grin-and-bear-it platitudes from the "buck-up" school of psychiatry.

There is no way of knowing what might have happened if Dr. N had simply introduced himself, quickly scanned the history, asked a few questions, then advised that Drew be admitted to a private school. And yet, even though he could not prove it, he found reason to believe that this single interview had worked a profound effect on Drew. Two years later, when asked if he recalled any details of the earlier interview, Drew had replied with an emphatic affirmative which clearly advised that it would not be necessary to spoil, by wordy repetition, his poignant recollection of what had happened then.

Dreams and "Dreams"

Dreams are ordinarily of limited usefulness in treatment of the adolescent. After his doctor has accustomed him to the idea of using his dreams in therapy, he is usually willing enough to recount them and sometimes even eager to do so. He may also attempt with varying degrees of success to make associations to them. Too frequently, however, he seems inclined to do this a bit too knowingly or with a pensive sobriety which is suspiciously foreign to his usual manner.

Dream content which is reported literally will naturally provide information about emotional themes which are important to him, but more often than not this same information has already become available to both therapist and patient from his history, direct verbalizations, and behavior. In fact, one frequently gets the feeling that the somewhat too-informative dream which the patient reports at critical points in treatment has been suggested into consciousness by some treatment transaction of a day or two prior. This does not necessarily mean that the content of the dream is spurious, but only that it is a little too late to add significantly to what is already known. As with adult patients, the bringing of dreams to the treatment session may also serve the aims of resistance.

Ginny, seventeen years old, had made gratifying progress during eighteen months of psychotherapy. As she neared the completion of formal therapy, she began to reexperience disturbing erotic feelings toward her therapist. With the resultant increase in anxiety she fell into more frequent and longer silences during interviews and was having trouble finding her way out of this impasse. When she suddenly began to bring in a number of dreams, once again she became more comfortable and verbally productive.

She realized that dreams have psychological meaning and that by recounting them and associating to them in extensive detail she could persuade herself that she was fulfilling her treatment obligations. Her dreams were rich in transference themes but contained nothing which she did not already know. When it was pointed out to her that she was using her dreams defensively, her anxiety again increased. She then began to make a variety of bitter, random complaints about many things, and it was this series of apparently irrational and overdetermined complaints which really constituted her own type of free association.

She passionately criticized a movie which had dwelt on the subject of homosexuality to lengths which, she asserted, defeated the aims of art. She also began to criticize a roommate, of whom she was very fond, for her vanity and immodesty. Her doctor was reproached at times for his disinterest, at others for his overattentiveness, and at still others because he was "too serious about everything." From all of this it was soon possible to assemble the scattered pieces into a coherent picture which could then be held up for her to see. Many of the wishes and fears which had been so dutifully and hastily sketched in her dream reports thus acquired details, color, and the third dimension of "emotional meaning" for her.

Some of the "dreams" which the adolescent patient reports prove never to have been dreams at all. These can sometimes be recognized by their cohesiveness and their quite literal pertinence to current events. They do not violate the laws of reality as sleeping dreams ordinarily do, and they also seem exceptionally purposeful in the ways they are reported:

A fifteen-year-old boy of average intelligence and some experience in psychotherapy reported: ". . . in the dream you didn't want me to go home on a pass, but finally you changed your mind and let me go anyway. When I got there, my father started a big argument with me and there was lots of trouble, but after a while he felt better and everything quieted down and we all had a good time. When I got back here and told you about it, you were glad you decided to let me go on the pass." As the therapist offered no immediate observations on this well-constructed dream, it was necessary for the patient to repeat it several times during the interview. In his frustration he finally wondered aloud, "I was thinking about asking to go home this weekend . . . Do you think the dream means it would work out all right?"

It turned out that the boy had not fabricated the dream. The narrative which he reported had occurred to him as a fantasy when he was in the process of awakening that same morning, which by his standards qualified it as a dream. He had also sensed immediately, of course, that it might have a somewhat greater commercial value if presented as a dream.

Celia, a sixteen-year-old inpatient, reported the same dream on three consecutive days:

"It is night time and I am in my bed getting ready to go to sleep. The room is dark and the only light I can see is coming through the door. Then I see a man standing in the doorway, and I am so scared I can't even move or say anything . . . he looks like he is going to come in and get me, but finally he goes away."

"Does the man look like someone you know?"

"It's hard to tell because it's so dark . . . Well, his outline reminds me of Mr. S, you know . . . that new attendant."

"I see. Has Mr. S ever come to your doorway after lights out? I mean really, not just in a dream?"

"Not very often."

"But when?"

"Just the last couple of nights, making rounds."

"Oh? But staff men aren't supposed to make rounds on the girls' side after lights out."

"Maybe he doesn't know that. I thought about telling him, but . . . well . . . I was too scared to say anything."

"Well, I'll look into that right away." (It turned out that this was as honest a misunderstanding as it is possible for such misunderstandings to be.) "Now, I guess what you're saying is that those dreams weren't exactly dreams."

"No, I guess I was awake when they happened. But I remember I used to have dreams like that when I was in kindergarten."'

Celia's alleged dream served several useful purposes. It enabled her to confide a significant irregularity in nursing procedure which she hesitated to do directly because of not wanting to get the attendant into trouble. It was also a cautious approach to examining some wish-fears of her early childhood in conjunction with their contemporary import.

Symbolic Gratification of Neurotic Wishes

Although not peculiar to the treatment of the adolescent, there are a few other venerable principles of treatment which require special consideration when applied to him. There is, for example, the problem of symbolically gratifying a patient's unconscious wishes in such a way as to increase his symptoms or diminish his motivations for treatment. Related to this is our constant concern about "playing into the patient's neurotic needs" by responding to his provocations as he expects. Both are more pronounced with inpatient treatment which regularly requires the therapist to do more than "just talk" with the patient and his parents.

Some of the reality problems which it is necessary to make decisions about may be theoretical "absolutes," but in practice we must often deal with them as though some are more realistic than others. Is it desirable to tube-feed an anorectic fourteen-year-old girl who is being treated by intensive psychotherapy? Her resistance to eating is partially a defense against certain unconscious sexual wishes which will be "mobilized" by the intubation. This can be a valid contraindication, but if her weight falls to such a level that there is reason to fear for her life, then it will be better to risk mobilizing her unconscious wishes than to have her starve to death.

Further, her anorexia is a passively hostile behavior as well as an intrapsychic defense. Her therapist and other members of the staff become just as frustrated about her eating habits as the parents were. Tube-feeding will sometimes thwart this aim and force her to a more realistic and accessible expression of her anger. In other instances it will confirm the efficacy of the behavior by encouraging the fantasy, "Ha! I've got him so desperate he's forced to this heroic measure! Now watch me force him to remove it!" There are no rules of thumb to answer questions like these—only judgment.

Therapist—Administrator

There are many times when we must sacrifice one treatment advantage in order to meet a reality demand of higher priority. The hope of avoiding this is one of the principal arguments in favor of dividing the therapeutic and administrative roles between two different doctors. In most instances the alleged sacrifice is fictitious. (See also p. 251.)

For example, the manipulating, masochistic youngster whose misbehavior demands that he be confined to the ward, if only as a protective measure, will invariably accuse the therapist of punishing him "just the way my father always does." He is, in effect, accusing the therapist of "acting-out in the countertransference" which is a cardinal sin among psychiatrists. Whether or not the therapist really is guilty of imposing premeditated punishment depends upon how confident he feels about his reasons for having taken the action. If he was indeed forced to it by his own anger, he will find it very difficult to convince himself that he acted primarily in the patient's interest. On the other hand, if he recognizes the neurotic aim of the patient's behavior early enough to curb it before he has approached his own breaking point, he can feel much more confident that his action was not punitively motivated. He does not wait until he is too angry to make a rational decision. The patient also has in this type of transaction an opportunity to learn something more about the nature of treatment. He expected much better cooperation than this from his doctor's aggression-inspired guilt. His indignation at being compelled to deal with unfamiliar, unpredicted responses from another person is further enhanced by his doctor's relative calm.

"What did you confine me to the ward for? I didn't do anything!"

"Well, you didn't do much. You left that tennis equipment out in the yard again last night."

"Sheesh! You're giving me the works for that!"

"Oh no, not for that. Getting confined to the ward is much too much punishment for a little thing like that."

"Then what are you doing it for? That's only the third time I left it out this week! I suppose if I leave it out there again I'll probably get twenty years for it!"

"Well, thinking back on how you used to get things going with your father, I expect you'd work at it until you got me just as mad as he used to get . . . or almost."

"You're worse than he is!"

"How so?"

"He'd at least give me another chance when I'd . . . well, you know . . . leave his golf clubs out or something like that."

"I gave you another chance. Remember? I reminded you twice about the tennis equipment."

"He'd give me a lot more chance than that!"

"How much more?"

"Well . . . I don't know—no special number. He'd just keep warning me about it."

"Then what?"

"Well, sure! He'd finally blow up and beat the hell out of me . . . but . . ."

"And you always knew he'd get around to that sooner or later?"

"Sure . . . I guess so. But look, getting stuck on the ward doesn't make any sense. What's that got to do with leaving out the tennis stuff?"

"Nothing—nothing at all. You're not on the ward for leaving out the tennis stuff."

"Well, what is it for then?"

"For treatment . . . for what leaving out the tennis stuff stands for . . . for automatically starting to do some of the same old things without even thinking about them."

"You mean you think I was going to keep right on leaving it out just to get you mad? I wasn't even thinking anything like that!"

"I know you weren't. You weren't thinking about it at all . . . you were just doing it . . . you couldn't even help it."

"Oh. Well . . . I can remember to bring it in. How am I going to prove it if I don't even get a chance to try?"

"Where did you get the idea that you weren't going to get a chance to try? I didn't have it in mind to keep you penned up here forever."

"Does that mean I can play tennis this evening?"

"No. That would be just another one of those old-fashioned warnings that your father had so much trouble following through on . . . the kind that never worked."

"But it's such a little thing!"

"It may look little, but it isn't. It has an awful lot to do with the reason for your being here. That's hard for you to understand, I know, but it's true, and you'll know it a little later on. We can afford new tennis equipment, but *you* can't afford to have me agree with you that it's just a little thing."

"Keeping me on the ward won't do any good. I could goof things up just as much here as outside."

"You sure could. Are you thinking that's what you want to do?"

"No! I was just giving it as an example! (Shrugs disgustedly) Oh well, you can't fight city hall. Just let me know when I can play tennis again."

"Of course, but you're going to have to let me know when it's all right."

"As far as I'm concerned it's all right now!"

"Is it?"

"OK! OK! How about next week?"

"Let me know what you think about it next week. And I'm not kidding about that. I want to hear what you think about it . . . not just whether you like it or not, but the other things you think about it."

"OK."

Destructive Aggression

The uncontrollably assaultive, aggressive, defiant adolescent patient presents a serious challenge to the office-therapist's concept of proper treatment technique, even if he has had experience with such problems in the past. One forgets painful things, often quickly and thoroughly, and these situations can be extremely stressful and threatening to a psychiatrist's feeling of competence.

Dr. B, a resident psychiatrist, anxiously approached his supervisor for emergency consultation about Charley, a muscular sixteen-year-old boy who had recently been admitted to the adult closed ward. It was evident from Charley's history that he had long been accustomed to taking complete charge of every social situation which he entered. The psychiatric ward was no exception. He drove the nursing staff to distraction with his insolence, defiance, insults, and threats. Dr. B's thoughtful ruminations on the cause and meaning of his conduct had no tangible effect on its rampant course. Charley had brought things to a crisis for which there appeared to be no appropriate psychiatric treatment.

"He got one of the other kids to smuggle him in a ball bat. He's down in the dayroom now swinging it around and threatening to bash anybody who comes close to him. I tried to talk to him, but he wouldn't even listen to me. What do I do now?"

"Do you have any ideas?"

"He'd been telling me I should give him some truth serum, so I could find out what was on his unconscious mind. Maybe I could promise to give him some Amytal."

"Then? Really give it to him?"

"I could. It wouldn't do any good, but at least it would get him to sleep . . . and it sure wouldn't do any harm to have him asleep."

"That would be all right if you don't mind having him be the doctor on his own case . . . and if you're sure you've got a good answer for him when he asks you why you lied to him about *why* you gave him the Amytal."

"I know, I know! But we can't just leave him down there like that."

"We certainly can't. From what you say, I'd guess he's really in a mood to use that ball bat on somebody?"

"He sure is."

"Then we'd better get it away from him pretty fast. Get several of the attendants together with a mattress in front of them and . . ."

". . . rush him like that? If I do something like that to him, he'll never be able to work it through in psychotherapy!"

"I don't think he'll consider it quite as terrible as you do. He wouldn't be able to work it through if we let him fracture somebody's skull with that ball bat, either. Nor would the fractured party."

"I guess so, but it doesn't seem like the right way to treat a patient."

"It isn't. It's just the least bad of a very limited number of bad choices. Tell him you're sorry he's made things so you can't treat him as a patient. Give him no threats and no false promises. Just tell him to put down the ball bat and walk into the seclusion room, or the attendants will have to do it for him."

"Wouldn't it be better to have just one or two attendants take him in?"

"No. Having a lot of attendants is going to make him feel much too important, but it's safer for everyone. For whatever good it will do, you might tell him that you got a lot of men for the job to keep *him* from getting hurt, and to keep them from getting hurt."

"I can tell him, but do you think I should be down there when all this is going on?"

"Why not?"

"Well, I'm just trying to think out loud about how this will affect his fantasies about me . . . doing something like this to him."

"I'd say that you're doing it for him, not to him. If you're not there, he'll have fantasies about that, too. He'd probably think you were hiding out somewhere, which you would be."

"What I mean is, won't it stir up his fantasies of homosexual attack . . . something like that?"

"Sure, but what of it? Is it a homosexual attack?"

"Well, no, but . . ."

"He'll know that, too, won't he?"

"Yes, sure. But is it good technique to make him *more* anxious, when you know it's going to happen?"

"Not on purpose, but the question is academic. Tell you what, go get the ball bat away from him before someone gets hurt. We can talk about theory later on."

"OK. Only I'm scared."

"Me, too."

"Do you think you should do it instead of me?"

"No, of course not. I would if I had to, but fortunately for me this one is yours. Try to think of it as a precious learning experience."

"Do you think it'll work?"

"When something has to work, you don't worry about whether it will."

"Well, here I go."

Dr. B followed through with the plan as discussed, and the boy put down the ball bat and cooperated without a struggle. Far from damaging the treatment relationship with his patient, this incident improved it. Both patient and therapist got a better idea about the meaning of reality in psychotherapy—that the relationship between reality and psychotherapy is not a mutually exclusive one. The importance of this relationship can be considered more thoroughly in connection with the residential treatment program on an all-adolescent ward.

PART III RESIDENTIAL TREATMENT FOR DISTURBED ADOLESCENTS

12

AN ALL-ADOLESCENT SERVICE

Beyond The Chaos Principle

A psychiatric inpatient service for the specialized treatment of emotionally disturbed adolescents is hard to find. Many of these youngsters are cared for today, as they were yesterday, in other types of residential facilities such as training schools, boarding schools, and reform schools. These are the institutions which have been so severely criticized in recent decades as primitive, abusive, and medieval. That psychiatry has been slow to provide for these youngsters can be explained in several ways, not the least of which is an unspoken or perhaps unconscious suspicion that psychiatrists could not handle the job any better than the "schools," and perhaps not even as well.

Although guided by the principle of retaliation, of punishing wrongdoers for their crimes, the various schools have at least supplied a useful degree of protection for the youngster and for society. This, of course, falls far short of the ideal aim of rehabilitation or reform. Even worse, it is a humble gain which has been achieved by methods which correspond very closely to those of adult penal institutions. The methods were decried; they were sometimes roundly denounced, sometimes ignored altogether, but no one rushed forward with better solutions.

Some of the very severe management problems presented by adolescent patients, acting individually and en masse, were described vividly by Curran in 1939 in his report on the children's and adolescents' ward at Bellevue [6]. This was a pioneering effort which survived the beginning hardships and flourishes to the present. The report is a valuable, forthright account of one of the earliest collisions between adolescents and modern residential psychiatry. It helps the inexperienced clinician understand why the reform school had so much difficulty living up to its name and why psychiatric hospitals have been so reluctant to put theories of treatment to the test with patients of this age.

Curran observed that aggressive and destructive behavior was routine. For example, some boys would urinate in the beds of other boys or in the bedside stands, steal clothing and candy, throw personal property out of the window, and would break up tables, chairs, and other ward furniture. Most of this was done deliberately with no effort to disguise their aims. "At times this was done so they could use the legs of chairs as weapons."

The first effort at solving the problem was made by replacing the old furniture with stronger furniture, whereupon the boys turned their attention to "locks, electrical fixtures, tearing mirrors off the walls, puncturing the sound-proofing equipment on the ceiling with broomstick handles which they secured by volunteering to help sweep the floors." They also broke windows with their shoes, smashed electric lights, unscrewed metal door checks, threw game equipment out the window, and stole furniture skids to wear on their heels for tap dancing.

Other popular activities included stuffing toilets with clothing, throwing dangerous objects out the window, smashing the telephone in the nursing station, and throwing food in the dining hall. It was also noted that food was used as a means of bribery by which a small boy could buy the protection of an older boy. Initiation rites which included brutal physical treatment occurred regularly, as did privately scheduled fist fights and the rapid formation of antagonistic racial groups. The "no smoking" rule was extensively violated, and the situation was brought under control only by depriving the entire ward of smoking privileges for a period of 24 hours in the event of a single violation. "In this way the pressure of enforcing this smoking rule . . . comes from the boys themselves rather than from the staff."

One method directed at handling some of this extreme behavior was proposed by the boys themselves. They were permitted to set up their own court for the purpose of trying offenders, with the understanding that punishment would be administered by the ward physician. The punitive measures proposed by the boys themselves included whipping, no food or water for 24-hour periods, and beatings which were to be meted out by other patients. The plan died a natural death because the older and more aggressive patients intimidated smaller boys and prevented their testifying in court. A few aggressive secret societies were formed with "vigilante" intent. Membership in these organizations was based primarily on racial and religious differences.

The disciplinary routine adopted by the staff began with an interview of the offending child. An attempt was made to understand the underlying motivation for his act. He was then given another chance and told that if he were to offend again he would be disciplined because such behavior could not be accepted on the ward. With the first repetition of the offense, he was required to remove his clothing and remain in pajamas for 24 hours. This measure singled the patient out and "also indicated to his relatives who visit him that he has been in difficulty."

The next step was to stop attendance at off-ward activities. In the event of violent, uncontrollable temper tantrums, forced seclusion for 15 to 30 minutes was used, accompanied again by the explanation that such behavior was not permissible. Repeated uncontrollable destructive behavior resulted in the transfer of the offender to an adult closed ward for a 24-hour period. Curran states that they attempted to avoid this as much as possible because they felt the procedure was not good for the patient or for the adults on the other ward.

Experiences similar to this are well known to hospital psychiatrists across the country. The dream of providing intensive, individual psychotherapy for the hospitalized adolescent seemed beyond realization. Keeping these youngsters in the hospital, alive and uninjured, and the hospital and its staff intact was job enough. The state hospital staffs have known for a long time that an adult "violent ward" requires less time and attention than a scant handful of disturbed adolescents. Although many institutions have undertaken the treatment of adolescent patients within the framework of adult programs, very few have attempted this on exclusively adolescent units. It is not a secret that rampant destructive and assaultive behavior of adolescent patients has forced the closure of some all-adolescent units. This alone is a persuasive argument for continuing the tradition of treating disturbed adolescents as minority members of an adult group. It has been widely observed that adolescents are far more easily managed when diluted in a liberal volume of symptomatically sedate adults.

Other clinicians, however, have continued to feel that there are sound reasons for choosing to treat the adolescent within a community group of his peers. Although adolescents have many things in common, this fact alone does not support the too-facile conclusion that it is ideal for them to be treated together. Only a small percentage of these youngsters who are seen for outpatient evaluation, and who need to be in residence, are deemed able to profit from intensive psychotherapy on an all-adolescent service. Other dispositions are recommended for the majority—those youngsters who need nonintensive residential care and treatment. Of these there are a great number who can profit most from a hospital program of work and activities which has been specifically designed for their age group, even though they share living quarters with adult patients. Hendrickson [17] has described some of the indications for selecting an all-adolescent or a mixed-ward setting for the individual patient.

In short, the celebrated lack of facilities is far from being the best explanation for the fact that most hospitalized adolescent patients are still being accommodated on adult wards. In particular ways, the all-adolescent setting is an exacting and extremely stimulating one to the young patient. For some this stimulation will hasten and increase their progress in treatment, but for many others it will demand much more than they are able to return.

All-Adolescent Service at University of Michigan Hospital[1]

From the beginning the Adolescent Service has administered exclusively to patients who qualify as adolescents by the single criterion of chronological age—thirteen to sixteen years old at the time of admission and rarely older than eighteen years at discharge. Patients older or younger than this do not present the same kinds of problems in treatment and should not be considered adolescents on the basis of one or two superficial, adolescent-like personality features.

The main service is housed on a single divided ward (boys' and girls' sides) one level above ground in the main hospital building of the Neuropsychiatric Institute. It is bounded above and below on several levels by adult open and closed wards, an EEG laboratory, adult occupational therapy shop, and administrative offices for adolescent and adult services. The adolescent ward and the entire building which it occupies are attached physically and clinically to the general hospital of the University of Michigan Medical Center.

[1] A twenty-five bed semi-open ward for ten girls and fifteen boys was opened at the Neuropsychiatric Institute of the University of Michigan Hospital, Ann Arbor, in September, 1956. An additional six to ten beds for adolescent patients were also made available to the service on the adult closed ward.

Operating within definite physical limitations, the ward was made as attractive and as nonhospital in appearance as possible. The physical plan is T-shaped, with separated boys' and girls' wards occupying the arms of the horizontal segment, and schoolrooms and dining room along the vertical segment. The closed nursing station is at the junction of the vertical and horizontal segments. Preexisting heavy steel doors were left in place for locking off boys', girls', and activities areas from each other and from the outside. Additional facilities available to this service, but physically separate from it and shared with the adult service, are an amphitheater for movies, a small gymnasium, and an unenclosed recreation yard behind the building. In the main hospital area are a newsstand, candy counter, recreational library, and a pleasant snack bar which the adolescents can share with the patients and staff of the general hospital.

The table of organization for staff personnel is ordered along conventional lines, with a generous clinical staff-to-patient ratio of about one to one. Under usual circumstances there are about five inpatients for each resident therapist, and one or two inpatients for each of the three senior staff members. Each nursing shift is supervised by at least one registered nurse, and each side of the ward by one to three psychiatric attendants.

A Philosophy of Inpatient Treatment

What is hospitalization supposed to accomplish for the adolescent patient? As far as general aims are concerned, there is little disagreement about this question. Most of us subscribe eagerly to the idea of offering the patient a rewarding emotional experience, opportunities for various kinds of gratification, satisfying interpersonal relationships, and—above all else—treatment.

Many nonpsychiatric institutions prove to be highly therapeutic for the disturbed adolescent despite the fact that no "therapy" is offered. Some psychiatric facilities provide treatment in profusion but achieve little in the way of therapeutic results. This is because the process by which results are achieved is far more important than the name given to the process. A common conception of inpatient treatment depicts hospitalization as a means of providing the patient with a benevolent boarding arrangement, a place where he can kill time between doctor's appointments by spending an occasional hour or two in a "therapeutic" school class, doing a little basket-weaving, kicking out an occasional window, and perhaps throwing a ball around the gymnasium free of the cruel and confining rigors of training and competition.

Ideally, a psychiatric residence for adolescents will offer more than this. In attempting to describe some of the important attributes of a good program, one runs the risk of drawing up a ready-reference, do-it-yourself manual, although something of this sort could be useful at the present time. In order to talk with others about the practical tasks of treatment, it is necessary to translate some of our psychodynamic expertise about treatment into more tangible, applicable terms.

There is a purpose in speaking first of the things which our patients have required us to do, and only then of theories about why and how our efforts were either effective or futile. It is appalling to see how far it is possible for theory to stray from the ordinary therapeutic forces which support the general society of healthy people. It is so easy to set aside the accumulated wisdom of centuries of cultural evolution as something which has all come about in some utterly random and purposeless fashion. In speaking of ego strengths, for example, or of reinforcing defenses, we have provided ourselves not only with useful conceptual tools but also with easy escape from examining those forces in our lives which really do the most to strengthen egos and reinforce defenses. The ideas connoted by such terms as *authority, moral standards, discipline,* and *ideals* have fallen under a heavy shadow of suspicion in our specialty, as though they are all bad. It is even bad to say "bad." But an active day on the ward has a way of reminding one that there is really no such thing as a good boy, at least not in the natural state. They have to become good, just as we did.

Although a therapist need not know whether the energy of the ego is autonomous or derived from the id in order to practice psychotherapy, he does need to appreciate, for example, that a person's ego does not develop in isolation from other people, that it does grow in relationship to other people—in response to their wishes, attitudes, expectations, demands, and gifts of pleasure. He must appreciate the destructive insult which is implicit in his failing to require the best which his young patient is able to offer. He should also find it difficult to imagine that he would voluntarily relinquish to another person the potent therapeutic agent of "administrative" responsibility on the perverse rationale that being realistic about realities might somehow interfere with psychotherapy.

THERAPIST'S ROLES: A FICTION. One of the alleged problems of the hospital psychiatrist is that of having to reconcile his dual roles as therapist and administrator.

Cameron [4] described a division of such functions between the senior and junior psychiatrists on the adolescent ward of the Maudsley. The junior physician tended to become more deeply involved in ward activities, he noted, and with individual cases in therapy. The senior doctor was also active on the wards and treated a few patients, but he functioned primarily as a representative of authority and control. In the beginning the psychiatrists felt that this simplified some problems in individual psychotherapy, but later in Cameron's experience the junior psychiatrist found the arrangement disadvantageous and preferred finally to "take over the total psychiatric role rather than the simple therapeutic role."

This problem of role division is derived more from theoretical considerations than from practical experience. The idea that fulfilling one's supervisory obligations to the juvenile patient will in some fashion interfere with treatment is a true paradox. The services of supervision and treatment are by nature inseparable. The parent who loves, feeds, and protects is also the parent who controls, punishes, and deprives. He is the source of that ambivalence which every individual must resolve in developing from instinct-ridden infancy to mature adulthood. Artificial attempts to separate the two functions seem an ill-advised effort to avoid interfering with the relentlessly positive, friendly-looking aspects of the treatment relationship.

In allocating to another person the responsibility for confronting the patient with realistic frustrations, the therapist loses the chance to draw these most critical emotional issues into treatment. Permitting the patient's reactive feelings to be deflected to another person may indeed support the positive transference, but it also reinforces the patient's maladaptive conviction that his troubles are due mostly to an unsympathetic and unjust external reality which is now represented in treatment by the malevolent disciplinarian. It persuades him that people who give him what he wants are good and that people who do otherwise are bad. Providing him one therapist who gives and one who deprives, rather than helping him resolve his neurotic ambivalence, actually encourages him to act it out.

THERAPEUTIC FORCES IN PROGRAM. As a minimum offering the psychiatric inpatient service should provide as fully as possible a *nonpathogenic* environment. This will serve not only as a background for individual psychotherapy but also as a program which makes its own unique contributions to comprehensive treatment [18].

The value to the patient of being away from the troubled family relationships which have tended to perpetuate his illness is an important gain in itself. However, there are many places other than psychiatric hospitals which can provide at least this much and sometimes even more. Perhaps the thing which most distinguishes the psychiatric residential treatment program from all others is the knowledgeable capacity of the professional staff for resisting the sick youngster's automatic efforts to recreate with them his old, familiar patterns of interaction with people. He brings to treatment his own characteristic ways of feeling, thinking, and behaving, all backed by an inexhaustible energy for carrying them with forceful impact into his relationships with staff members. The system which aspires to treat such a patient, through helping him to correct his understandably distorted conceptions of reality, tries not to repeat the errors of the past. In more positive terms it must supply the means by which these distortions can be corrected, and must further provide the motivation which will enable the young patient to bear the stress of accepting and internalizing an improved version of reality. This applies whether his presenting problem is predominantly a complex of symptoms, of antisocial behavior, or, as it usually is, of both.

The first and most startling of the realities which confronts the new patient is our conspicuous disinterest in treating him as though he were crazy, helpless, and utterly incapable of taking some responsibility for his own actions. If necessary, he is assured with directness and confidence that there are others, who reside elsewhere, who exist for the purpose of providing physical controls for the uncontrollable. This is not offered as a threat but as a fact which he is entitled to know. We presume him to be a youngster who is, in the final analysis, capable of worrying about himself and his effect on other people. Incredible though it may seem, he is expected to be obedient, and this without the support of manhandling and high-security confinement. One may question how a youngster who has been long accustomed to acting immediately and unreflectively on impulse can adapt himself to such a physically permissive setting. The answer to this, in general terms, is that the physical permissiveness is not as delightful in the eyes of the young patient as we are inclined to think.

The effects of Adelaide Johnson's "sanctioning" on our adolescent patients are glaring and routine. The youngster has little reason to believe that adults are capable of meaning what they say or of knowing what they mean. Their own parents were easily frightened, perplexed, manipulated, and controlled. Far too often his further experiences with adults, in his sometimes circuitous transit from the home to the ward, have done little to dissuade him from his conviction that no one can really stop him—or help him. Psychiatrists, teachers, counselors, social workers, probation officers, and judges in this era of psychological enlightenment bend over backward to avoid being punitive. By the time the patient enters the hospital, he is usually wallowing in a quagmire of omnipotence and is wretchedly unhappy about it. He sees no alternative to testing and retesting the validity of his fantasied supremacy over the entire adult world.

Cultural Tone of the Ward

The therapeutic answer to this test is a long time in the making. It begins with his doctor's simple description of the basic expectations he is to meet as a part of his treatment. Words mean very little to him at first. The possibility that we might really mean what we say begins to dawn on him with his first opportunity to sample the *cultural tone* of his new community.

This is an atmosphere which is continually generated by a complex of staff attitudes which are meant to demonstrate that one's words are not always contradicted by his actions. No effort is made to protect the patient from the knowledge that he resides on a psychiatric service and that he is there for psychiatric treatment. At the same time it is made clear to him that much effort has gone into providing him with as attractive, rewarding, and comfortable a living situation as possible. This is offered on the assumption that, for our group of patients, it is not necessary to bolt down the furniture, strip the walls, and lock off all physical equipment which might be liable to damage or destruction. He is able to see with his own eyes that we do not anticipate a need to rely on detention screens or locks to keep him out of trouble. Nor do we comfort him with the notion that *he* can rely on them, either.

When the service was opened, home-style furniture, draperies, mirrors, and other colorful and ornamental appurtenances were installed, and a liberal attitude was taken toward the nonpermanent decoration of rooms. No effort was made to develop high-security routines for prophylaxis against suicide. Glass mirrors are included among the furnishings, as are such potentially dangerous "sharps" as knives and razors, if there is a good reason for their presence on the ward.

Although the entire unit is kept locked much of the time, the freedom of movement of individuals and groups between the ward and other activity areas, both inside the hospital and out, is consistent with the verbal assertion that penal detention is not our business. Escape is so simple that it does not deserve the name. One may run away, but it is impossible to escape.

A flexible policy of privileges enables a certain percentage of patients to have unsupervised freedom within the hospital building for limited periods of time throughout the day. Fuller privileges are also granted to youngsters who are deemed sufficiently self-responsible to go alone from the hospital for relatively longer periods of time.

PRIVILEGE OF RESPONSIBILITY. Other evidences of this apparent permissiveness could be enumerated. The point to be made here is satisfied by the foregoing, and might stimulate some wholesome doubt in persons who have had experience with the "in-service" treatment of disturbed and frequently antisocial adolescents. The distinctive philosophy of treatment on the Adolescent Service is aptly reflected in the view that a privilege is not really a privilege unless it has first been successfully discharged as a responsibility. It is not incidental to treatment, but a part of it.

From the patient's point of view privileges are not as popular as one might expect. They cannot be won by acquiring points or gold stars nor lost through demerits. Although they must be earned by the patient, no one is quite certain how this is done. It depends, essentially, on a process by which doctor and patient develop a gradual understanding about the ways in which a privilege of any sort might or might not contribute to the long-term goals of treatment. A common name for this process is *psychotherapy.*

The ideas of permission and prohibition in psychotherapy should be examined in the light of the patient's fantasies about his therapist's reasons for giving him or depriving him of anything. If some special privilege is conferred as a cheap payoff for a short term of "good behavior," the patient will know about it, and he will also have found a reliable guide to the future exploitation of his doctor's equivocating, conciliatory approach to the treatment process. If a privilege is withheld to foster the youngster's efforts to stand on his own feet and to feel better while doing it, he will know that also. He probably will not like it at first, but he will appreciate it.

Viewed in this way, it is easier to understand that a program which offers the consolation of physical confinement, along with its codified and predictable system of controls, can be experienced paradoxically by the antisocial adolescent; for him it is an indulgence. He is familiar with the talion mode of operation and within its framework can practice his acquired talent for achieving short-term pleasures with surpassing skill.

Although the patients on the adolescent ward enjoy an unusual degree of physical freedom in the various activities, there are certain other requirements which they feel to be stringent, painful, and, most important of all, bewilderingly novel. It is the sum of these requirements and the attitudes of the patients and staff toward them which are indispensable to the maintenance of the ward community's cultural tone. On first examination some of these requirements might seem arbitrary and picayune, but all of them together constitute a background of social reality which can best potentiate both program-treatment and intensive, individual psychotherapy. Many of the standards which are imposed upon the group correspond closely to the popular conception of social conventionality. Living up to these standards is very difficult for most of these youngsters. And, for the majority of the staff, living down to them is equally painful.

STAMPING OUT MENTAL HEALTH: A TEMPTATION. There is nothing special nor distinctively psychiatric in the scenes which an outside observer could recognize in the course of an average day. The surface routine is so ordinary that there are long periods of time during which it is almost impossible for the patient to maintain a clear mental image of himself as a proper mental patient, and for the professional staff person to preserve the personally supportive picture of himself as a skilled psychiatric specialist. In both patients and staff there is a surprisingly strong, if subtle, compulsion to foster an atmosphere of ongoing psychopathology which will be consonant with the popular stereotype of what a mental ward ought to be like. A doctor or nurse never feels his worth more keenly than during times of plague, but this does not warrant his going about spreading the disease. He is supposed to cure it.

It is understood, for example, that swearing is strictly forbidden, even though we recognize that in the privacy of their rooms a certain amount of this kind of activity will be surreptitiously enjoyed as forbidden fruit, which is indeed a vital staple in the adolescent diet. This is inevitable but not harmful, and only our own unconscious sadistic strivings could prompt us to deprive them of this sweet pleasure, by giving them official permission to practice in public that which is most enjoyable when violated in private.

It is also required that all the professional staff be addressed by title and approached with the customary signs of respect. The same courtesy, of course, is extended to the patient. In other psychiatric settings where obscene salutations have routinely replaced "hello" and "good morning," we have noted some highly antitherapeutic consequences. This is the kind of "magical" address which enables the patient to take a generic as opposed to an individual view of the adult. In the patient's fantasies it capably degrades the staff person while simultaneously enhancing his own illusory sense of omnipotence. There is nothing "moralistic" in the staff's taking a stand against it; it is just that there is no worthwhile treatment aim to be served by taking a stand *for* it.

Conventional clothing must be worn in school as well as in most other group and individual activities. Off the ward, while in the public eye, appropriate clothing and conduct suitable to the situation are insistently expected. All members of the staff take an exceptionally active interest in the grooming, cleanliness, and personal presentability of the patients and comment on such matters quite openly—though tactfully—as need arises.

These details are described to put meat on the bones of the all-too skeletal principle that "it's good to set limits." The prevailing atmosphere of the ward society can be further defined and developed in a subsequent review of certain core problems encountered in staff training and in relation to the therapeutic management of some common forms of antisocial behavior (acting-out) on the ward.

The positive social tone is partly maintained by the ultimately effective persistence of the staff in expecting the patient to do his best. Although it is acknowledged that exceptions to these basic expectations are numerous and recurrent, there is still a vast difference in the significance attached by patients to the misbehavior which they carry out *in spite* of the staff's vigorous expectations, and that which occurs without contest because of staff's apathy, neurotic inhibition, or unconscious need for vicarious satisfaction.

THE CONFORMING REBEL. The professional staff, like the individual therapist, cannot make patients better. They can only create the conditions which might make it possible for a patient to get better. A point which must be repeatedly emphasized is that this fundamentally prosocial organization could not possibly be maintained without the strong support, however unconscious and indirectly expressed, of this manifestly hostile, rebellious, and antisocial group. Even as a youngster protests the unreasonable stringency of our idealistic expectations, he still continues to demonstrate in many ways his intense, personal investment in the order as it stands. By subscribing to the demands of the ward society, he enjoys a distinct increase in his estimation of himself. He becomes dependent upon the dividends of his investment and is secretly antagonistic to any force which threatens the stability of the corporation in which he holds stock. Abundant proof of this is found in direct and indirect testimony during individual treatment sessions but is even more persuasively demonstrated in the reactions of the larger group to the "bad apples" in their barrel.

To date we have repeatedly observed what seems to be, in contrast to some experiences elsewhere, a paradoxical reaction of the group to misbehavior by one of its individual members. The patient "acts out" partly under endogenous pressure to communicate something of his internal conflicts and to allay the anxiety resulting from them. On the adolescent service he usually finds that he must act without the support of the group. Instead of infecting the others he frightens and drives them away, and is thereby deprived of some of the exciting, supportive secondary gains of his aggressive and sexual acting-out. He is not seen in the role of leader, incitor, champion, and is not applauded. He finds himself appealing impotently to a grimly neutral or even antipathetic audience, and the defensive aims of his behavior are partially frustrated. This outcome leaves him with stronger motives for dealing with the internal implications of his behavior in the therapeutic work with his doctor.

We often hear references to the need for converting the character neurotic to a symptom neurotic as an essential first phase in the treatment of the relatively anxiety-free, antisocial individual. Applicable recommendations for accomplishing this end, however, are seldom elaborated to a useful degree. Experience here strongly suggests that at least one basic prerequisite to this transformation is a living situation which acts against pathological character defenses. It has been most rewarding to observe a number of initially "cool," untroubled, aggressive delinquents undergo this conversion, with the parallel development of a marked increase in free-floating anxiety and such psychogenic physical complaints as vomiting, diarrhea, and skin disturbances.

Mary, a fifteen-year-old girl, had been previously hospitalized elsewhere with a history of ungovernable behavior in the home and sexual promiscuity. Among her hospitalized peers she quickly achieved status through her sex play with several boys on the ward. This naturally excited much interest in the others and resulted in some "spreading" of sex play within the group. When the problem was brought directly to her attention in individual therapy, she shrugged it off indifferently and carried on as before.

For several reasons she was later transferred to the Adolescent Service where she quickly became involved in an incident of gross sexual misbehavior. She returned from this experience eager to publicize it to the other girls, with the expectation of earning their open approval. She was shocked and unnerved by their coldly critical reception. This was one of the major factors which motivated her to internalize her defenses and to suffer the anxiety arising from certain problems which she had previously warded off by acting them out. She could turn only to her therapist for help.

Some of the more popular antisocial group activities, such as room-barricading,[2] wrist-slashing, and obscene verbal assaults against the staff, have achieved little social success here. Because the group has entered into an undeclared alliance with an essentially prosocial tradition, its individual members are much freer to test themselves and others without fear of destroying the structure which supports them.

It is curiously rare, for example, to find the boys' and girls' sides of the ward hyperactive, testing, and agitated on the same night. It is also uncommon to find more than one or two individuals on either side to be inordinately cantankerous at a given time. During the first several years of operation there were very few prolonged periods of tranquility, but only rarely was it necessary to contend with more than two or three very troubled or troublesome patients at one time. On other occasions we have anticipated serious trouble as a result of transient staff shortages, but these fears have seldom been realized. As a rule the youngsters respect those of our weaknesses which we really cannot help. In these ways the importance to the group of preserving the prosocial tone is easily demonstrated. This can be recognized despite the ceremonious belligerence of its individual members.

There are some patients, erroneously admitted to the service, who are simply unable to get along in this atmosphere of *relatively* self-controlled civility. It demands too much of them, and they invariably recognize

[2] About two years ago we finally installed antibarricade doors to patients' rooms. In defense of this action it is only fair to say that the original construction included in-swinging doors and room lengths exactly equal to the lengths of two beds and the width of one chair. This was an almost irresistible invitation to adolescent patients. We have not been able to figure out a way to "beat" the new antibarricade doors but have no doubt that they could. The fact that they have not even tried lends support to the idea that they are greatly disposed to cooperate with any good purposes which are expressed with sufficient clarity and determination.

their incapacity earlier than we do. Although they find it difficult to confess this openly, they will do so if sufficiently desperate. As a rule, however, they prefer some other way of signaling that we have overestimated their ability to tolerate so much stimulation, freedom, and general emotional prosperity.

A sixteen-year-old boy with a long record of multiple delinquencies struggled bitterly with the question of his ability to survive in this setting. He provoked the staff repeatedly with aggressive and defiant behavior, much of which was directed at securing firmer external controls. When this was explained and demonstrated to him, he became extremely anxious and inhibited. He kept a careful chart on his conduct and was finally able to point with incredulous pride to a record of twenty days of "good behavior." He found that the mild praise he earned for this was too much to bear. He could not accept this much esteem or the burden of personal responsibility which it imposed upon him. On the twenty-first day he ran uncontrollably wild and had to be transferred to the adult closed ward, where he settled down almost at once.

When such a patient is transferred for treatment on the adult closed ward, it is not as a regrettable act of expedience but in response to positive treatment indications for making such a move. With the secure, externally controlling protection of a locked ward, he usually becomes much more comfortable and can finally liberate for other purposes some of the energy which was previously monopolized for impulse-control. It is true that this much protection may also foster his tendency to relinquish his own controls, particularly if antisocial character mechanisms predominate in his illness. With rare exception, however, the youngster who is acting-out ungovernably will walk to the closed ward with no active resistance, no matter what his diagnosis. But weeks of careful work are required to overcome his anxiety about moving to the adolescent ward, where he knows he will have to enter a challenging social competition with peers.

In managing individual problems of misbehavior, it is useful to respect the diagnostic acumen of the patient group. They are often more sensitive than the staff in distinguishing between symptomatic "loss of control" and that which is more-or-less deliberately antisocial. As a group they can tolerate a limited amount of aberrant behavior from the former type of patient, but will become angry, anxious, and intolerant if we delay too long in curbing the transgressions of the latter.

Their formulations are not made at an entirely intuitive level. In one girls' group therapy session they registered bitter complaints against a girl who had *openly verbalized,* "I get high (hyperactive) and talk too much when I'm upset."

The conclusion which they promptly reached: When a person knows his behavior is the result of painful feelings, he is in a position to do something about it. They held her responsible for her behavior instead of excusing her on the grounds of being helplessly sick. Thus, the medical staff are justified in temporizing with "symptomatic acting out" but are expected to act promptly and decisively in instances of apparently *will*ful[3] misbehavior. The patients are less tolerant than we about excusing delinquency "by reason of mental illness."

The Privilege of Punishment

Seclusion on a maximum security ward is sometimes necessary in the treatment of many disturbed adolescents but is never used as an elective measure. All four of the preexisting seclusion rooms on the adolescent ward were converted to workshops, lounges, and patients' rooms prior to opening.

A patient suffering an acute episode of excitement, agitation, or panic may be placed for a short time in his own room to insulate him from overstimulation and to reassure him with a concrete demonstration of our ability to "take over" should his own controls fail. This is not a euphemistic expression for concealing retaliatory motives. The patient who can profit from a brief period of time in seclusion is the one who has genuinely lost self-control and is terrified that he may be permitted to act ungovernably. The "bad actor" is secluded only when there is no other choice. He must *not* be temporarily, punitively secluded if he is thought to have the capacity for inhibiting himself. Short-term confinements for routine infractions would contradict our assertion that the burden of responsibility for controls rests, ideally, upon the patient. The knowledge that he might be secluded at any moment would free him from the painful labor of directing his own actions with maximum effort.

[3] This term is used here as in the expression *free will.*

There are some rich secondary profits to be realized from seclusion, especially when our abuse of the method permits the youngster to perpetuate the old fantasy of courageous, justified rebellion. Taking his dialogue from the "heroic gangster" movies of twenty-five years ago, which are now available on late TV, the offending boy will boast that he can "do seclusion time standing on my ear." Imprisonment provides him with the supreme opportunity for dramatizing his masculine independence while enjoying the ultimate in dependency gratification. If given the chance, delinquent boys will compete with one another to win this distinction. With his exquisite sensitivity to the importance of being independent and hairy breasted, the imminent availability of structured punishments helps him pretend to the role of the indomitable, testosterone-drenched hero without requiring that he expend the energy necessary to actually becoming such a person.

From the boy's standpoint being a hood, a criminal, or a hard character is a far, far better thing than being mentally sick. That he should choose[4] to be antisocial is something which we regard as a symptom of mental illness, rather than an illustrious character trait, and we therefore offer him the *long-term* application of the only feasible measure which can protect him and others from the consequences of his behavior. This is closed-ward care. Short-term transfer to a security unit registers too little concern for the seriousness of his illness. The personality processes which determine his characteristic choice of antisocial defenses are not changed in a few days' time, and therefore brief excursions to a closed unit can only be regarded as pointlessly, ineffectively punitive.

Empty threats, bluffs, and punishment must be avoided, not merely because they are neurotically motivated but because they do not work. The staff person who takes recourse to them betrays his own uncertainty, which fact is readily recognized and capitalized upon by the patient. This is not necessarily an argument against certain forms of punishment if they are *known* to help in controlling problems of otherwise intractable antisocial behavior, but is rather to point up the fact that pro-

[4] We assume the existence of free will which is capable of transcending the force of psychic determinism. This assumption is necessary to the conduct of any psychiatric treatment, just as it is to living. The philosophers may have the rest of this question for the time being.

grammed punishment is not the natural function of a hospital. Other institutions can provide penal services far more effectively and economically than we. To tell an aggressive, defiant adolescent that he will go to the closed ward if he does not behave himself is ethical enough, but it is also equivalent to saying that we are in the penitentiary business. Instead, when our own estimation of a patient's psychological situation decisively indicates that he really needs this kind of management, he is transferred *without* a lot of redundant warnings. Intimidation, in short, is not an instrument of our profession.

At the same time it would be equally unrealistic to conceal from the patient that there are agencies in society which operate with a somewhat less humanistic consideration for psychogenic misbehavior. When a boy runs away from the hospital and steals a car, which *is* a felony, we would be doing him a serious disservice to withhold the explanation that, although we are willing to view this as symptomatic, it can be examined in quite another light under the law and can possibly result in his being removed from our relatively benevolent sphere of influence. He has a right to know this, and we have an obligation to tell him. In some psychiatric settings it is too easy for the antisocial adolescent to nourish the delusion that his status as a patient automatically exempts him from all other legal, moral, and religious responsibility. Many of us who should know better give comfort to this delusion. Parents, schools, and, interestingly, even some legal authorities are often remiss in helping the offending adolescent understand that certain of his actions might get him into serious and unpleasant difficulties. This is a trenchantly insulting infantilization of a youngster who is trying very hard to grow up.

Kenny, aged sixteen, ran away from the hospital and stole a car. It was recovered a few hours later, and he was returned to the ward. His therapist was contacted by a police detective who generously offered to drop all charges because he did not want to "interfere with the boy's treatment." He presumed that it would be harmfully traumatic to subject this "emotionally disturbed juvenile" to an interrogation about the car theft.

Kenny's therapist was naturally mindful of the psychological conflict which prompted the behavior but could not neglect the fact that the behavior itself was illegal and therefore a matter of justifiable concern to the police. The detective was assured that his investigation of the case was expected. Following a lengthy interrogation by the officer, Kenny began to show for the first time some awareness that his behavior, however symptomatic it might be, could still get him into the kind of trouble which he never really believed possible. He also began to develop a greater respect for his doctor's skill at appraising and judiciously blending some of the apparently immiscible aims of mental illness, psychotherapy, and society, instead of sweeping them under the rug of jurisdictional self-righteousness: "The only good is treatment."

As punishment and legal correction are not functions of the adolescent service, we are in no position to mete out determinate sentences for specific offenses which have been perpetrated against the ward society either. The antisocial adolescent who is contemplating "a job" of some sort is always very apprehensive about "what will happen to me if I do it?" He needs this information to make his plans. Although a judge could answer such a question, we cannot. We can only explain to him that our decisions in such matters are always based upon a great deal more that the act itself. "You're asking me how I'll punish you for staying sick? You want me to submit a bid for a job I don't even want you to do? Just what is it you want to know?"

The talion principle holds much comfort for the social offender, oddly enough. As noted earlier, a fixed sentence is something he can predict, ergo, something which he can cause whenever he wishes. It also enables him to see his problem as an inevitable conflict between an immutable character, himself, and an immutably alien environment. There is nothing more disconcerting and prohibitive to the scheming adolescent than to be told, in effect: "Well, I don't know what would happen exactly, but you know very well that no matter what happens, we will always try to do *the thing that is best for you,* corny as that may sound." The patient senses that "the best thing" would probably not reinforce his delinquent aims, which leaves him at a decided tactical disadvantage with respect to his further planning [16].

It is no easier to tell the reader "what will happen *if,*" because it really is an unknown. One patient is unexpectedly transferred to the closed adult unit for no *apparent* reason. Another kicks out the screen in his room, drops to the ground, and roams free for many hours, only to have his previous "privileges" fully restored immediately upon his return to the ward; the other patients can see that he is in no way prosecuted. A third returns five minutes late from a building-pass and has his privileges indefinitely suspended, while still another—who has consistently abused his privileges—continues unrestricted. This apparent inconsistency is such only with reference to the talion principle. A careful individual analysis of each of these incidents would reveal that there were excellent treatment reasons for the highly varied responses to similar-appearing misbehaviors. When the patient sees this principle in action, he believes it and feels unfamiliarly impelled to an attitude of critical self-appraisal of a kind which is not encouraged by the comforting promise of uniform punishments.

13

THERAPEUTIC MANAGEMENT OF COMMON GROUP PROBLEMS

There is practical advantage in examining in greater detail some of the commoner behavior problems and their management. The ubiquity of certain patterns of aggressiveness, escape, theft, riot, destructiveness, and defiance of authority indicates the need for a better understanding of the etiology of such behavior in adolescent groups. Some factors of causation are "latent constants," always present when adults and adolescents get together. The point of view taken in the following discussion emphasizes, in addition to general causation, some of the conditions which *permit* the development of crises in group behavior, and some field-proved ways of understanding and dealing with them therapeutically when they do arise.

Riot

Pathogenesis of panic and riot. Many of the staff person's fears about the bad things which adolescents might do originate within himself and are defensively ascribed to patients. At the same time it must be allowed that this projection is at least strongly potentiated by some genuine threats inherent in the structure of an adolescent group. Psychiatry and the law both recognize that delinquent adolescents are too young to be considered criminals, but they can still be dangerous. People who have worked with large groups of adolescents are familiar with an ever-lingering sense of uneasiness about "what would happen if they decided to take over?" This can happen—through a malignant process which leads by a progression of interpersonal "infectiousness" to final expression in epidemic rioting.

The successful development of this sequence requires that a high group valuation be placed upon antisocial modes—by which they temporarily become "prosocial"—and that an equally strong negative value be assigned to the conventional virtues. It also requires the active cooperation of supervisory adults, which will work even if it is unintended. The net effect of the forces leading to riot can be catastrophic.

Retrospective examination of riots among adolescents which we have observed in other situations (there have been none here on the Adolescent Service to date) reveals a rather constant pattern of development. The following formulation is oversimplified and, of course, variable in detail, but it is still a useful model for understanding a complex group process:

For whatever personal reason, a patient acts in a way that is incompatible with the expectations of a psychologically dominant medical staff. He may, for example, tell an attendant to "go to hell." The act may be minor as far as immediate consequences are concerned, but the offending patient and the others who are so carefully observing the reaction of the staff will accord it special significance. The staff person would ordinarily settle this acute strain in their relationship by having a little chat with the lad about the ways of the outside world, where teenagers do not consign their elders to hell, at least not with impunity, even with provocation. No special reason is given to explain *why* this is not done, except perhaps to point out that things of the inside world, the ward, are meant to correspond as closely as possible to those of the outside.

This is what is usually done. Occasionally, however, the staff person might respond otherwise, perhaps with feigned indifference if not a frankly shameless retreat. Perhaps he does not want to "start trouble" or thinks it best to "let sleeping dogs lie." His solution to the problem is neglect. He leaves it. In this case the patient or one of his anxious allies will deem it necessary to test this response with another, more insistent action of similar significance. The staff member, feeling himself being drawn in deeper, tries placation and appeasement, or accelerates his retreat in the illusory hope that the misbehavior with all its murky implications will "just go away."

The patient is now both excited and troubled by this substantial tribute to his own power and demonstration of the weakness of the staff upon whom he leans. He experiences a heightened sense of omnipotence, the validity of which must be further tested, then tested again, and again, and again.

The vicious cycle is fed by the continued withholding of a realistic staff response. It has, in effect, become a staff-sponsored activity. The staff person desperately resorts to additional ill-advised measures of expediency which further betray his fear, uncertainty, and unwillingness to do what must be done. With the spreading of excitement the fascinated spectators leap in to join the "fun," but with the *conscious* assumption, or hope, of eliciting a quick and decisive suppression of what they also recognize as a terrifying trend. In a short time the impotence of the staff is proved, and the patient group has no choice but to take charge. They find their unexpected power quite unbearable. Panic with riotous destruction, assault, and mass runaway may conclude the sequence.

Prevention is the best answer to adolescent rioting. This can be done with comparative ease in the earlier stages of development but becomes increasingly difficult as the process continues. A healthy group of adolescents in some conventional group setting, like a picnic or a camping trip, will commonly administer the same kind of "test." They are much better prepared to accept a supervisory answer, however, because they started with a much finer appreciation of their own limitations. In spite of their clamoring to the contrary, they are wholesomely aware, as too many psychiatrists are not, that the administration of a democratic government is the responsibility of adults. The disturbed youngsters, harried by unresolved feelings of infantile impotence, omnipotence, and plain ignorance, and frightened by their understandable mistrust of adult effectiveness, require a concrete and emphatic answer to any questions bearing upon the staff-patient power balance. The psychiatric residential program is not a democracy, nor should it be, nor do our patients really want it to be. This point may be somewhat at variance with Ruth Eissler's appraisal [10] of this type of disturbance among adolescents.

One of the early signs of trouble is the increased irritability and impatience of staff members and patients alike. Close inspection reveals that the former are slowly evacuating a sinking ship. They begin to find more and better reasons for spending larger amounts of time away from the patient group: in conferences, at writing progress notes, or in reading books and articles. Their growing uneasiness is unconsciously displaced from their own faltering relationship with the youngsters to a number of trifling and petty concerns about rules and policies. They demand absolute administrative edicts about routine matters which they are customarily able to decide with a quiet, firm confidence in their own judgment. They want to know how loud they should permit radios to be played. They call for a flat ruling on whether or not patients should be allowed to dance the twist, further requesting exact specifications on the appropriate amplitude and frequency of hip swiveling—all of which is to be rendered in circular degrees and twists per minute. No longer able to trust themselves, the staff members suddenly need laws in black and white which, in foolish desperation, they hope will cover every contingency. A reminder that doctors are also "staff" should be superfluous, but probably is not.

Specific precipitating events are usually obscure. But, as a general rule, we are quite safe in interpreting these early omens to mean that we are missing something very important. Fortunately, instituting measures which will bring the group under more secure and comfortable control does not require that we know immediately the precise nature of precipitating causes, although it is essential that we try to find out. It is usually some time after a reasonable level of harmony has been restored that the patients are once more sufficiently safe and trustful to let us know what got things started.

It may have been that a newly admitted patient had been making homosexual advances, that a very sick youngster was threatening suicide or a runaway, that one of the ritual, pedestrian romances had begun to sprint beyond safe limits. In any case it is almost certain that it was something which had been able to develop through the special agency of staff neglect. A doctor had been "taken in" by his patient and had allowed too much freedom at the wrong time. Or, for some unexplained reason, the nursing staff had begun to avoid the darker and more remote corners of the ward or were making "rounds" less frequently even though there was reason to make them more often.

Until the focus of the trouble is found and remedied, an overwhelming septicemia can be averted by palliative measures. The grip of authority is tightened. Each clinical detail of the recent past and immediate present is scrutinized with great care by the therapists during individual interviews with their patients, and by the ward staff in their minute-to-minute contacts with the whole group. The limits of self-responsibility are made tighter and more restrictive for the group, although individual patients who have clearly succeeded in disentangling themselves from the deeper currents of the process will continue as before. No special little parties, recreational outings, or "late nights" are planned with the idea that this will make them feel better and love us more. This will occur only when we have restored their safety.

The general progression of events which builds to rioting will not reverse spontaneously after it has passed a certain point, one which is usually reached quite early in the process. It must be actively reversed by the intelligent understanding and determined actions of the supervisory staff.

It is worth emphasizing that our treatment aims are necessarily and temporarily modified after a riot has started to build. Adequate protection for patients and staff, and program survival, receive top priority. This, of course, is a departure from our approach to patient behavior under usual circumstances, when it is dominated by the aims of intensive, individual treatment.

INTERPRETING ILLUSORY OMNIPOTENCE. The adolescent-at-large, though beginning to attach more importance to verbalized ideas, still relies heavily on motor activity and other outward "signs" to communicate his feelings. A confusing mixture of verbal and motor telegraphy is especially favored by the disturbed adolescent, who has a more than average mistrust of spoken language. There are many things which he can say only through the language of behavior, and we must learn how to decipher this before we can help him to greater proficiency in adult patterns of "exchanging emotional information."

The management of all acting-out behavior, i.e., not just in the limited antisocial sense, is directed at (1) the undermining of those defensive machinations which make it possible for the patient to choose and exercise motoric modes and (2) helping him to resolve intrapsychically, by any useful means, the old childhood conflicts which are constantly pressing him into maladaptive motor expression.

The emotionally significant meanings of a given act are not specific, either for the act or for the individual who performs it. The theft of a cookie, for example, may serve directly to satisfy hunger, to incorporate symbolically an unconsciously desired attribute of another person, to express aggression, to prove masculinity, or to satisfy a sadistic need. The emotional meanings of the act may have no visible relationship to its manifest content, which naturally restricts our chances for understanding them. This, in turn, would theoretically leave us to infer more—and from less valid data—than would be the case with a patient who can tell us about his feelings in words. If this were true, which is debatable, then it might seem that we would have to settle for "superficial" treatment, as opposed to "deep therapy," for the acting-out adolescent. This is not generally true.

As a rule, it is quite impossible and probably unnecessary to determine the elusive and perhaps mythical underlying cause of every action with which we must deal. It is possible, however, to achieve valuable understanding at various levels short of this theoretical ideal. The arboreal complex of forces leading to the single actions and thoughts of the present need not necessarily be traced to every tiny little rootlet of origin to be favorably influenced in treatment. Working at the surface can have deep-reaching effects on a person, just as pruning and sunlight have on a plant. The idea of "treating behavior" does rankle a little, but it often yields the best results. For many adolescents (to say the least) it is the only way to achieve any results. An understanding of dynamic principles is not at all essential to good "surface work," but it can help immeasurably if adequately understood in application as well as in theory.

Most individual instances of antisocial behavior depend heavily, for example, upon the patient's immediate feeling of omnipotence. Ideally, the treatment question implicit in any such action should be resolved promptly and directly, and its various meanings then translated, if possible, into "verbal ideas." If this is not possible, the therapist can only proceed on his inferences about the behavior. It is often easier to sense that a youngster is being troubled by resurgent feelings of omnipotence than to diagnose it by objective signs, although some useful indicators can be crudely identified.

The patient's "parting shot" helps to preserve his sense of control over others. He has had the last word. He customarily tosses this over his shoulder in a deceptively casual manner, and the staff person is understandably tempted to drop the matter there. To do so only postpones the problem.

It is very easy for a staff person to ignore a fleeting facial expression which connotes silent contempt, or to see it but misinterpret its meaning. Usually it has no great clinical significance, but sometimes it will be the only available indication that a patient is feeling a superiority which transcends all realistic considerations. To take note of such signs openly, to raise questions about their possible meanings, effectively persuades him to compare his fantasies with the realities which they violate.

"Escape"

Runaways. Our patients have subscribed to the idea that unauthorized departure from the sphere of staff supervision is too easy to be designated "escape." It is called "running away," "taking off," or "cutting out."

Before this idea was adequately clarified with them, there were several incidents which illustrated their need to keep it alive. On one occasion two of the youngsters, a boy and a girl, tied sheets together, kicked out a screen, slid to the ground, and "escaped." After being returned to the ward, their initial boasting implied that they had surmounted the insurmountable, but they were unable to sustain this fantasy when other patients pointed out to them that they could have left by the front door with much less effort. There are innumerable opportunities throughout the day for walking away from the hospital. It is clearly understood, for example, that a patient leaving the group from a supervised walk without permission will not be pursued by accompanying staff members. They will be told not to go, but no effort will be made to restrain them physically. There is little romance to the game under these conditions, and on a number of occasions various youngsters have found it necessary to create a challenge where none really existed.

Although running away occurs periodically, it has never been a highly valued diversion. This tactic is seasonal and epidemic; it seems to support a variety of purposes. Of all the aims which it might serve, the least is a genuine wish to be permanently away from the hospital. Several observable patterns of behavior suggest some of the attraction which running away holds for the adolescent. Sometimes it seems to climax and terminate a period of slowly rising tension within an individual or a group.

Quite often a passive boy is strongly impelled to accomplish an heroic, symbolic resolution of a suspected but unidentified problem. Girls, as a rule, are able to accept the passive role imposed by hospitalization more easily than boys, and would be expected to have less need to demonstrate their capacity for active aggression. Actually, they take French leave as frequently as the boys, although their motives for doing so seem somewhat different.

It is common to hear from girls just returned from escape adventures many direct and indirect allusions to spirited sexual close calls which suggest "something terrible almost happened to me, but it didn't." Parents in our society are understandably concerned about having their daughters on the streets at odd hours, unattended, because of the sexual dangers to which this exposes them. One sometimes gets the impression that a girl's escape is sexually climactic in a somewhat metaphorical sense. They seem to be placing themselves in a reality situation of slight sexual danger which supports thrilling fantasies of great sexual danger—a threat which does not materialize.

Rarely is a runaway aimed at the discovery of a brave new world of independence and self-determination. The patient who impulsively runs away seems to have no particular conscious aim or direction, and will usually just wander about until he is picked up by a patrol car. Many times he will go to great lengths (not always unconsciously) to attract the attention of police and so insure his prompt return to the hospital. Seldom does he leave with a specific goal in mind and as a result finds himself back in the hospital within a few hours. One girl ran off with an ex-patient and was gone for eight days. Her boy friend, fortunately, was much less determined than she and finally contrived to steal a car which he promptly drove into the waiting arms of the law.

The patient who is planning to run away typically manages to drop a number of obvious clues to his intentions which can be picked up readily by alert staff persons. In such an instance, as with so many other rebellious but essentially nonfelonious delinquencies, the youngster approaches the misdeed with ample evidence of his conflicted feelings about it. In the standard prelude he spends anywhere from a few hours to a few days working up a sort of a war dance, often by straining clamorously to pick absurd fights with his doctor over miniscule issues which are known to be of little genuine concern to him. On the eve of the great venture he attempts to withdraw all his allowance money with unnecessary fanfare, insultingly demands that he be released to go out on pass privileges, and noisily confides his "secret"—complete with destination and time schedule—to his worst enemy. In this way his friends can at least see that he is *trying* to make a break. The illustration is not overdrawn.

For boys, running away is often a denial in action of their dependent wishes. They are most likely to run away after any experience which has enhanced feelings of passivity and submissiveness, as in losing out in a psychological power struggle with a member of the staff. It is intended to prove his ability to function with total autonomy. Similarly, running away frequently "saves" the patient who is threatened by increasingly strong transference feelings for the therapist, and saves him from the concomitant pressing to consciousness of passive-receptive sexual wishes. In still other cases it pointedly communicates the patient's fear that we were failing to appreciate fully the seriousness of his illness.

Carl, aged sixteen, came to us with a long history of truancy, rebellious behavior in school, and repeated auto theft. After the first few hectic months he began to make progress and some months later seemed ready for discharge to his family.

Throughout the entire course of his treatment he had insisted that he was ready to go home and could best be treated as an outpatient. When this propositon finally came under active consideration, Carl suddenly ran away and went straight to his home. After returning to the hospital, he was able to express openly the fear that his therapist would misinterpret his months of good behavior, place too much confidence in him, and perhaps send him home before he really felt able to keep himself out of trouble. When he was helped to understand that his therapist had not so interpreted his improvement, he was able to view the implications of his discharge more realistically.

THE NEED TO BE DEPENDENT. The need to be cared for, recognized, and appreciated is always woven into the complicated motivation underlying any antisocial behavior. It is one to which untrained staff seem most sensitive. They are quick to theorize, correctly as a rule, that a child's misbehavior is prompted by a desire to get attention. All forms of so-called attention-seeking behavior covertly communicate this need for the affectionate care and approval of a loving adult. To express this need openly is difficult enough for the disturbed child and virtually unthinkable for most adolescents, disturbed or otherwise. Freely admitting to the need for support from others is one of the cardinal sins of adolescence. Gifts of love from others must be obtained deviously, in ways which belie the motivating need while compelling a type of response in which the affectionate content will also be concealed:

"I'd just like to see you try and keep me here!"
"I'm going to try!"

When the adolescent complains *openly* of being unloved, he usually does so for the purposes of controlling a vulnerable adult. Only with the greatest difficulty could he make such a humiliating confession with sincerity. Hyperactivity, teasing, overdetermined expressions of hatred, and much angry and rebellious behavior are directed either at securing a limited serving of dependency gratification, or at defending prophylactically against the threats of frustration or exploitation which he perpetually, transferentially expects from any affectionate relationship.

In working with the depressed adolescent, it is vital that the therapist keep this idea in mind, no matter how flagrantly defiant and "independent" the patient may appear. Wonders can be worked by imposing firm and realistic prohibitions *against the behavior itself*. This is a positive form of attention which speaks volumes of friendly interest without a lot of superfluous embarrassing words. A verbal interpretation of the motivating need would probably force the patient to continue his denial-in-action with renewed energy. He will find the behavioral clarification far more palatable.

"Don't do that."
"Why not!"
"Do you want me to tell you?"
"No, never mind."

Authority: Compliance and Defiance

Group supports for the flagging sense of identity. A wide variety of the adolescent's acting-out patterns seem to have as their principal aim the confirmation of fantasies about what kind of person he is. Familiar customs, such as the elaborate intrigues, gossiping, clique-formation, and razz sessions (mutual criticism in social groups), all help in some way to fill in his picture of himself as a single individual whose unique personality sets him distinctly apart from all others. There is no higher compliment for the adolescent than to be told by a peer, especially one of the opposite sex, "You're different from the others," or "You have a wonderful personality," or "You're the understanding type."

Clinically, there is range in the kind and severity of identity disturbances which will influence our treatment approach. Many of these we recognize and respond to quite automatically with the adolescent patient, much as we would with friends and family. The fact that these measures require very little conscious reflection should not disqualify them as valuable agents in psychotherapy. Well-earned praise that is bestowed conservatively and dispassionately is a good example of this. Once again, the matter of "complicating the transference" is of secondary importance. Many of the girls who are admitted to the service, for example, have been protecting themselves from their own sexual exhibitionistic wishes by contriving to render themselves as unattractive as possible. Mild obesity or anorexia, sloppiness, bizarre overgrooming, repugnantly garish makeup or no cosmetics at all, are a few of the ways in which their conflicted wishes about being sexually attractive are simultaneously conveyed and defended against. When a girl with this kind of problem begins to improve in treatment, it is advisable to express a little matter-of-fact appreciation for her efforts to make herself attractive. Offering this when she has finally succeeded in resolving some of her painful uncertainty about herself will not stimulate any untoward or damaging transference fantasies. If she has put much honest labor into restyling her hair or making an attractive dress for herself, it would probably be more damaging to withhold comment. She might secretly wonder if her therapist has gone blind, but would be even more likely to marvel at the magnitude of his inhibitedness. Fantasies which are aroused by the therapist's more personal remarks can be used to good advantage in clarifying transference distortions. The latter are more likely to become explicit in the interview if her therapist, instead of freezing, simply comments to the effect that "Your hair looks very nice—you've changed it":

"Oh . . . well, the other girls told me I ought to."
"I see. You apparently thought it was a good idea, though?"
"It seemed like a good idea at the time, but now I don't like it this way. I wish I could change it back."
"Why? It looks nicer the way it is, doesn't it?"
"Not to me. I'm not worried how it looks to other people."
"You're not? Now, that isn't true, is it?"
"I care some, but . . . with this kind of a hairdo the other kids will think I'm trying to be Miss America."
"How do you get that idea? Did any of them say something like that?"
"No . . . it just seems like that to me." She trailed off thoughtfully.
"Didn't you ever fix your hair up nice when you were younger? I remember what a mess it was when you came into the hospital. How about before that—a year or two ago?"
"I did once and my mother told me I looked like a chorus girl. She made me put it back in braids . . . she and my father got into a big fight about it."
"A real fight?"
"Well, they didn't hit each other, but for a while I thought . . . They were really mad . . . well, that's the time I cut it all off real short and did it ever look horrible. I looked like a boy."

This open expression of appreciation on the part of the doctor naturally carries a hint of sexual interest. As such feelings are inevitable anyway, any effort to write them off entirely as "countertransference" will be correctly interpreted by the patient as an act of emotional cowardice—

an uneasy withdrawal from the very kinds of feelings which she finds so difficult to tolerate in herself.

ART OF AUTHORITY WITH THIN-SKINNED SUBORDINATES. After a difficult day with one or several of the boys on the ward, one sometimes gets the impression that they are all dedicated to no more complex a cause than the incessant proving of their physical strength, sexual potency, and wretched independence. Some of the built-in features of the routine activities program which make positive, realistic concessions to this need will be considered shortly. In our more personal contacts with a boy, there are some other ways in which we can demonstrate the respect which he deserves and needs so much.

He must always be approached by members of the staff, for example, with the same courtesy which is required of him. He should never be addressed by a nickname unless he approves of it and it is certain that this has no belittling connotation to him. Genially hostile salutations like "sport," "buddy," or "buster," are strictly out of line. There is no place for condescension or other humiliating techniques in the treatment of the adolescent.

It is painful for an adolescent boy to take orders gracefully and a fine art for the staff members to give them graciously. We need to develop a keen appreciation for the difference between rebellious and face-saving behaviors. The staff person who directs a boy to pick up a piece of paper which he has thoughtlessly thrown on the floor is asking too much if he expects him to comply immediately and without some sort of mildly desultory rejoinder. Ideally, such instructions are delivered in a tone which conforms to the magnitude of the job, rather than to the quality of the response which is anxiously *expected* from the boy. The characterologically hostile, rebellious boy is adept at conditioning the staff person to anticipate a full-dress battle on every issue. If he is so disposed, the attendant will find himself exercising even the slightest measure of authority as though he were commanding a regiment of infantry into battle. A piece of paper on the floor deserves attention, to be sure, but very little emotional investment.

"Jerry, you dropped a piece of paper on the floor."
"Well, what of it?"

"So pick it up."

Jerry rolls his eyes hopelessly skyward, expressing the futility of it all, "Oh boy, what a place! Now I'm a janitor!"

The attendant finds that no response is necessary, unless he is amused, in which case a reflex smile would really not be out of order.

These relatively routine and automatic measures are gauged to be age-specific and sex-specific, meaning, for example, that we try to avoid treating a sixteen-year-old girl like the nine-year-old tomboy she feels herself to be.

PSYCHOTIC NEGATIVISM. Other youngsters, who are much sicker, become so deeply involved in trying to establish whether or not they exist at all that they have little energy left over to embellish a mental picture of themselves with the finer details of character.

Doris, fourteen years old, was admitted with a lifelong history of severe affectional deprivation. The most prominent clinical feature of her illness was negativism. To a new nurse who introduced herself as "Mrs. White," Doris simply replied, "No, you're not."

If told to stand, she sat, and if told to sit, she stood. There was copious evidence of her lack of a basic sense of identity. She had changed her own first name many times. For months she referred to all women generically as "ladies" and did not refer to men at all. She identified no one by name.

It was suggested to the staff that they always approach Doris with some concrete tribute to her existence. Specifically, they were to call her by name, comment in detail on her appearance and actions, and above all to answer the need expressed in her negativism. To Doris a passive and kindly response to her negativistic behavior would have defeated its adaptive aims. Sanctions were offered to the nursing staff for entering into protracted verbal struggles with her for the purpose of reinforcing her feeling of being an individual apart from other persons. Her subsequent improvement, after a period of months, was due partly to this management. She came to identify people concretely, e.g., "there is the lady with the black hair who is always smiling," and to address a few people by title and name.

Julia, aged sixteen, suffered an adolescent psychotic illness which was marked by extreme affective swings between frank depression and elated hyperactivity. She always became very concerned about the attitudes of other people toward her as her mood rose. In a formal group therapy session, talking under great pressure, she proposed that they conduct a "razz session" in which the girls would criticize each other candidly. The others, perhaps needless to say, were not enthusiastic about the project and gave her little support. In a frantic effort to sell the idea, Julia finally exclaimed: "It's all right—you can start with me—say anything to me you want—don't be afraid of hurting my feelings—tell me anything about myself you want to because I want to know—I don't even know what I'm like and I want everyone to tell me—please tell me what I'm like!" She was agitated and on the verge of tears. Her request for multifocal reassurance about the reality of her existence was literal and sincere.

Relief from guilt. The adolescent who willingly confesses to having committed a social misdemeanor is likely to be regarded by his peers as a fellow-traveler of card-carrying adults. Confession, though possibly good for the soul, is terribly hard on the adolescent's self-esteem and could ruin his social standing altogether. Unrelenting feelings of guilt from either conscious or unconscious sources must ordinarily be relieved by means other than public penance. One of his "preferred" unconscious mechanisms is to act in a way which will provoke a certain allotment of punishment which can then be re-allocated intrapsychically to assuage all other fantasied sources of guilt as well. A special refinement of the mechanism offers the exceptional advantage of provoking punishment which can be represented publicly as blatantly unjust. This defense by righteous indignation provides the guilt-ridden youngster with a legal precedent for declaring all previous accusations, however accurate they may have been, to be invalid and inadmissible [16].

Kenny, spoken of elsewhere, had been having more than his usual share of trouble with the staff. His manner was provocative, irritating, and generally offensive. His therapist recognized these as earmarks of unalleviated guilt but had not yet found a way to deal with them.

At evening snack-time, when the supervising aide's back was turned, one of the other boys threw several slices of bread over her head and then surrounded himself with an aura of Tom Sawyeresque innocence. The aide whirled around and surveyed the group with a swift glance, then pointed her finger accusingly at Kenny and ordered him out of the room.

He left with cries of outraged innocence and indulged himself in an orgy of bitter recriminations against the ponderous injustice of adult authority. He was so unassailably secure in his righteous anger that it soon became necessary to call his therapist.

After repeating his heated account to his doctor five or six times, he was finally able to settle down and review the precipitating incident in detail. As he finally explained it, still afire with the unfairness of it all, "I'm not going to tell you who threw the bread! Go ahead and blame me! I'm admitting it—I did it—she accused me of it so I did it! Of course she didn't even see who really *did* do it, but I'm still the guilty party. There were four other kids there. I don't know why she picked on me. So *maybe I had a guilty look on my face!* Does that mean I did it?"

Through his overdrawn sarcasm and the mask of guilt which he wore constantly, Kenny contrived to array the bulk of the evidence against himself in the hope of seducing some staff member into making a reckless accusation which he could then refute in his own fantasies, and, along with it, every other accusation that had ever been made against him by himself or anyone else [16].

THEFT

CONFLICTING LOYALTIES: A PROBLEM IN ETHICS. There has been little difficulty with stealing on the ward. A few patients have had specific problems with compulsive stealing, but as one might expect, their activities have been consistently "open" and accessible to the work of therapy.

There is no highly organized system for preventing theft beyond urging the youngsters to be careful with their own possessions. On those rare occasions when an item is stolen, its recovery is not so urgent that we cannot wait for it to turn up in fact and in therapy.

The psychological value of stealing naturally varies with the individual patient and is not an issue here. Certain consequences of this kind of behavior crystallize other issues which are of utmost importance to the group and often extremely delicate and difficult to handle. As an antisocial action which has occurred in a tightly woven group, theft, or anything like it, invariably challenges our standard of values. We are not free to assert only that "stealing is wrong," because we will also have to give an opinion as to whether it is more or less wrong than betraying a friend, placing other patients in danger, punishing "all for one," or "searching without a warrant."

Following the theft of medications or a ward key, for example, we are likely to be more concerned by the fact that they are in the possession of a patient than by any deep psychological implications of the act itself. For obvious reasons we are not justified in being too leisurely about recovering such items, which poses a delicate question of procedure. Although it is well understood that members of the staff are empowered to enter and search any area of hospital property at any time, we would choose to do this only under rather exceptional circumstances. Even then there would be little excuse for failing to enlist the aid of the patient in conducting the search. "No, I'm not calling you a liar. I'm just saying you might be one. Come on, let's go down to your room and look. You do the looking and I'll watch. Let's get this thing settled."

Ward-wide "shakedowns" are honest enough but extremely impractical. It is an approach which challenges the group to a contest which most of them would contemplate with a justifiably cheerful anticipation of triumph. Most important of all is the fact that such methods are quite incompatible with our otherwise consistent expectation that we, and they, will be able to handle such problems more forthrightly than this.

A ward key was carelessly left on the office desk by a staff member and found to be missing a short time later. Because there were some good reasons to suspect that one of the other staff people might have inadvertently picked it up or otherwise mislaid it, we were not immediately concerned that it had fallen into the hands of the patients.

After several days the key had not turned up, but a few vague verbal clues from the patient group had. No sudden, sweeping action was taken. Instead, one of the staff psychiatrists on a routine sojourn through the ward casually inquired as to the whereabouts of the key from one boy after another, as opportunities to do so arose. This process was repeated several times a day, and with each new contact the field of culpability narrowed a little more. It quickly became clear that the purloined key had become the joint property of a group of four boys; interestingly, virtually all the information which pointed to this group was provided, bit by bit, by its individual members.

The frequency of contacts with these four was then increased, and heavier psychological pressure of a certain kind was brought to bear. Each of the four boys refused to "testify" on the grounds that it might incriminate him. On the other hand they all took pride in admitting to having knowledge of the act and were eager to accept some of the blame. None of them wanted to turn chicken and squeal on the member who was in actual possession of the key. They were repeatedly advised that we were more concerned about recovering the key than catching the culprit, even though we regretted having to admit this. We freely acknowledged that we were in no position to put our finger on the guilty party and were not interested in doing the kind of detective work which would make this possible. We presumed, instead, that the guilty party and others involved would eventually see this, in effect, as a manifestation of personality disturbance and consider it a matter of treatment. At that moment, however, we wanted the key back and were insisting that it be returned.

The four boys were directed to meet together and select one of their number to return the key. By this time they were all becoming quite anxious, raising questions about what would happen to their various privileges if the key were not returned, openly suggesting that if we were to restrict the entire ward from all activities that the key would probably be returned promptly, and finally begging for permission to be released from the responsibility of participating in this increasingly noxious group project.

None of the restrictive pressures which they had proposed were invoked. We agreed that general ward restriction would probably do the trick, but felt that it was unnecessary to resort to such infantilization when it was within their power to return it without this kind of pressure. They finally met together in a session which lasted for more than an hour. Every few minutes one boy or another would leave the meeting room perspiring unhappily and step into the bathroom to void. The tension in the group was immense, but at the conclusion of the meeting one of the boys returned the key.

The most interesting consequence of this appeared during their regular group therapy session on that same afternoon. Long and bitterly they complained of the tremendous pressure which had been brought to bear upon them by the staff. At first they were unable to admit that the only pressure had been the staff's repeated, firm insistence that the key be returned, along with a clear explanation of the very important reasons for this. They were so threatened by the growing realization that they had chickened-out, as a group, in voluntarily complying with an important adult code that they had to perceive the pressure as having come exclusively from outside of themselves. During the formal group therapy session, as the facts of the several preceding days were reviewed, they were finally unable to support this illusion any longer and were impelled to acknowledge their gross complicity in an act of social virtue.

Destructive Aggression

Physical assault and the destruction of property are dealt with, in those extremely rare instances when they have become imminent issues, by a simple but effective technique: emphatic prohibition. All these youngsters had, of course, successfully defied many prohibitions before entering the hospital and therefore entertained good reasons for questioning the security of such a rigid stand. It had to be tested.

Shortly after the ward was opened, a nurse discovered a small set of initials carefully painted with fingernail polish on one of the doors and another set on the tile wall. This single effort taken by itself was more ornamental than destructive, but in those circumstances it was a recognizable test of our treatment aims and moral stamina. If this minor occurrence had been ignored, we could have predicted with reasonable assurance, on the basis of experience elsewhere, that it would have been followed in time by artistic endeavors of Sistine scope and Rabelaisian content.

It was not ignored. The artists, two of the girls, were immediately put to work removing the polish, and the site was inspected many times that day by one unsmiling staff member after another. No effort was made to conceal our genuine concern over these little dabs of polish. The effect was remarkable. There have been no serious problems with deliberate property destruction to this time, because it is sincerely expected not to happen.

A number of months later a group of the boys removed the pins from a recreation room door in a "spirit of fun," which is the way all such tests usually begin. They were not at this time manifestly defiant and rebellious. The psychiatrist on night call struggled with the temptation to let the matter ride until morning. His good judgment won out, however, and he came in that evening. Upon entering the ward he passed mutely and soberly through a group of inquisitive, sheepish-looking boys and spent fifteen awkwardly silent minutes scrutinizing the unpinned hinges. One by one the "mischievous boys" drifted down to the recreation room and began offering unsolicited proclamations of innocence. They volunteered to help and began turning up hinge-pins from the most improbable hiding places. After they had replaced the door, a hospital maintenance man was called immediately to examine the job and check the door lock. It is noteworthy that they had destroyed nothing in the process of determining whether or not we would accommodate destruction as a part of the community's social tradition. There was little room left for their doubting the sincerity of the sacred edict: Thou Shalt Not Destroy.

The idea of physically attacking a staff member has been raised by one or another patient no more than two or three times, and our ready and heartfelt response has always included a visible, unfeigned shock-reaction of perplexity and disbelief. The staff do not touch patients[1] for purposes of coercion, and it is likewise understood that the patients do not touch staff members with assaultive intent. This has not been a problem.

Fist fights between patients have been rare and well controlled. The boys have demonstrated a truly remarkable skill at assaulting each other brutally without raising so much as a lump or a bruise. They manage not to hurt each other. In this connection it has been interesting to observe that the two toughest boys on the ward are less likely to fight it out for the position of supremacy than are the two weakest, who wish desperately to escape last position in the pecking order.

Sex and Sociability

The problems involved in drawing the line on open sexual behavior among adolescents are very trying for most adults. These are somewhat simplified with inpatients because of the clear-cut situational inappropriateness of physical romancing in a hospital setting. On this ward the

[1] In the six years since the opening of the adolescent ward it has been necessary in only one instance—that of an extremely psychotic fourteen-year-old boy who needed to be transferred to the closed adult unit—to use physical measures with a patient.

limits are set to exclude any tenderness-tinged physical contact between patients unless they are dancing, skating, or similarly engaged. They naturally protest this vehemently, just as we protest it in silence, but are usually cooperative in practice. The adolescent seems far more interested in the picture which he has of himself participating in a thrilling and forbidden adult adventure than in the adventure itself [11]. If he enjoys some reputation as a lover, he will not be too concerned about a scarcity of real action. Repeated observation strongly suggests that the ideal teenage romance occurs in the purest troubadorian tradition.

Fran and Jack, both sixteen years old, fell deeply in "love" and became "engaged" after several weeks of desultory courting. Fran made a great deal of noise about her romance, flaunting it before the other girls and challenging the staff to "try and keep us apart." Jack was commended by his peers as a smooth operator. His occasional moments together with Fran were uneasy ones, and the relationship seemed to survive mostly from the support of staff prohibition. To a large extent it was the protection of supervision which made it safe for them to appear so voluptuous. However, as they attracted less and less attention from the other youngsters, they began to lose interest in each other and started looking around for new partners. At this point a change in Jack's clinical situation, which was incidental to his love-life, prompted his transfer to the closed adult unit, whereupon the dying romance came miraculously to life.

They railed angrily against the staff for transferring Jack just to keep them apart (which was pure fiction) and exchanged letters dripping with sentiments of everlasting love. One note from Jack began with the telltale salutation, "Dear Fran—I never want to be any farther away from you than I am right now . . ." (nor, by deft implication, any closer). Safely separated, they were free to love ethereally and without fear of consummation.

There is less likelihood of serious sexual acting-out in this population than might be expected, but reliance upon neurotic inhibition is not an adequate substitute for good supervision and the enforcement of conventional taboos. All mixed groups are carefully chaperoned, and it is hard to know whether this is more comforting to the staff or the patients. The patients themselves have made it clear in many ways that we cannot afford to be derelict in this duty. A report of sexual misbehavior seems to pass the squealing barrier more easily than others.

A related problem has less to do with the control of gross sexual acting-out than with the need to organize some mechanisms for heterosocial insulation to protect against excessive stimulation. The ward had been in operation for several months before we realized that the youngsters were immersed in a far more liberal coeducational system than could be found in any other legal and proper social situation. This was brought to our attention by a group of the girls who specifically requested a two-hour period in the evening during which they could enjoy one another's company in the privacy of their own side of the ward. The request was allowed. The boys, hearing of this, rose in manly protest and declared that only the most extreme measures could prevent them from practicing their hairy animal prerogatives wherever and whenever they wished. They termed this period of privacy "evening lock-up," making it sound as though they had been bricked in forever. The fact was that we had only closed the door, not locked it. It has taken us five years to learn just how conflicted and irresolute we adults are about this issue. It has, indeed, been far harder for us to provide consistent chaperonage than for them to accept it.

Such matters may seem too minor to rate so much attention, and yet the whole of any social structure is built up from a vast number of apparently minor things. Each of these alone might indeed be negligible if it could be eliminated, altered, or forgotten about all by itself. This is not easy to do, however, because the same attitude which sanctions the neglect of one "minor" issue will also operate in the resolution of many other equally minor issues. We have repeatedly stressed the conviction that the therapeutic milieu for anyone, and perhaps especially for children and adolescents, should be made to correspond as closely as possible to conventional, nonpsychiatric group living situations. These youngsters have enough internal reminders of their mental state without our adding more. They don't want to live in a "nut house," and we should not require them to do so.

14

STAFF, PATIENTS, AND PROGRAM

Qualifications of Staff

It is evident that members of the staff should be well qualified, but general stipulations are obviously insufficient guides for the actual selection of personnel. It might seem that no one could be better qualified for working with disturbed adolescents than a person who has had intensive training in dynamic psychology and a deep interest in sick personalities. There are excellent reasons, both practical and theoretical, for believing that this is not so. In reviewing the work records of ward personnel (most of whom were college students) on the Children's Service of the Neuropsychiatric Institute, University of Michigan, in the early 1950's, Rabinovitch [29] confirmed a long-standing suspicion that there is a definite relationship between one's personal career interests and the probability of his contributing usefully to a therapeutic program for children.

Interests and motivation of staff. Our own experience, which parallels these findings, indicates that persons with interests and prior training in such fields as psychology, social work, philosophy, law, and medicine are as a group less likely to function well in a children's psychiatric treatment program than are those whose central interests lie a little further away from academic fields of human psychology.

Although the explanation for this is not established, several possibilities come readily to mind. There is the popular and not necessarily erroneous notion that many people select psychology and related fields because of aptitudes based upon extraordinary and perhaps "abnormal" insightfulness or in an effort to "distance" their own personal problems by professionalizing them. These people would be relatively more disturbed to begin with, and their ineptness in a psychiatric treatment program could be explained on that basis.

Another possibility is suggested in the traditional warning that a little knowledge is a dangerous thing. A person with some training in a field relating to human psychology might well overestimate his abilities and try to reach beyond them. Formal knowledge also has a limiting effect on spontaneity. When a good golfer starts thinking about his muscles, he is lost. Whatever the answer may be, the fact remains that an applicant's professional interest, in a statistical way at least, does tend to influence us in the selection of ward personnel.

We are also interested in the prospective attendant's approach to employment and are inclined to be especially inquisitive about the motives of the person who expresses a deep interest in joining the staff because of his strong, preexisting interest in the dynamics and treatment of disturbed adolescents. Conversely, persons motivated primarily by a desire for steady employment and a living wage are somewhat less suspect than those with a deep yearning to help the mentally ill.

At the risk of propagating a jurisdictional dispute, it must be confessed that we also make a point of hiring teachers from a regular public school system rather than those who have been trained in special education. This is certainly not without some loss, but a careful examination of the pros and cons of the question has led us to the conclusion that it is better, in the long run, to draw sharp lines between the various professional staff disciplines. This is not related to any stand against "lay therapy." It is just that if teachers become therapists and school becomes therapy, who will do the teaching and how will it be done?

Members of the permanent and resident psychiatric staff are not exceptions to this general view of personnel qualifications. In some ways we psychiatrists have more difficulty in our routine ward contacts with patients than do a number of the untrained nonmedical staff. To say it simply, it appears that the personal qualities of an individual staff person are—with respect to his effectiveness in this work—considerably more important than his professional training.

Every applicant for a position which requires patient contact is interviewed at length by one or two staff psychiatrists and by the head of the unit in which he might be working, e.g., nursing, occupational and recreational therapy, or school. We naturally look for glaring personality disturbances, for too much or too little self-assurance, into avocational as well as vocational interests, work history, social and marital status, and for signs of the all-important "ability to get along with other people." In plain terms we like to see people who by the grace of their own past experiences have come to adulthood with a liberal endowment of kindness, conscience, and good judgment, the exercise of which will not depend too much upon their having to think about each of them.

Staff and patients. Adolescents are exquisitely sensitive to any evidence of artificiality in the people around them. They recognize instantly when a staff person attempts therapeutic pretenses which are unnatural to him. That the adult should *need* to do this will be interpreted as an evidence of his uncertainty about his own competence. The adolescent can handily diagnose such deficits and exploit them at will. He is interested in boldly exposing adult inadequacies, just as he feels his own feeble pretensions to be transparent and scorned. "Pretending" with him gives him the chance to lead from strength. It enables him to switch from defense to offense, a move which he will gleefully make at almost any opportunity. He begins to mimic that which is spurious in the adult's manner, to ridicule him, and to undertake the testing of other points in this powerful figure's presumably impregnable ego armor. The youngster's pleasure in such a triumph is short-lived, spoiled, as it is, by the price he must pay for it. He loses more than he gains.

Time after time we have heard the unhappy, realistic complaints about the staff person who "tries too hard," "thinks he's a doctor," "is an easy pushover" in an authority contest, and seems always to be trying to figure out what he is supposed to do in any routine conflict situation with a patient. Complaints are also registered against the most proficient staff people, but these are made in some clearly self-contradictory manner: "he thinks he's the boss . . . he's always right just because he's on the staff . . . he got mad at me just because I told him to get the hell out of my room . . . he doesn't like me."

It would be unfair and inaccurate to leave the impression that a graduate student in psychology, social work, or philosophy could not possibly be a good ward attendant. If this were true, then the clinical psychiatrist might be the last to qualify for such work. We could theorize, of course, that he would not have to qualify as a good attendant to work well as a psychotherapist, but our current impression is that an outstanding individual therapist, for reasons already partly implied, will prove equally adept in the unstructured, informal group setting.

The ward nursing assistants are referred to as *aides* (women) and *attendants* (men). Some unsuccessful attempts have been made here and elsewhere to avoid the medieval, custodial connotations of such titles, in line with similar efforts in psychiatry to substitute a more lyrical expression for *electroshock treatment*. These verbal decals probably fail simply because the old terms are more concise and accurate than their somewhat sunnier alternatives. By any name, however, the main job of the attendant is to attend to the needs of the patients in his charge. Various other terms which have been proposed are even less desirable because they are inaccurate (*counselor*), dishonest (*mother*), or misleading in some other way.

They are not "ward parents." The argument that role-playing parents can answer an unmet need of the patient is untenable. Most patients, particularly older ones, would see this effort as a somewhat poetic distortion and could survive it without great strain, although they would be obliged to interpret it as just another example of disappointingly silly adult posturing. For other children this misrepresentation may seriously strain their reality-testing capacities. If they have indeed been neglected, deprived, and are without parents who can provide for their minimum requirements, they may be strongly tempted to participate in an illusion which makes cruel demands and offers hollow promises. An employed staff person is in no position to be a parent to his patients. He may do a lot of the superficial, ritual things which parents do for their children, but cannot be expected to make the same emotional investment in these activities that the healthy parent would with his own children. Nor can he fulfill the parental obligation to stay on the job until his child is adequately prepared for independent living.

When patients complain that the attendant is not really interested in them and is just working at the job to make money, it is best to be in a position for giving only a very straight answer. This is the only kind that will be accepted. It is well enough for us to see that the patient's attitude has been experientially determined (i.e., a transference attitude), but it is very hard to explain to him if we have literally tried to present him with parents who work on an eight-hour shift and do not look, act, or feel like parents. We would have justified his bitterness and encouraged his persistence in an irrational, dysfunctional pattern of displacement. It is far preferable to acknowledge without apology that the attendant is indeed a paid employee before attempting any maneuver aimed at helping the patient to understand that his feelings about the attendant are misdirected.

Though not a parent, the attendant can be, in addition to his regular duties, an older friend, a coach, a teacher. The fact that he is on salary does not prevent his being genuinely interested in many of the important things of concern to the patient. The fact that they will not remain together geographically for an indefinite number of years does not alter the fact that they can, in a relatively short time, influence each other in significant and lasting ways.

Training of Staff

Training for ward staff is "bed side" rather than theoretical. The chief goal of training is that each member of the staff shall come to regard himself as being immediately and seriously involved in the treatment of patients, which in fact he certainly is. Academic lectures on psychopathology contribute little enough to the resident psychiatrist and even less to the attendant. The didactic approach may lead the attendant to believe that we expect him to become an "analytic" type, which is not the case. Instead, his presence is required at regularly scheduled round-table meetings which are attended by all shifts of the nursing staff and several of the individual therapists. In this informal discussion group an anecdotal approach to the reporting of current ward activities is encouraged. The attendants describe in ordinary narrative terms the various perplexing or interesting experiences which they have had with patients. These are then discussed, analyzed, or simply enjoyed by the other members of the staff. One of the most important functions of these meetings is that of exciting and sanctioning a humanistic interest in the patients, and to insure in every way possible the preservation of an atmosphere of harmonious staff integration. It is also valuable for detecting early signs of staff *dis*integration.

These aims are further served by the relationship which exists between physician, attendant, and patient in experiences on the ward. The adolescent is keenly aware that doctors occupy positions of administrative authority, and he will often attempt to capitalize upon this in his incessant, ambivalent power struggle with attendants. It is a common occurrence for a patient who is usually cooperative to suddenly become defiant and resistive toward an attendant when a doctor comes within earshot. It is his intention to degrade the attendant by going over his head successfully. If the doctor simply goes about his business as he should, the youngster may make a more direct confrontation and deliver himself of an especially eloquent, heartrending, and winning appeal for a "stay of execution." The therapist's specific response will always include a casual tribute to the supervisory competence of the attendant, along with some sign that he is not going to step into this carefully baited trap.

At times the attendant will find it necessary to come directly to one of the therapists about some problem he is having with a patient. If an evaluation of the problem favors our intervention, we do this, but even then we attempt to conclude our resolution of the difficulty by returning it to the attendant if this is at all appropriate. Further, it is impossible for any member of the staff to ask a question about his work which does not rate a thoughtful, respectful answer. Even the busiest doctor is well advised to avoid the expedient of answering such questions with general, irrelevant aphorisms and clichés.

One of the most treacherous and obscure pitfalls in the able management of adolescents lies in the staff person's eternal quest for potent verbal formulas and for infallible, magical techniques. The roots of this need are easily unearthed. The attendant knows he has been hired to "take care of the patients," and if he is as conscientious as we would like him to be, *any* apparent failure on his part will be very disturbing to him. This particular source of anxiety rests squarely on the popular myth that all conflict situations between people can be handled on the spot if one knows just the right thing to say or do. As legend has it, the one person who can always do this is the psychologist (i.e., any of us) who is commonly seen as omnipotent by virtue of his vast understanding of human motivation. If we fail to clarify this majestic delusion for the staff person, we force him to conceal from us episodes which have provoked in him some thoroughly undeserved feelings of anxiety and guilt.

This fable of psychological omnipotence is sometimes inadvertently perpetuated by the therapist who advises the attendant that in some similar future situation he might say to the patient, "Now I understand that you are upset about this, but you are able to realize that . . ." and so forth and so on. These are not the attendant's words, and he knows it; and if he should ever try to use them, the patient will also know it. It is preferable that a careful attempt be made to illuminate the incident in question, to dissect from it the hidden meanings of the patient's communication, and then to mumble a little something about our concept of the *kind* of response which might make the most sense. This gives the attendant a chance to proceed with actions which are more natural and comfortable for him.

STAFF GUILT OVER PSEUDO-FAILURE. The nonmedical staff person's difficulty in accepting his own periodic "failures" is further complicated by his having to stand by at times and watch someone else succeed where he has apparently failed. After spending fifteen minutes at an unsuccessful effort to get a boy out of bed in the morning, he may turn helplessly to the patient's doctor, who rouses the slugabed with little more than a snap of his fingers (sometimes!). Here again it must be carefully and clearly explained that such occurrences are not only expected but confidently predicted in the community as it is organized. Recalling that many of these youngsters have come to us because of intractably aggressive and defiant behavior of one sort or another, they could hardly be expected to become suddenly passive and compliant just because of a change in address. They will threaten trouble, and we will keep them safe from it.

The anxious, depressed patient who tends too easily to "defense by aggression" can look around and see not an impregnable system of confining walls but a concentric system of personal, psychological barriers which extend finally beyond the limits of his vision. What the staff person takes for granted as a simple administrative hierarchy, the patient regards as a sort of "DEW Line." The attendant is in front and behind him is the nurse, then the therapist, the chief of service, the director of the institute, the juvenile court (which enforces as well as symbolizes the laws of society), and then beyond these a variety of other controlling social structures. If in this setting his own internal pressures *compel* him to aggressive acting-out, this can occur without his having to fear that he might successfully burst through a single line of authority and find himself pathetically independent.

Kenny, aged sixteen, unconsciously regarded himself as passive, effeminate, and impotent. His main line of defense against these feelings was a swaggering, rebellious manner reeking of masculine protest. In certain routine situations which obliged him to submit to the authority of a male staff member, he seemed able to protect himself from resurgent, passive wish-fears only by becoming actively hostile and defiant. After an outburst of this type he would saunter up and down the hall, shouting imperious orders at the staff and warning them that it would do no good to call his doctor. His doctor would then arrive, hear him out, offer some direct reassurance, and then lay down the law in positive terms. At this point, after having proved his strength and valor in successfully crashing the first two lines of authority—attendants and nurses—he was ready to capitulate with honor intact.

As he improved in treatment, he tended to continue in this pattern even though his need to do so was no longer urgent. When this was recognized by the therapist and clarified with Kenny in a straightforward manner, he was able to abandon it entirely.

If the attendant is not helped to understand that these occurrences are inevitable, though short of ideal expectations, he will feel guilty about fancied failure and perhaps feel that he has been inadequately supported by the medical staff. He might start avoiding the patient in order to spare himself the pain of further failure [16].

Allocation of staff responsibilities. Patient care in any situation is the full and immediate responsibility of nursing personnel, which includes the registered nurses, aides, and attendants. They may retire to the background during school time or join casually in an ice-skating activity which is under the supervision of a recreational therapist, but they are always prepared to act as an extension of the therapist in the latter's absence.

There is probably no delicate way of stating this principle without diluting its meaning, and it is too important to be neglected. It is essential that "adjunctive" staff respect the nurse's authority in all clinical matters in order to relieve them of any inclination to compete for popularity with patients. The point is emphasized especially for new services, where it is common to find several of the adjunctive disciplines jockeying for positions of administrative advantage; and the staff of an adolescent service dare not be divided.

The adolescent patient, with his many troubled feelings about other people and his relationship with them, has a strong predilection for condensing all adults into one great, faceless integer, cast in the model of a rather bad and manipulable parent. It is worthwhile to avoid as much as possible anything which might support his homogenized perception of people. It is well not to let irate outbursts against the "staff" pass without expressing some curiosity about exactly which specific individual has provoked him so.

CONSISTENCY AND NONUNIFORMITY. The natural heterogeneity of people is concretely represented on the ward in the nonuniform dress of nursing staff, and it is further reflected, within reasonable limits, to certain of their attitudes, tastes, and beliefs. The fact that we do not always do and see things the same way gives the youngsters many rich opportunities to groan darkly of our inconsistencies. After observing that Mrs. X is much more liberal about hand-holding than Mr. Y, they like to defend our heretical disregard for legal principles. They, and we, would indeed find more comfort and security in a uniform code, but catering to these needs would cost them many of their finest and most strenuous opportunities to regard people as individuals who desire and deserve tailored consideration. This is one of the most effective ways in which they are pressured to discriminate between the exacting realities of the present and the maladaptive, "transferred" misinterpretations of it which have derived from their own past experiences.

Staff's Countertransference

The fascination of adolescence. The idea of working with disturbed adolescents intrigues and attracts many, but captivates few. There is widespread reluctance to deal with them at the clinical level, and, indeed, a generous percentage of adults find them hard enough to tolerate at the family and social levels [16].

One finds in discussions with colleagues, as well as in the psychiatric literature, many allusions to clinical experience with adolescents. A little further inquiry often reveals that these are mostly prepubertal or barely pubertal youngsters or, even more frequently, young adults in the age range of eighteen to twenty years. It is commonly proposed that these latter, who are really postadolescents, still have a lot of *adolescent-type* problems.

This reasonable generalization applies to most adults, but the fact remains that there are significant changes in attitudes and defense preferences which bring an end to clinical adolescence at around seventeen or eighteen years of age. These changes influence, and are influenced by, other concomitant alterations in the individual's legal and social status. As noted earlier, it is at about this time that he finishes high school, becomes eligible for military service, may leave home to live beyond parental jurisdiction, get a job, marry, and come under the adult legal code. He also rather abruptly becomes a far more reasonable prospect for outpatient psychotherapy than he was a year earlier. Psychiatrists are suddenly willing to consider him for treatment.

Dr. M, an able and experienced general psychiatrist, telephoned to make an emergency referral of a fifteen-year-old boy who had got seriously out of hand. Wilson's parents had been divorced six years earlier, and he had lived alone with his mother since then. On the day prior to referral, she had anxiously informed him of her plans to remarry, following which he went into a violent rage. His prospective stepfather was a house guest at the time. Wilson gathered together all that he could find of the interloper's clothing and luggage, drenched them with gasoline, and used them for a spectacular bonfire in the back yard.

Dr. M's referral information included a comprehensive, carefully detailed history based on a two-and-a-half hour interview with the mother, which he then followed with the request that Wilson be admitted to the hospital. He was asked about his findings and impressions with respect to the patient and replied apologetically, "Well, the boy's sitting out in my waiting room, and he doesn't look very cooperative. I got the whole story from the mother, so I didn't think it would be necessary to see him."

This is not unusual. Although there are many things which the adult finds interesting about *adolescence,* the intensity of his interest tends to vary directly with his distance from the *adolescent.* The psychology of adolescence lends itself admirably to abstract consideration. It has become an increasingly popular subject for articles, books, and panel discussions at professional meetings, but it is still difficult to find someone who is willing to accept an adolescent patient for treatment. Clinical work with the disturbed adolescent is, in fact, extremely interesting and rewarding, but it is also an experience which constantly reminds one that there are many easier forms of livelihood. Even an experienced psychiatric ward staff accustomed to dealing with adult and child patients has little inclination to accept the innumerable opportunities to participate in this beguiling work.

With his doctor's approval, Ben, aged sixteen, was transferred at his own request to the adult closed unit because he found himself uncomfortably overstimulated on the adolescent ward. His behavior had never been violent or aggressive. Shortly after the transfer his therapist, a resident psychiatrist, received an urgent call for help from the adult service staff because Ben was quietly refusing to shave. After answering this call, the resident observed, "They (clinical staff) aren't afraid of the most psychotically paranoid adult, but if an adolescent boy refuses to shave in the morning they want to call a general conference to discuss the theory and technique of managing rebellious adolescents."

RECAP: THE PROVOCATEUR AND THE PROVOKED. Some of the reasons for this common adult's-eye view lie in the adolescent's embodiment of strong drives, poor controls, and adult strength. It is more probable, though, that the adult's vague uneasiness results more from internal problems of his own than from real external threats.

As adults, time and our own defenses afford us greater protection from the travail of childhood than from the frequently painful struggle of adolescence. At the onset of "second latency" the emerging adult enjoys substantial success in covering over some of the aims, modes, and values which we so commonly associate with adolescence. But at best the labors of the age are still incomplete and remain a source of continued conflict throughout life.

A person ordinarily relies upon his natural faculty for selectively recalling the pleasurable memories of the past. It would seem to be far easier for him to achieve vivid, detailed recollections of his adolescence than his childhood, and he probably could—if he would. The painful events of this period seem more suppressed than repressed. They are more available to consciousness but in some ways no less threatening than earlier conflicts partly *because* of their greater availability. The child who is pathologically dependent upon his mother becomes the adolescent who is noisily rebellious and "independent." Later, as a young adult, he will regard this adolescent style of defense as beneath his station, but still far more acceptable than his abandoned infantile ways of dealing with regressive pressures. Because the adolescent modes are so close and accessible, any sudden stress from without or within will favor a reversion to them first. For the average adult there is a significant source of anxiety in this tendency.

A common and very threatening stress is activated in the attendant when his ability to "dominate" or "control" a defiant boy is placed in serious question. He is less likely to be troubled if his authority is challenged by one of the girls. New attendants routinely raise questions about what course of action one should follow if physically assaulted by one of the boys. This particular issue is much less important to the nurse or the aide. The attendant's anxiety is founded in good part on the projection of his own continuing need to compare his virility against that of the patient who challenges him, and such typically adolescent modes as quarreling and brawling press uncomfortably to the fore.

Nurses and aides, on the other hand, seem to have more difficulty with formulating and implementing reasonable standards of sexual behavior among the girl patients. The same woman who on one occasion retreats uncertainly from a darkened corner, where she has surprised a couple in tender embrace, may later become highly incensed at the sight of the same couple idly holding hands in front of the television set. From a more positive point of view, male staff members are prone to extol the aggressive physical accomplishments of boy patients, whereas women staff are more inclined to enjoy a little vicarious participation in the intense but short-lived romances of the girls.

Occasionally it is helpful to strengthen an attendant's position by assisting him to a better understanding of the source of his anxiety but in a way which does not carry with it the threat of treatment. It is usually enough to generalize about the nature of the problem, conveying the idea that "we would all tend to get pretty mad if someone suggested he could beat us up. And of course we'd feel even worse about hitting one of the kids than about getting hit . . . and that's what really scares us when they start to get tough."

Staff as Fallible Agents of Reality

Correctly representing reality to their adolescent charges is a fundamental treatment obligation of the staff, but being a well-adjusted and well-trained adult does not automatically qualify one for interpreting it more accurately than the patient. At times we speak rather glibly of reality as though it were something which one either does or does not understand. We are on fairly firm ground with respect to gross hallucinations and delusions but must acknowledge that beyond this it is possible for several intelligent people to make quite different interpretations about the "reality" of a given situation. This points to a common difficulty of staff people who are participating intimately in the residential treatment of manipulative, argumentative adolescents.

When the patient is right. When the parents disagree or when nursing staff and psychiatrist disagree, a youngster's prospects for controlling the conflict situation are greatly increased. Although he may have mixed feelings about doing this, the temptation to profit from the weaknesses of others is hard to resist, even when he senses that yielding to it will not be in his best interests.

Donna came to her doctor's office following a recreational basketball game. She complained that the staff man in charge of the game had "tried to fix it." Whenever one team got ahead, he would join the other side or favor the losing side by deliberately tossing them the ball. At one point in the game, when Donna's team was behind, he charitably passed her the ball even though he was at the moment on the other team. She became angry, threw the ball down, and indignantly "told him off."

In the ensuing discussion her therapist could only agree with her view of the principle involved, but was not too distracted by this to point out that she had seized upon the attendant's error to humiliate him publicly. She was aware of this and quickly acknowledged that it would have been better had she simply explained to him privately her position regarding this one aspect of reality—one which he had not appreciated with sufficient sensitivity. The reality? That a competitive game loses its meaning to the participants when the element of competition is eliminated, and that his action was also condescending, implying as it did that mental patients cannot bear the threat of losing a game.

THERAPEUTIC USE OF ARBITRATION. On occasion a staff member will take an untenable stand with a patient in such a way that the therapist must decide whether to approach the problem through the staff person or through his patient. It is very useful to bear in mind that members of the nursing staff, living in such close emotional proximity to patients, are perpetual targets for strong transference feelings and fantasies. Approaching special incidents with this point of view often helps greatly to decide how best to interpret to the patient his neurotic distortion of reality. Doing this also requires that one first have a reasonably good understanding of the realities of the conflict incident. Sometimes a staff person is simply and unequivocally wrong, for example, and does not realize it.

An unrecognized tension had arisen between one of the teachers and the nursing staff over the division of authority between them. One day the teacher was showing an educational film which had not run its length by the end of the period. With good intentions she told her class that they were free to decide whether to remain for the rest of the film or leave the class and go on to their next assigned activity.

Although the youngsters had some mixed feelings about it, they could not help taking a certain delight in this legitimate chance to be late for an activity which they knew was required. In the resulting confusion Dr. G was called by the head nurse, who explained that these patients were attempting to manipulate the staff.

After talking with the nurse, Dr. G promptly spoke with the teacher and with one of his patients who was involved in the episode. Of these three the patient was the only one capable of presenting a coherent and credible account of the incident. It was evident that the fault lay entirely with the staff.

This group of patients could not have left the classroom on time without flouting the teacher, but by remaining they appeared to be violating a stringent program policy. The fact that they enjoyed the situation made it possible for the several staff people involved to point an accusing finger at them and thus avoid direct conflict with each other. In order to resolve this rather routine type of "crisis," it was necessary for Dr. G to speak directly to the staff people about their unwitting contribution to the trouble, after which he pointed out to the patient that his feeling of injured innocence, though justified, need not be overplayed.

One of the leading risks in untangling these snarls is that the therapist will share his patient's indignation and attack the staff people involved. This does not help. Realistically, we simply cannot pretend to perfection. The only thing we can really guarantee in this regard is that we will make mistakes even though we try to keep them to a minimum. This is how it should be presented to the patient who attempts to make too great a gain from such an incident.

In another general type of staff-patient entanglement it becomes apparent that both parties are contributing to it about equally.

Sara complained that Miss W, one of the nurses, made her very uncomfortable by attempting a probing, psychological "analysis" of her personality whenever she looked the least bit unhappy or anxious. In examining this with her it was evident that she herself was unwittingly seeking out opportunities to provoke Miss W into approaching her this way. She was actively helping the nurse to be "wrong" for the sense of control which it gave her. In bringing this to her doctor, she also sought to incite him against a "mere nurse" for violating his professional jurisdiction. She had little difficulty in recognizing this but then added, accurately enough: "But I only started doing it after I found out she liked to pretend she was a psychiatrist."

In this instance Sara's therapist might have talked directly with this still relatively inexperienced nurse about some of the psychological subtleties of her decidedly impractical approach. This, however, would have deprived the nurse of a valuable opportunity to learn from experience in a situation which could tolerate temporizing. It would also have been an unwise collaboration with Sara's neurotic aims. She had tried to set doctor against nurse, just as she had so often pitted her parents against each other. Instead of this, Sara was advised to work out the problem with the nurse. This naturally required that she do something which was new to her. "But how am I supposed to do that—lie down and let her psychoanalyze me?"

After some give-and-take on this rhetorical question she was able to construct the general model for a suitable answer with very little counsel from her therapist: "Well, Miss W, I'm feeling kind of nervous, but I know from experience that talking about it wouldn't help" or "The reason I'm looking so sad is because I feel sad, but it's about something personal. Do you ever feel sad?"

In practice this worked out very well, for the nurse as well as for Sara. In this vignette the patient's efforts to restructure the present to conform to her own past were not verbally interpreted at first. To have presented her with such an intriguing idea at this point would probably have delighted her ("you mean I think that she's my mother and you're my father?"), but no good would have come of it. Rather, she was asked first of all to explore the minute and concrete details of her current relationship with the nurse, and was then simply advised to think of some way to break up her own automatic tendency to repeat her contributions to the inevitable antagonism which arose between them.

It was some weeks after this that she make a passing reference which reflected her awareness of the "transference" aspects of the exchange, but it would not have been surprising—nor any great cause for concern—if she had never mentioned it. That she had quietly, privately extracted her own interpretation from the experience was adequately demonstrated by her ability to alter it by altering herself and then to maintain the alteration.

The example also explains the rationale for regarding this kind of transaction as a bona fide treatment measure. The patient is expected and assisted to go as far as possible in making his own way with the standard frustrations visited upon him by other people. Doctors and nurses, like other mortals, make mistakes, have bad days, and do not try to live their lives by a few simple and superficial principles of psychotherapy. The major effort is directed toward helping the patient adapt to reality, i.e., to people as they really are, and not to custom-tailoring the staff to accommodate themselves to the patient's illness. It is not desirable for everyone to be a therapist. There still exists a great need for "people" in a properly constituted treatment program.

Another common snare is one which the staff person sets for himself by making a correct judgment regarding a stress situation and then defending it with the wrong reasons.

For some weeks the girls had been in good spirits and doing very well when, over a period of several days, they started to become unexplainably restless. They proposed some sketchy plans for a Saturday night slumber party, discussing the project at some length in their regular "group sessions." Dr. L, though inclined to favor the idea, fittingly referred them to the head nurse to negotiate a final decision. Miss M immediately sensed something wrong with the idea and finally turned it down after a brief and essentially business-oriented discussion with the girls. Then, in reply to their inevitable and angry demands for an explanation, she answered uncertainly that they had not planned the activity "far enough in advance."

The girls immediately countered with an impressive array of evidence to the contrary, and a heated debate was on. An impromptu review of the matter between Miss M and one of the staff doctors confirmed the correctness of her intuitive decision and established also that it was correct for a reason other than the one which she had given to the girls under pressure.

In a second discussion with the girls she cleared the air by acknowledging that they had planned quite carefully and then went on to point out that she felt just as sure of her decision as she was uncertain of her reasons. She reflected, without attempting to explain, that a slumber party is a special and rather exotic activity and that they had already had several of these during the several preceding months and were in danger of ruining the fun of the activity by making it routine. This was readily accepted by the girls, and shortly thereafter they began to let the staff know in various small ways that the plan for the party had been largely inspired by a wish to emphasize their social exclusion of a new girl who had just been admitted to the ward.

VALUE OF "BREAKDOWN" IN STAFF COMMUNICATIONS. The so-called communication breakdowns between staff members do not just happen. These, too, are caused. Whenever a stress situation of this sort develops, some member of the staff can be counted on to throw away a rich treatment opportunity by designating it as "just a breakdown in communications."

Jane, aged fifteen, reached an agreement with her doctor that she could attend a movie with some of the other girls. Soon after returning to the ward he learned that she had become very angry and testing with several members of the nursing staff. Viewing her behavior in context, he interpreted it as a "message" that she should not go to the movie after all. He advised a nurse accordingly and added that he would talk to Jane about the change in plans.

Another urgent matter arose, and he left the hospital without doing so ("I just forgot"). When it was time for the movie, Jane made her appearance with the other girls. The nurse, assuming that she had been informed of the change in plans, became irritated by what appeared to be an additional test. Jane naturally became angry and charged that the nurse and/or doctor were either lying to her or being evasive. The nurse regarded herself as innocent of all charges. She felt with some justification that she had been left holding the bag. Not realizing that much of her anger at Jane was displaced from the doctor, she counterattacked unprovocatively, and a major scene developed. Jane quickly became unmanageable, and not too surprisingly the nurse could see no alternative to calling her doctor. By this time he was in the middle of dinner, which fact, combined with the unconscious guilt which he felt over having neglected a duty, prompted him to lather the nurse with blame through a series of ingenious rationalizations.

MATERIEL OF PSYCHOTHERAPY. These scrimmages are the major media of inpatient treatment. Within them such ephemeral ideas as countertransference, displacement, sibling rivalry, jealousy, hostility, and oedipal struggle, to name only a few, all acquire a fresh and genuine emotional meaning for the people involved. It is difficult to describe the extent to which the therapist concerns himself with the finest details of his patient's seemingly routine daily activities. He is very attentive to such things as telephone calls, mail, quality of school work, performance in other prescribed activities, cosmetics, haircuts, clothing, and choice of television programs. The idea of *attending* to these things does not imply that the patient is always *directed* about them, i.e., that his mail must be censored or his shoes shined. It is done because we have learned that whether by conscious intent or inadvertence the patient of this age has a considerable predilection for communicating difficult information about himself by the most circuitous of routes. Much of psychotherapy progresses through the retracing of these pathways, starting with the immediate present—the urgent business of the moment—settling this as realistically as possible, and then wending slowly backward from there.

Guy was fifteen years old at the time of admission. He was referred by the juvenile court with a two-year history of increasing truancy, loitering with known delinquents and becoming involved in various petty violations with them, carrying a lethal weapon without a permit (a revolver), and for slugging the maiden aunt who had reared him since early infancy.

His mother had died of tuberculosis several weeks after his birth and when Guy was eleven his father had died with a chronic organic brain syndrome which had left him psychotic for the last two or three years of his life.

The family was devoutly Catholic, and Guy had been reared with high moral standards. Until the eighth grade he was a good student and was well liked by the adults in his neighborhood and by his own friends. He had always put much time and interest into church activities. His school grades, which were very good through the sixth grade, began to fall shortly after his father's death. This also marked the beginning of the delinquencies which prompted the referral.

When he entered the hospital, he wore sideburns, black leather jacket, Levi's with a low-slung waist line, taps on his shoes, and the rest of the trappings as well. From history and interview findings it was evident that he was not a chronic, dyssocial delinquent. He had failed in many ways to live up to the ill-fitting "emergency role" which he had formed for himself in a time of crisis. He was ambitious, intelligent, articulate, and much too effective in his general social aggressiveness to qualify as a hood. He attempted to carry himself with an air of contemptuous superiority but, much to his chagrin, made frequent slips of the tongue and of behavior which betrayed his basic liking for people and his high ideals.

In spite of this he managed to put up a good battle for the first few weeks following admission. It was necessary to keep him on the adult closed ward, and he even contrived to spend several days in a seclusion room. When he was finally "cleaned up," mostly through his doctor's unrelenting application of authority, he was transferred under duress to the adolescent ward.

There he complained that he felt naked in his clean, conservative, and neatly pressed clothing and especially with his close-to-the-scalp hair cut. Although it was touch-and-go for a while, he soon became deeply involved in the work of psychotherapy, and his over-all course was steadily uphill. Because of his intelligence, high verbal capacity, and ability to enjoy and tolerate his feelings for people, he was able to profit from a much greater than average examination of some of the unconscious psychogenetic determinants of his neurosis.

After a year and a half of inpatient treatment he appeared ready to leave the hospital. His parents were dead, his aunt had died while he was in the hospital, and there was no home for him to go to. He was enrolled in a small liberal arts college, where we realized he would have to assume almost completely independent status. He was understandably frightened by this prospect and several weeks prior to his discharge underwent what seemed to be a total relapse.

To the extent that the necessary props were available, he once again donned his old role of the hardened delinquent. But this time he had to work it through without the support of his therapist's authority.

As some of the more evident defensive aspects of his *ersatz regression* were pointed out to him, he could no longer find sanctuary in them. His anxiety mounted steadily, until finally all the problems in his world seemed to be focused in the long, carefully groomed sideburns which he could not bring himself to shave off. In therapy sessions with his doctor he struggled courageously with this problem, and for this period of several weeks he endured intense, unremitting anxiety. At the conclusion of each session he would resolve with great sincerity to shave off the sideburns, only to return next time quite ashamed and almost incoherent as he tried to rationalize his failure. During one of these interviews his anxiety reached a critical level, and he suddenly blurted out, "I know why I can't shave them off, but I can't tell you. The reason I can't do it isn't even real . . . but it seems real to me!"

After a moment of tormented silence he finally explained, "I'm afraid I'll cut my face . . . for some stupid reason I'm afraid I'll cut my f——g face if I try to shave them off."

He was able to say no more than this at the time, but once more resolved to shave them off. His therapist later learned that he had first borrowed an electric razor from one of the other boys, but had returned it immediately without using it. Then, with his own safety razor, he cautiously set about resecting his sideburns. Perhaps not surprisingly, the "warded off" returned, and he "accidentally" inflicted a superficial but unsightly laceration on the side of his face.

Shortly after this he and his therapist had an unplanned meeting on the ward. Just as they began to talk, one of the other boys stepped out of his room and caught sight of Guy. With uncanny sensitivity and sadistic perversity he sang out with malicious glee, "Hey, Guy! I see you nearly cut your head off shaving your sideburns!"

Guy was enraged. His face turned a flaming red, and he unleashed a stunning volley of obscenities at his critic, who by this time was effecting a triumphant retreat into his room. Guy spontaneously regained his composure almost immediately. In the interview which followed he expressed —with a greatly expanded breadth of awareness—the fear which filled him as he contemplated leaving the hospital. The sideburns had saved him from the feelings of utter helplessness and impotence which flooded to consciousness at that time. These feelings, the memories connected with them, and his projected fantasies of the future were examined carefully as he produced them. The "ultimate interpretation" (castration anxiety) was not made explicitly, as he had made it far more effectively himself. As this point the words of his therapist would only have spoiled what he had accomplished by reexperiencing and surviving these old feelings of his childhood in a realistic crisis of the present. There he found them to be invalid, or rather less valid, less real, and far less serviceable than before.

He was discharged from the hospital soon thereafter and his subsequent adjustment was excellent, which proves nothing but suggests a great deal.

15

THERAPEUTIC VALUE OF NONTHERAPY ACTIVITIES

The psychiatrically hospitalized youngster can hardly turn a corner without being "treated" by someone or something.

Our immense interest in psychopathology for its own sake, which has already been hinted at fifteen or twenty times, is further reflected in our promiscuous use of the word *therapy*.

The patient can scarcely avoid noticing his inescapable position at the business end of a magnificently efficient "treating machine" which grinds exceedingly fine and incessantly as well.

At our insistence he must submit passively and dependently as we gather our highly trained team together for the purpose of treating his passivity and his dependency.

The adolescent, departing reluctantly from the familiar if somewhat dubious satisfactions of childhood, will resist and protest against the increasing responsibilities of his approaching adulthood. With it all he is still eager to achieve the maturity of which he can conceive only vaguely. He fully expects to support his candidacy for adulthood with some real proofs of eligibility. His wish to be more self-reliant in every way is certainly among his most intense wishes and worst fears. He wants to contribute something which is a measure of his ability to assume responsibility, to work well in the present for a remote future reward, and to bring credit to himself and to those people who "make a difference" to him.

A Real School

Although the school program plays an extremely important role in treatment, it has not been included with the treatment groups because of the distinctive position which it occupies in the patient's community. The school program is therapeutic because it is *school* and not another form of therapy. It is conducted by full-time teachers who take pride in their work, know very little about psychotherapy, and could hardly care less. A willing resident psychiatrist learns more about education while on the service than the teacher does about the dynamics of therapy. It was planned this way.

Others have regarded the school as a valuable opportunity for direct treatment, as another form of group therapy in which the child might work out some of his problems by writing themes concerning his dreams, fears, wishes, and fantasies. Such productions might be read aloud and group discussion of common problems moderated by a therapy-oriented teacher. Zachry [33] has also advised combining school and therapy with the further suggestion that a teacher with training in psychoanalysis would be best qualified for this job.

There may be some advantages to these approaches but none which could not be obtained with equal benefit in nonschool treatment groups. For the adolescent patient, at least, we have felt that there are some immensely important reasons for preserving the school program in its traditional form and for avoiding overemphasis of the treatment theme.

Most adolescents who become inpatients have histories of attendance, learning, and conduct problems in school. There is an incredible readiness of referring sources, including school personnel, to find the explanations for truancy and refusal in the school itself or in the child's relationship to the school. It is not out of the ordinary to find youngsters referred with such highly deferential complaints as "nothing seriously wrong, just a little truancy" [16].

A little truancy is to be expected from virtually every child, sooner or later, but simple law "enforcement" (i.e., by family and in school) satisfactorily corrects the overwhelming majority of these problems. The average child learns his lesson quickly and does not offend again, or at least not for a respectable length of time. The patient who is referred for psychiatric evaluation because of "just a little truancy" is really referred because of other psychological symptoms which are only limelighted by the unsuccessful efforts of family and community to make him a happy and law-abiding individual.

It is in this patient's anxiety, guilt, rage, defiance, and depression that we find the clues to a degree of illness far greater than could be accounted for by even a very bad school. In a few exceptional cases, such as undiagnosed mental deficiency or frank physical disturbances of hearing and vision, there might be some direct antagonism between the adolescent and conventional teaching processes. In most instances, however, it is not the school which needs to be changed.

As the cause of truancy is usually not to be found in a *real* rift between the truant and school, it follows that any "treatment" of his truancy should not include continued truancy in any form. As a rule, the patient himself has already been successful in externalizing and rationalizing many of his problems in terms of "crummy schools, lousy teachers, snobbish kids, worthless subjects," and so forth. It is easy to strengthen his resistance to treatment, through tacitly agreeing with his version of the realities involved, by offering a school program which is heavily diluted, optional, or a substitute activity which simply passes by the name of "school." The better alternative is to disagree with him and insist that he join us in seeking answers to his alleged school difficulties within himself.

This quality of the adolescent patient's illness and the kind of treatment which it requires are, of course, just as applicable to his many other neurotic adaptations as to his school adjustment. For purposes of concrete illustration, however, the part played by the school program serves admirably to illustrate how some of the technical operations of traditional office psychotherapy can be made far more real and effective by introducing them into the youngster's life as well as into his therapy. The school, by being no more than an ordinary school, can often "interpret" unconscious wishes and disordered patterns of defense, and with deeper reaching consequences, than could possibly be achieved by office techniques alone.

The school is especially good for this purpose because it is about the closest thing to a pubertal rite which our society has to offer. Even though it covers many years, and its ceremonies are diffuse and complex, it is psychologically similar as a test of maturity to having one's front teeth knocked out without flinching or to spending three days alone on the desert without food, water, or clothing.

In our country today adolescents are too young to work and too old to play around the house. School is the only honorable occupation available to most of them.[1] Whether good or bad, it probably does more than any other contemporary social institution to "separate the men from the boys."

The new patient is cordially and sometimes rather strenuously accepted into the school program of the Adolescent Service. It is not an elective activity. Standard high school subjects are offered from ninth to twelfth grades, inclusive. The curriculum has teeth in it. Depending upon his individual needs and abilities, the student will carry from two to six subjects a day. Classes are scheduled tightly and definitely, as indicated in the following standard schedule of daily activities:

7:00– 7:15	A.M.	Out of bed, morning ablutions, dress
7:15– 8:00		Breakfast
8:00– 8:30		Room cleanup and prepare for school
8:30– 9:15		First class period
9:15–10:00		Second class period
10:00–10:45		Third class period
10:45–11:50		Art, crafts, woodwork (occupational therapy)
12:00– 1:00	P.M.	Lunch
1:00– 1:45		Fourth class period
1:45– 2:30		Fifth class period
2:30– 3:15		Sixth class period
3:30– 4:30		Physical education (recreational therapy)
4:30– 4:45		Showers
4:45– 5:30		Dinner
5:30– 6:30		Required evening study hall
6:30– 9:30		A relatively free time for a variety of on and off the ward activities. However, the time is often used for a second, or even a third, required evening study hall for the student who needs it
9:30–10:00		Nourishments (refrigerator raiding, really)
10:00–10:30		Prepare for bed
10:30		Lights out and all quiet

[1] The service is not large enough to warrant the varied program which would be needed to accommodate youngsters who cannot profit from secondary level education. Patients are selected for intensive inpatient treatment with this limitation in mind. There are many other "real work" activities which would serve just as well for these youngsters and which are, in fact, available in many of our larger high schools, for example, auto mechanics, domestic sciences, and training in a variety of other trades.

Most of the youngsters have an hour to an hour and a half of free time during the morning or afternoon which is not reflected in the schedule above, due to the staggered scheduling of boys' and girls' activities. There are no recreational activities during school hours—no radio, phonograph, television, or games. The patient who is not in school will have nothing to do except sit quietly in his room meditating on the dynamics of the school-refusal syndrome.

Standard required courses in English, history, government, and general mathematics are offered, along with courses in French, German, Latin, physics, biology, chemistry, algebra, and others in the academic category. Commercial courses include typing, accounting, office practices, business law, and sometimes shorthand.

The entire curriculum is carried by three full-time and one half-time teachers. Credits are also granted for music, physical education, and sometimes, by special arrangement in the "OT" program, for fine arts. Although under the nominal supervision of the school director, physical education is actually conducted by two men and one woman (shared with the adult service) who are listed on the table of organization as recreational therapists. This is only a technical misnomer and does not interfere with the primary work of the "RT's," who are really skilled athletes with extensive coaching experience. They are dynamic more in the physical than in the psychological sense, and probably nowhere in the country do high school students work so hard so often for so few credits.

Special projects and periodic examinations are required as in the average public school. Grades are not given for morale purposes; they are earned. Students who fail in a subject are graded accordingly, and there are no "social promotions." There is full reciprocation of credits with the public school systems of the state, and in most instances the patient's home school awards the diploma. Many patients attend public school during the latter part of their stay in the hospital, although this is not decided solely on the basis of whether or not they are well enough to handle this much self-responsibility.

The schedule is somewhat lighter during the summer session, but it is still school. In addition to routine course work the summer provides a good opportunity for making up courses which have been failed. In addition, remedial reading, the fundamentals of grammar, and general mathematics are provided for those students who need them. A few of the better students are assigned to rapid reading drills or are given special tutoring in subjects for which there is usually little demand.

Stress of Leisure

By far the most difficult times of the year, from the standpoint of general ward morale, are the extended vacation periods which come at Christmas time and between the summer and fall sessions. The youngsters are able to tolerate a maximum of about seven to ten days without school, after which they begin to develop indolent decubitus ulcers of the ego. Following a year of sustained grousing about the cruel demands of the regular schedule, it is a little pathetic to watch them in their losing fight against the temptation to complain aloud about the awful burden of vacation. It is ordinarily sometime during the third week of leisure and recreation that their courage finally fails, and they begin to ask openly, heads hanging, about when school will start again.

After the first two or three years a great number of the initial treatment policies became tradition. Although they still require more time, energy, and supervision than any other age group, this becomes somewhat less as a new service evolves its traditions. When these have become firmly established, the newly admitted patient is somehow indoctrinated by his fellow patients. He learns how things are—what is done and what is not done. This apparently is not accomplished primarily by direct instruction but rather by a variety of subtle and powerful social gestures of approval and disapproval.

If he comes onto the ward in the morning, he will get settled in his room, have lunch, and be in regular classes by afternoon. For the past several years there has been little question or trouble about school attendance, perhaps partly because of some slight, gradual change in the "types" of youngsters admitted but even more importantly because of the increased confidence of the staff. Any lingering doubts about the desirability of breaking with certain long-standing conventions which have governed the inpatient treatment of adolescents have been entirely erased.

The staff are now thoroughly convinced that the right to attend school is a privilege first and a requirement second. The patients see it this way, too. On occasion an individual patient will have trouble, but as a rule he is soon attending and working after first experiencing a systematic failure of all the old ruses and dodges which worked so well for him in the past. Angry and defiant, he initially goes to class with an attendant, nurse, or doctor at his heels. Once there he may sit in solemn silence, ignoring the teacher and his classmates, in which case we can wait a while and see how he gets along. Should he decide to launch a deliberate campaign of disruption, the teacher will direct him to return to his room and remain there until he has his doctor's permission to return. This may be granted at once or withheld indefinitely, depending on what the patient and his doctor are able to understand about the reasons for the trouble. If the youngster is simply testing our sincerity, it will often suffice to return him immediately to class with little comment.

If he remains militantly defiant, there is no choice but that he be "prescribed out" of school, and without this there is no good prospect for long-term treatment. He may not go even if he wishes to, and it is made clear to him that it is he, and not his doctor, who has chosen to suspend his treatment. No abstract gestures of therapy are made at this point. It would be like treating an overwhelming speticemia with aspirin. The question immediately arises as to "what happens next," and nobody knows the answer to it. The therapist begins to think about other dispositions which might be more realistic for this youngster, because he is keenly aware of his inability to carry out a successful program of treatment which has been designed by his patient rather than himself. The recalcitrant patient senses this and begins to relent, but suspects a bluff. After careful deliberation he expresses his willingness to go to class but not to physical education, to business law but not to English, or to "go a couple of days and see if I like it," and so forth. These propositions do not offer an adequate basis for prescribing his return.

The process is partly one of seriously considering alternative treatment plans and partly the bringing to bear of a high degree of psychological pressure. It is vital that the doctor not wedge himself into a do-it-or-else position. His patient does not *have* to go to school, but he may have to be returned home or to the juvenile court, to mention most of the very few suitable disposition possibilities. Only rarely does it prove to be in the youngster's best interest to follow through with "other arrangements." Usually he successfully convinces himself that he is missing out on a promising opportunity and returns to school with a vast public display of disgust and a secret determination to succeed.

It is not unlikely that he will fail to complete his daily assignments and perhaps fail some of his first examinations. These lapses are also very soberly considered with him by his doctor, and it is made as clear to him as possible that the work of treatment is mostly his burden to bear. He is supported in every way possible, with extra study halls as needed, by being spared the distraction of other and perhaps more pleasurable activities, and by the pervading atmosphere of the service. He cannot count on the friendly support of other patients and will recognize at once that the only encouragement for continuing his resistance emanates from those several youngsters who actively dislike him.

Among his other feelings the boy is more than a little surprised that he had been failed in the kind of a hospital which, in many other ways, has demonstrated its willingness to reward him well for small achievements. He is also unnerved to learn that his psychiatrist looks upon his school failure as a symptom of illness. He is also startled to find that his doctor has a curiously direct and unapologetic way of speaking about such matters, when he speaks of them at all, and a marked disinclination to compromise on questions of treatment.

He is no longer able to convince himself and others that the school has *caused* his troubles. With great embarrassment he slowly begins to work, and during this phase he is exquisitely sensitive to any open expressions of praise, approval, or confidence in him. These would be, for him, derisive accusations that he is a conformist, and that his earlier rebelliousness had been no more than a defensive sham. For the time being it is still necessary for him to believe that he is working only because of tyrannical external pressures, despite the fact that a few weeks earlier he had stated with indisputable accuracy that no one could make him work if he did not want to.

His first scholastic success, e.g., a superior performance on an examination, is often a time of crisis for him. Meritorious achievement in a class which makes very few concessions to "emotional illness" could result only from his own efforts. After this he will probably need to miss a few more assignments, whereupon his doctor might note in passing that "it's pretty hard for you to stand the idea of being a square, but let me tell you something right now—you're the one who can't stand the idea, not other people. And stop worrying that I'm going to praise you and get all sloppy about things. I'm not going to ruin your reputation by being proud of you . . . well, maybe a little bit, but I'll try not to talk about it too much."

Except for the size of the classes the school is comparable in a very important sense to a regular school. Because of the way we feel about it the youngster who has previously found an "out" in unconscious parental sanctions discovers that the escape hatches have been closed. Almost against his will the unhappy, defiant youngster begins to succeed as a student and as a member of a social group and enjoys a contribution to his self-esteem which could not be matched by anything which we might do *for* him or say *to* him.

Psychosis is not a contraindication to school attendance. Many very sick youngsters can make remarkable gains in their fight against illness by participating in the school program, even when they have not been able to participate successfully in the simplest of the recreational ward activities.

The attitudes which govern this approach apply equally to most other aspects of his life in the hospital. Much is expected of him, because it is our feeling that he deserves this tribute to his worth. In the past he has expected only the worst from himself and will strive heroically to have us share this estimation of him and to adjust our hopes for him accordingly. We consistently make a strong point of declining this invitation.

The success of this approach has exceeded our highest expectations. There is no proper psychiatric term or expression to describe a treatment program which is not therapy, but merely therapeutic. The concepts of "structuring," or patterning, are little more than anemic efforts to expand our jurisdiction by professionalizing the ordinary. If one hopes to succeed in treating the disturbed adolescent, he must be willing to be a *non-therapist* as well as a therapist.

Other Therapeutic Group Activities

This fruitful coalition between psychiatry and the commonplace (a regular school) proved to have far-reaching effects on the entire program.

According to plans made prior to the opening of the service, school would occupy the special position described in the foregoing. It was assumed, however, that some of the traditional adjunctive therapies, namely occupational and recreational therapy, would be carried out along traditional lines. In general theory this meant providing the patient with activities which would "reinforce his mechanisms of defense" and permit him to "release some of his dammed-up instinctual energy."

For the delinquent adolescent boy, especially, it was felt that recreational athletics would provide an excellent opportunity for him to relieve himself of aggressive tensions while having some "fun" at the same time. The theory was a good one, even though our combined years of experience with adolescents on the adult service gave us no reason to entertain it.

The loosely organized pickup games of basketball, volleyball, and touch football never seemed to produce the desired results. Our hopes that the boys would return from the activity bright-eyed and wholesomely weary in the aftermath of battle were not realized, and we naturally attributed this to their illness. It was disappointing to find them unable to avail themselves of this opportunity for a constructive and acceptable outlet. Scheduled recreational therapy was very unpopular with the patients. They seemed to dislike it even more than school, and conflicts between staff and patients over attendance were frequent and strenuous.

Taking their illness into account, we tried ever harder to make it enjoyable for them by widening the variety of games and allowing them as much freedom as possible in choosing what they wanted to do. On the basis of our superior knowledge of the threats posed by unconscious instinctual strivings, we did not even consider such activities as boxing and wrestling.

The evolution of a "RT" program from these rather lunatic beginnings resulted from a one-sided contest between psychological theory and sand-lot empiricism. As the person immediately responsible for the activities program at the time, I can best describe this most important process by relating, in the first person, what actually happened.

At the outset I had very few doubts about how the recreational therapy program should work. Miss B, who was then in charge of girls' "RT," proposed that they all be required to attend a weekly swimming class, and I confidently advised her that this would be unwise. "All people," I explained, "have an inherent phylogenetic dread of water," and we could logically expect this to be pathologically exaggerated in mentally ill persons.[2] Swimming was declared an optional activity and failed after several weeks of trial because none of the girls attended.

A similar plan for instructing the boys in the fundamentals of various physical skills was proposed by Mr. K, director of "RT" for the boys. I pointed out to him the need for emphasizing the recreational aspects of this activity, and further urged that competition and score-keeping be omitted in order not to intensify the low estimation in which our patients already held themselves.

The "RT" staff strove conscientiously to carry out the program as it had been precisely and asininely defined, but in spite of their best efforts the patients refused to cooperate. They were scornful, rebellious, and utterly perverse in their refusal to have fun while discharging their pentup aggressive energy. It was all very disappointing, and once again I reminded myself that one could hardly expect more from sick, delinquent youngsters. They were told they needed the exercise, and we tried to convince them of the therapeutic value of having a good time. Although they were rather casually required to attend the regularly scheduled daytime "RT" sessions, individual patients who were unusually "threatened" by fear of physical injury or competition were frequently excused.

A few months after the opening of the service, I began to hear disturbing reports from several of the boys about how things were being changed in "RT." Jerry, a fifteen-year-old delinquent boy, explained in persuasive detail his reasons for refusing to attend the activity any longer. He explained that it wasn't fun any more. For the past three weeks, five days per week, they had done nothing but figure eight basketball drill, shooting practice, and running laps. Mr. K, Jerry observed, was a "mean bastard" who gave them neither praise nor respite. He was routinely requiring each boy to run an additional lap for each deliberate "mistake" made during drill and was holding them overtime, making them late for

[2] The reader will understand that the recollection of this incident worked upon me a distinctly emetic effect.

dinner whenever the entire group lagged in completing the day's exercises.

Calisthenics, deep knee bends and push-ups, were required for warming up at the beginning of each hour. And to make matters even worse, Mr. K had started coming up on the ward before each period for the purpose of applying firm, personal, though unobtrusive pressure on each of the boys to attend.

It was a grim picture indeed, and in light of Jerry's proved capacity for revising reality to suit his convenience, there was little reason to believe that it could possibly be true. I spoke with Mr. K about it, and he modestly confirmed every detail of Jerry's account. It seemed to me that no great harm had been done, so I simply advised him to "ease up on the patterning approach and get back to recreation."

But, as it developed, there are some things too great for the human soul to endure—cruelty to children being one of them. Mr. K stood firm and courageously defended his approach without benefit of theoretical rationale. He simply insisted that "it's better for them."

We called in the head nurse, and she confirmed my suspicions that for the past several weeks the number of complaints from the boys about the "RT" sessions had increased markedly. However, she also noted that attempts to refuse the activity had fallen almost to zero. I decided to see for myself, and it was immediately apparent that Jerry had understated his complaints. After they had finished their grueling workout, I finally saw what I had long since despaired of ever seeing. The boys left the gymnasium perspiring, panting, and bone-weary. They complained lavishly and in chorus. They were bright-eyed, square-shouldered, and flushed with pride in the aftermath of battle. The evidence was incontestable.

From this moment on, "cruel regimentation" became the official guiding policy, and "recreation," in this area at least, gave way to physical education.

Explaining the psychological rationale for this paradoxical reaction was a simple matter, after the fact. Mr. K was advised to proceed according to his own judgment, with the added assurance we would be happy to provide the theoretical explanations for his successes after he had accomplished them.

Since then problems centering around the "RT" program have been isolated and infrequent occurrences. The physical education program, like the school, functions without a respectable rationale which can dignify it as therapy. The boys follow a year-round schedule of coaching in tackle football with full equipment, basketball, boxing, baseball, and track. Each of these endeavors requires many consecutive weeks of monotonous drill, all without a prospect of immediate reward. When they have acquired sufficient skill and strength to qualify for competition the boys are forthwith subjected to the "threat" of winning or losing. The approach has provided them with an *earned and well-deserved* sense of masculine accomplishment.

The physical education program for the girls also emphasizes the teaching of physical skills, although it is not nearly as demanding as for the boys. Basketball, swimming, volleyball, modern dance, and choral music are stressed. Periodic courses in some of the fundamental do's and don't's of hairstyling, cosmetics, clothing, bearing, and posture are also included.

Despite their symphonic complaints the patients are as a group more dedicated to these activities than are the staff. They understand and readily accept the idea that intercurrent psychological symptoms are insufficient cause for their failing to fulfill this obligation to themselves.

Eric, aged fifteen, was admitted with an unremarkable inventory of hypochondriacal symptoms which resulted, in part, from a lifetime of excessive maternal solicitude.

Within his own family and group of friends he was renowned as a "frail boy," and his mother led us to understand that undue physical strain would seriously impair his health or perhaps kill him. General medical evaluation revealed no basis for this concern.

All direct forms of communication between Eric and his mother were suspended for a few weeks and he was entered into the athletic program as a peer. On the first day he collapsed in the middle of basketball drill and was unconscious for five minutes. An on-the-spot medical and psychiatric examination pointed strongly to psychogenic syncope. Although it was recognized that he was not malingering, it was decided that his interests would be best served by requiring him to make up his "coma time" after the regular session. He was able to do this without complaint.

When talking about it later with his doctor he was in tearful misery, not because he had been required to make up the time but because he had fainted in the first place. He openly voiced his feelings of shame and inferiority, and his fear of being considered a sissy or a queer by the other boys.

Arrangements were made for Mr. K to offer him some extra periods of special tutoring, and he worked as though preparing for the Olympics. He never became a "star" but did develop into a capable athlete; he later had many occasions to enjoy the admiration and respect of the others for his abilities.

When Eric's mother was advised of this she became acutely anxious, and it was necessary to double the frequency of her casework visits. His success threatened her with the loss of the clinging, sick, asexual infant whom she needed so desperately to fulfill her own needs. For weeks she verged on signing him out of the hospital despite her intellectual appreciation of the fact that he was improving. "I know he's getting better but I can't stand to have him in here any more. I don't know why, but he's got to come home!"

When Eric caught wind of this, he lent passionate support to her demands that he be discharged, but without waiting for an answer he ran away from the hospital just long enough to make a telephone call to her. His wild harange against the hospital so frightened her that she decided to leave him there. "You're just making him worse . . . look what he's doing now . . . but he can't come home when he's that sick." And Eric, for his part, settled for the philosophical observation that "if she won't take me out of the hospital I guess there's nothing I can do about it." He was able to resume his treatment, and with good results.

A little more freedom of choice and expression is allowed in the real recreational activities, and in occupational therapy, than in the school and athletics programs. Recreation, in the literal sense of the word, is reserved for scheduled periods in the evenings, on weekends, and during vacation periods. A number of these activities are supervised by the "RT" staff, but just as many or more develop spontaneously within the ward setting. Record dances, slumber parties, bridge tournaments, theater parties, and picnics are just a few of the superabundant conventional pleasures available.

Availability of recreational variety is no problem in itself. A far more serious difficulty lies in the fact that recreation has proved to be an inadequate solution to the problem of leisure. The most frustrating part of the program planning, by far, is the thrice-yearly task of finding enough legitimately productive work projects for the patients to leaven the corrosive effects of too much fun.

Unfortunately, custodial service in the hospital is so structured that it was only through the exercise of considerable influence in high places that we could arrange for the patients to do some of the routine furniture refinishing and equipment maintenance. Suitable part-time employment is also extremely difficult to obtain because of the high university student population in the community. We continue to look, though not too hopefully, for better answers to this problem. Occupational therapy provides the youngsters with greater latitude than the other activities, but it still requires regular attendance and a demonstrated respect for the importance of working well and with good purpose.

This part of the program was developed from the beginning with the idea that its major therapeutic effect would be achieved through its contributions to the adaptive aims of the ego, rather than through the jejunely theoretical reinforcing of defenses and venting of instinctual pressures.

This view appears to represent a general trend in the subspecialty. A few years ago the psychiatric occupational therapist did not appreciate being looked upon as a teacher of skills. There was a distinct tendency to depreciate and minimize the importance of this function in favor of more dynamic, and therefore more distinctive, formulations. We no longer hear much about the innate value of leather-pounding as an acceptable outlet for aggression nor of clay-modeling as an ingenious contrivance for the indirect discharge of smearing impulses.

The patient's attitudes about his OT projects, the effect which it has upon his conception of himself, and how it influences the attitudes of other people toward him are beginning to be recognized as the things which really count. The principle here is identical to that concerning the relationships between instinctual strivings and age-appropriate routes of gratification, as discussed in connection with the RT program. Whacking away at a piece of leather might provide some transient relief from "tension," but can offer little more than this because it does not provide the unconsciously desired aim or target. An inanimate object is incapable of reacting to a beating as a person would, and it is not the person toward whom the aggressive, destructive strivings were directed in the first place. For purposes of psychic energy discharge it has only limited value, and even then only if it is repeated in perpetuity.

Competition, motivated by a desire for personal gain, comes much closer to permitting the dissipation of aggressive strivings. This may not be morally good, depending upon one's philosophical outlook, but it does appear to be the way of things.

Just as a passing reflection, it has often seemed that the people most able to develop healthy appearing reaction-formations against their aggressive, competitive strivings, are either those who have lost so many times that they have given up trying, or those who have won so much that they can afford to relax in their efforts to get more. Controlled aggression, discharged according to the rules of society, is really not so bad as many psychiatrists make it out to be.

Whether a person functions as one who deserves reward for his intrinsic nobility of character or as one who consciously seeks it by working and selling, his goal is still a substantial reward for accomplishment. And aggressiveness is the means by which he achieves it. The moderately healthy adolescent is a natural competitor and achiever. He has a deep hunger for new skills, and whether these are social, intellectual, or manual skills matters less than that they better prepare him to become something more than the dumb, clumsy, impulsive child which he fears he might remain for the rest of his life.

With all of this one might wonder if we are advising that the adolescent patient be treated, in effect, by hanging a carrot in front of his nose, just out of reach, and then mercilessly goading him on to goals which he cannot achieve without great effort. Cannot he ever have any fun at all?

The proposition here is that he has the most fun, and experiences the most satisfaction, when he is meeting the challenges of reality to the best of his ability and, with this, feeling himself to be a more worthwhile person.

Summary

Individual psychotherapy and the therapeutic residential program operate synergistically. Though mutually supportive, each offers something which the other cannot. The following are special contributions which a properly constituted residential program might offer:

Removal of the patient from an environment exercising antitherapeutic influences which could, ultimately, outweigh any gains that might be made in individual psychotherapy.

Protective controls over the kinds of acting-out behavior which are liable to be irreversibly damaging to the patient or to someone else: suicide, homicide, imprisonment, pregnancy, chronic school failure, seducing and being seduced, anorexia, and the frequently tragic consequences of accident-proneness. Indeed, getting such a youngster through adolescence "in one piece" is in itself often a major therapeutic achievement [16].

A more favorable climate for spontaneous improvement, for learning skills, and for testing psychological realities in relationships with other people who can help him do it safely.

The therapeutic management of the patient whose behavior problems, though not delinquent, serve as a resistance which cannot be adequately dealt with on an outpatient basis.

The benefits which accrue from prolonged association with peers and knowledgeable adults in a supervised practice-field for social living.

An opportunity for the isolated patient to feel less lonely and frightened by observing that other "non crazy" youngsters have problems very similar to his own.

The unfailing attention of an "administrator-therapist" who aids and is aided by a staff of cotherapists, all of whom are prepared to answer the questions of adolescents by word and act.

And the adolescent is a rewarding patient. Not only does he have a strong tendency to recover spontaneously from his illness, thus enabling us to take credit for "cures" to which we are often not entitled, but he serves also as an ever-dependable hone for keeping the finest possible edge on his therapist's professional acuity. He will not permit us to retire to routine procedures and stratagems. We are kept alert and versatile by his impatience with contrived therapeutic techniques and stereotyped methods [32]. His keen diagnostic sense and his urgent need for a wise and respectful brand of help for his real problems constantly force the therapist to expect of himself an inventive, imaginative, and freshly inquisitive approach to each new patient—whatever the age of that patient might be.

REFERENCES

1. Alexander, F. The neurotic character. *Internat. J. Psycho-Analysis* 11, 1930.
2. Alexander, F., and French, T. M. *Psychoanalytic Therapy, Principles and Application*. New York, The Ronald Press Company, 1946.
3. Balser, B. *Psychotherapy with the Adolescent*. New York, International Universities Press, Inc., 1957.
4. Cameron, K. Group approach to in-patient adolescents. *Am. J. Psychiat.* 109, 1953.
5. Carek, D. J., Hendrickson, W. J., and Holmes, D. J. Delinquency addiction in parents. *Arch. Gen. Psychiat.* 4, 1961.
6. Curran, H. J. Organization of ward for adolescents in Bellevue psychiatric hospital. *Am. J. Psychiat.* 95, 1939.
7. Dubo, S. *Personal communication*. 1956.
8. Eissler, K. R. Some problems of delinquency. In *Searchlights on Delinquency*. New York, International Universities Press, Inc., 1949.
9. Eissler, K. R. Ego-psychological implications of the psychoanalytic treatment of delinquents. In *The Psychoanalytic Study of the Child*, V. New York, International Universities Press, Inc., 1950.
10. Eissler, R. Riots. In *The Psychoanalytic Study of the Child*, III/IV. New York, International Universities Press, Inc., 1949.
11. Erikson, E. *Childhood and Society*. New York, W. W. Norton and Co., Inc., 1950.
12. Fraiberg, S. Some considerations in the introduction to therapy in puberty. In *The Psychoanalytic Study of the Child*, X. New York, International Universities Press, Inc., 1955.
13. Freud, A. *The Ego and the Mechanisms of Defense*. New York, International Universities Press, Inc., 1946.
14. Freud, A. *The Psycho-Analytical Treatment of Children*. London, Imago, New York, International Universities Press, Inc., 1946.
15. Gitelson, M. Character synthesis: The psychotherapeutic problem in adolescence. *Am. J. Orthopsychiat.* 18, 1948.

16. Hendrickson, W. J. *Personal communications.* 1954–1963.

17. Hendrickson, W. J. Adolescent Service, Neuropsychiatric Institute, University of Michigan, *Bulletin* of the Michigan Society for Mental Health 13: 1, 1957.

18. Hendrickson, W. J., and Holmes, D. J. Control of behavior as a crucial factor in intensive psychiatric treatment in an all adolescent ward. *Am. J. Psychiat.* 115:11, 1959.

19. Hendrickson, W. J., Holmes, D. J., and Waggoner, R. W. Psychotherapy of the hospitalized adolescent. *Am. J. Psychiat.* 116:6, 1959.

20. Hendrickson, W. J., and Holmes, D. J. *Institutional Psychotherapy of the Delinquent; Progress in Psychotherapy,* V. New York, Grune & Stratton, Inc., 1960.

21. Josselyn, I. M. *The Adolescent and His World.* New York, Family Service Association of America, 1952.

22. Johnson, A. Sanctions for superego lacunae. In *Searchlights on Delinquency.* New York, International Universities Press, Inc., 1949.

23. Juracsek, V. *Personal communication.* 1955.

24. Katan, A. A. The role of "displacement" in agoraphobia. *Internat. J. Psycho-Analysis* 32, 1951.

25. Liu, Hsi-Yen *Personal communication.* 1962.

26. Lowery, G. *Personal communication.* 1962.

27. Pollard, J. P. *Personal communication,* 1962.

28. Potter, S. *Lifemanship, or the Art of Getting Away with It Without Being an Absolute Plonk.* New York, Holt, Rinehart and Winston, Inc., 1951.

29. Rabinovich, R. *Personal communication.* 1956.

30. Salinger, J. D. *The Catcher in the Rye.* Boston, Little, Brown and Company, 1951.

31. Szurek, S. A. Notes on the genesis of psychopathic personality trends. *Psychiatry* 5:1, 1942.

32. Waggoner, R. W., and Holmes, D. J. Import of the Adolescent to Psychiatry. Visiting lecturer address given at the Ohio State University, College of Medicine, Columbus, January, 1963.

33. Zachry, C. B. A new tool in psychotherapy with adolescents. In *Modern Trends in Child Psychiatry,* N. D. C. Lewis and B. L. Pacella (eds.). New York, International Universities Press, Inc., 1945.

INDEX